Test Copying Masters

- MULTIPLE-CHOICE (STANDARDIZED) FORMAT TESTS
- FREE-RESPONSE FORMAT TESTS
- ANSWER KEYS
- MANAGEMENT FORMS

Grade 4

Harcourt Brace & Company

Orlando • Atlanta • Austin • Boston • San Francisco • Chicago • Dallas • New York • Toronto • London

http://www.hbschool.com

ISBN 0-15-311173-9

7 8 9 10 170C 2003 2002 2001

CONTENTS

▶ Formal Assessment

▶ Management Forms

Multiple-Choice Format Tests
(Standardized)

The multiple-choice format is provided to assess mastery of the learning goals of the program. These tests assess concepts, skills, and problem solving. The use of these tests helps prepare students for standardized achievement tests.

There is an Inventory Test which tests the learning goals from the previous grade level. This can be used at the beginning of the year or as a placement test when a new student enters your class.

There is a Chapter Test for each chapter and a Multi-Chapter Test to be used as review after several chapters in a content cluster. Also, there are Cumulative Tests at the same point as the Multi-Chapter Tests. The Cumulative Test reviews content from Chapter 1 through the current chapter.

Math Advantage also provides free-response format tests that parallel the multiple-choice tests. You may wish to use one form as a pretest and one form as a posttest.

Choose the letter of the correct answer.

1.   6
  +3

A. 3
B. 9
C. 10
D. not here

2. Which subtraction fact is related to this addition fact?

$8 + 6 = 14$

A. $14 - 6 = 8$ **B.** $8 - 6 = 2$
C. $14 + 6 = 20$ **D.** $14 + 8 = 22$

For question 3, estimate the sum by rounding.

3.   22
  +51

A. 70
B. 80
C. 90
D. 100

4. Mike has 16 stickers in his pocket and 25 stickers in his book. How many stickers does he have in all?

A. 31 stickers
B. 35 stickers
C. 39 stickers
D. 41 stickers

5.   51
  −18

A. 33
B. 43
C. 47
D. 49

For questions 6–7, tell what time it is.

6.

2:36

A. 6 minutes after 2
B. 6 minutes after 3
C. 23 minutes after 6
D. not here

7.

A. 7:20   **B.** 7:25
C. 8:24   **D.** 8:30

8. Mr. Clark spent $11.50 for a shirt and $21.00 for slacks. He gave the clerk $50.00. How much change did he receive?

A. $15.00   **B.** $17.50
C. $17.60   **D.** not here

For questions 9–10, use the calendar.

April						
Su	**M**	**T**	**W**	**Th**	**F**	**Sa**
		1	2	3	4	5
6	7	8	9	10	11	12
13	14	15	16	17	18	19
20	21	22	23	24	25	26
27	28	29	30			

9. How many Fridays are there in the month?

A. 2 Fridays   **B.** 3 Fridays
C. 4 Fridays   **D.** 5 Fridays

10. What is the date of the second Monday?

A. April 14   **B.** April 15
C. April 21   **D.** April 29

For question 11, round the number to the nearest hundred.

11. 780

    A. 800   **B.** 700
    C. 600   **D.** 500

12. A cabinet had 5 shelves with 6 glasses on each shelf. How many glasses were there in all?

    A. 11 glasses   **B.** 20 glasses
    C. 30 glasses   **D.** 40 glasses

13. $1 \times 7 = \underline{\ ?\ }$

    A. 0   **B.** 1   **C.** 7   **D.** 17

14.
$$\begin{array}{r} 8 \\ \times 4 \\ \hline \end{array}$$

    A. 12
    B. 16
    C. 28
    D. 32

15. $28 \div 4 = \underline{\ ?\ }$

    A. 4   **B.** 5   **C.** 6   **D.** 7

16. Ann bought 15 goldfish. She placed an equal number of fish in each of 3 bowls. How many fish were in each bowl?

    A. 2 fish   **B.** 5 fish
    C. 6 fish   **D.** 9 fish

For questions 17–18, use the table.

STUDENTS' FAVORITE VACATION	
Place	**Votes**
Beach	卌 卌 |||
Theme Park	卌 ||||
Campground	卌 ||
Home with Friends	卌	

17. How many students answered the survey?

    A. 24 students   **B.** 28 students
    C. 30 students   **D.** 35 students

18. How many more students liked a theme park than liked a campground?

    A. 1 more student
    B. 2 more students
    C. 3 more students
    D. 4 more students

For questions 19–20, identify the solid figure that is like the object shown.

19.

    A. sphere   **B.** cone
    C. cube   **D.** cylinder

20.

    A. cylinder   **B.** sphere
    C. cone   **D.** rectangular prism

21. Chen drew this figure. She matched it to make the other half. What does the complete figure look like?

A. 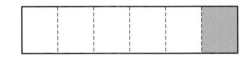   **B.**

C.   **D.**

For questions 22–23, use the picture.

22. How many parts make up the whole?

A. 4 parts   **B.** 6 parts
C. 8 parts   **D.** 10 parts

23. How many parts are shaded?

A. 1 part   **B.** 2 parts
C. 6 parts   **D.** not here

For question 24, find the words that name the part of the group that is shaded.

24.

A. one half   **B.** one fourth
C. one sixth   **D.** one eighth

25. Mrs. Fine has 8 cupcakes to frost. She has frosted 2 cupcakes so far. What part of the cupcakes is frosted?

A. $\frac{2}{8}$ **B.** $\frac{3}{8}$

C. $\frac{5}{8}$ **D.** $\frac{8}{8}$

For question 26, measure the length to the nearest half-inch.

26.

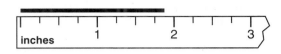

A. 1 in.   **B.** $1\frac{1}{2}$ in.

C. 2 in.   **D.** not here

For question 27, find the perimeter of the figure.

27.

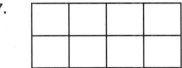

A. 8 units   **B.** 10 units
C. 12 units   **D.** 14 units

28. Dan is replacing a window that is 5 feet high and 3 feet wide. How many square feet of glass does he need?

A. 8 sq ft   **B.** 12 sq ft
C. 15 sq ft   **D.** 16 sq ft

29. A party table has 6 trays on it. Each tray holds 15 cookies. How many cookies are on the table?

A. 60 cookies   **B.** 90 cookies
C. 95 cookies   **D.** 100 cookies

30.
$$\begin{array}{r} 23 \\ \times\ 6 \\ \hline \end{array}$$

A. 123   **B.** 129
C. 138   **D.** 139

31. $9 \times 71 = \underline{\ ?\ }$

A. 161   **B.** 169
C. 638   **D.** 639

32. $56 \div 6 = \underline{\ ?\ }$

A. 9   **B.** 9 r2
C. 10 r6   **D.** not here

33. Mrs. Flynn had 50 party prizes. She gave the same number to 8 children at the party. How many prizes did each child get and how many prizes were left over?

A. 5 prizes each; 0 left over
B. 5 prizes each; 8 left over
C. 6 prizes each; 2 left over
D. 7 prizes each; 6 left over

34. A paint box has 42 tubes of paint. If 7 children share the paints, how many tubes will each child have?

A. 6 tubes
B. 9 tubes
C. 294 tubes
D. 296 tubes

Solve. Then choose the letter of the correct answer.

1. $5 + 4 = \underline{\ ?\ } + 3$

   A. 3   B. 4   C. 5   D. 6

2. $8 - 2 = 7 - \underline{\ ?\ }$

   A. 1   B. 2   C. 3   D. 6

3. $\underline{\ ?\ } + 0 = 9 - 1$

   A. 8   B. 9   C. 10   D. 11

4. $11 - 5 = \underline{\ ?\ } + 2$

   A. 3   B. 4   C. 5   D. 6

5. Find the perimeter.

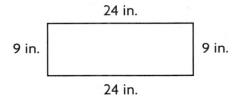

   24 in.
   9 in.   9 in.
   24 in.

   A. 56 in.   B. 66 in.

   C. 68 in.   D. 156 in.

6. Find the perimeter.

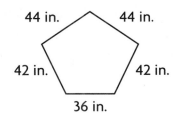

   44 in.   44 in.

   42 in.   42 in.

   36 in.

   A. 104 in.   B. 198 in.

   C. 208 in.   D. 214 in.

7.
   16   A. 51
   22   B. 59
   +13   C. 61
               D. 69

8.
   25   A. 95
   15   B. 105
   +65   C. 110
               D. 115

9.
   57   A. 154
   36   B. 163
   +71   C. 164
               D. 173

10.
   98   A. 135
   34   B. 139
   + 17   C. 145
               D. 149

11. A rectangular garden has a perimeter of 80 ft. The garden is 25 ft long. How wide is it?

    A. 15 ft   B. 25 ft

    C. 30 ft   D. 55 ft

12. Leila made a rectangular dog pen. She used 12 fence sections each for the long sides, and 8 sections each for the short sides of the pen. How many fence sections did she use in all?

    A. 20 sections   B. 32 sections

    C. 40 sections   D. 48 sections

13. What is 319 rounded to the nearest hundred?

    A. 300   B. 320

    C. 400   D. 500

14. What is $67.25 rounded to the nearest $10.00?

A. $60.00   B. $67.00
C. $68.00   D. $70.00

15. Which is the best estimate of this sum?

$$
\begin{array}{r}
209 \\
187 \\
+326 \\
\hline
\end{array}
$$

A. 500
B. 700
C. 800
D. 1,000

16. What is the best estimate of this difference?

$$
\begin{array}{r}
\$52.99 \\
- \ 29.53 \\
\hline
\end{array}
$$

A. $10.00
B. $20.00
C. $40.00
D. $50.00

For questions 17–18, use the price list.

Corn	$2.89 a dozen
Potatoes	$3.19 a bag
Lettuce	$1.09 a head

17. About how much change will Jere receive from a $10.00 bill if he buys a dozen ears of corn and a bag of potatoes?

A. about $2.00   B. about $4.00
C. about $6.00   D. about $7.00

18. Felicia bought 2 heads of lettuce and 2 bags of potatoes. About how much did she spend?

A. about $4.00
B. about $6.00
C. about $8.00
D. about $10.00

19.
$$
\begin{array}{r}
\$6.34 \\
- \ 2.78 \\
\hline
\end{array}
$$

A. $3.56
B. $4.44
C. $4.56
D. $4.66

20.
$$
\begin{array}{r}
\$2.45 \\
1.79 \\
+ \ 4.11 \\
\hline
\end{array}
$$

A. $7.25
B. $7.35
C. $8.35
D. $9.25

21.
$$
\begin{array}{r}
\$11.75 \\
- \ 6.64 \\
\hline
\end{array}
$$

A. $4.11
B. $4.89
C. $4.99
D. $5.11

22.
$$
\begin{array}{r}
\$14.55 \\
+ \ 18.25 \\
\hline
\end{array}
$$

A. $22.70
B. $23.80
C. $32.80
D. $33.70

23. Valerie bought a salad for $3.49, juice for $1.19, and pie for $1.50. How much did she spend in all?

A. $4.68   B. $5.08
C. $6.08   D. $6.18

24. Alan uses a $5.00 bill to buy lunch. He buys a sandwich for $1.75, lemonade for $1.25, and a cookie for $0.50. How much change should he get?

A. $0.50   B. $1.50
C. $2.50   D. $3.50

Form A • Multiple-Choice   A6   ▶ **Stop!**

Name _____

Solve. Then choose the letter of the correct answer.

1. The perimeter of this figure is 542 ft. Find the missing length.

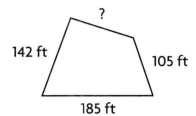

A. 100 ft   B. 110 ft

C. 200 ft   D. 432 ft

2. The perimeter of this figure is 1,260 ft. Find the missing length.

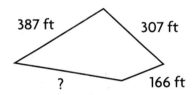

A. 373 ft   B. 387 ft

C. 400 ft   D. 473 ft

3. The city planted 170 plants on the four sides of a parking lot. There are 48 plants on one side. There are 35 on another side and 53 on the third side. How many plants are on the fourth side?

A. 34 plants   B. 36 plants

C. 44 plants   D. 136 plants

4. A rectangular field has a perimeter of 624 yd. The field has 2 sides that are each 212 yd. What is the length of each of the other two sides?

A. 50 yd   B. 100 yd

C. 200 yd   D. 212 yd

5. Which place-value positions should be regrouped to solve this problem?

$$3,000$$
$$-1,000$$

A. Regroup all places.
B. Regroup hundreds.
C. Regroup 3 thousands.
D. Do not regroup.

6. $$800$$
$$-428$$

A. 228
B. 372
C. 382
D. 482

7. $$300$$
$$-106$$

A. 194
B. 196
C. 204
D. 294

8. $$8,000$$
$$-6,917$$

A. 1,083
B. 2,083
C. 2,093
D. 2,183

9. $$40,000$$
$$-29,195$$

A. 1,915
B. 9,105
C. 10,805
D. 11,195

Form A • Multiple-Choice   A7   **Go on.** ▶

10. Salmon swim 6,000 mi when they migrate. Dogfish swim 2,500 mi. How much farther do salmon swim?

   A. 2,500 mi   B. 3,500 mi

   C. 4,500 mi   D. 8,500 mi

11. The zoo planted 3,400 red tulip bulbs and 1,850 yellow tulip bulbs. How many more red tulip bulbs were planted?

   A. 850 bulbs   B. 1,050 bulbs

   C. 1,150 bulbs   D. 1,550 bulbs

12. The soccer team has won 5 games, lost 4 games, and tied 2 games. Their season has a total of 16 games. How many games does the team have left to play?

   A. 3 games   B. 5 games

   C. 7 games   D. 9 games

13. Tori chose a number. She added 6. Then, she subtracted 8. Last, she added 5. The result was 13. What number did Tori start with?

   A. 10   B. 16

   C. 22   D. 27

14. What is 377 rounded to the nearest hundred?

   A. 300   B. 370

   C. 380   D. 400

15. What is 5,298 rounded to the nearest thousand?

   A. 5,000   B. 5,200

   C. 5,300   D. 6,000

For questions 16–18, choose the best estimate of the sum or difference.

16.   192   A. 500
      313   B. 700
     +267   C. 800
                     D. 900

17.   7,384   A. 2,000
     −3,871   B. 3,000
                     C. 5,000
                     D. 9,000

18.   5,688   A. 4,000
     +1,924   B. 7,000
                     C. 8,000
                     D. 9,000

For questions 19–20, use the table.

VISITORS TO BAXTER STATE PARK	
Month	Visitors
May	1,279
June	1,872
July	2,943
August	3,295
September	1,061

19. How many people visited the park in May and June?

   A. 1,593 people   B. 1,607 people

   C. 2,007 people   D. 3,151 people

20. How many more people visited the park in August than in September?

   A. 2,154 more   B. 2,234 more

   C. 4,256 more   D. 4,356 more

Name _____

Choose the letter of the correct answer.

1. Which answer choice tells how many times Carla walks her dog in 5 days?

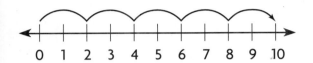

A. $2 + 5$
B. $5 - 2$
C. 5×2
D. $5 + 2$

2. Which answer choice tells how many sticks of gum Tonya bought?

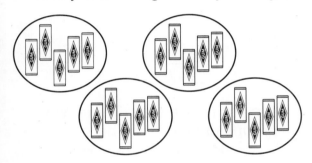

A. 5×5
B. 4×5
C. $4 + 5$
D. $5 - 4$

3. Which answer choice tells how many flowers there are?

A. 3×6
B. 6×6
C. $6 + 3$
D. $6 - 3$

4. Elaine bought 2 packages of film. Each package held 3 rolls of film. How many rolls of film did Elaine buy in all?

A. 3 rolls
B. 6 rolls
C. 7 rolls
D. 9 rolls

5. Ali feeds his cat 2 times a day. In one week, how many times does he feed his cat?

A. 2 times
B. 9 times
C. 12 times
D. 14 times

6. Which number sentence shows the Order Property of Multiplication?

A. $3 \times 1 = 3$
B. $3 \times 3 = 9$
C. $3 \times 2 = 2 \times 3$
D. $3 \times 0 = 0$

7. Which number sentence shows the Zero Property for Multiplication?

A. $5 \times 6 = 6 \times 5$
B. $5 \times 1 = 5$
C. $5 \times 5 = 25$
D. $5 \times 0 = 0$

8. Which number sentence shows the Property of One?

A. $4 \times 1 = 4$
B. $4 \times 0 = 0$
C. $4 \times 2 = 2 \times 4$
D. $4 \times 4 = 16$

9. $120 \times 0 = \underline{\ ?\ }$

A. 0
B. 1
C. 12
D. 120

10. $1 \times 7 = \underline{\ ?\ }$

A. 0
B. 1
C. 7
D. 8

Form A • Multiple-Choice   A9   **Go on.** ▶

11. $8 \times 4 = 32$ $4 \times 8 = \underline{\ ?\ }$

    A. 24   **B.** 32
    C. 48   **D.** 84

12. $(2 \times 3) \times 4 = \underline{\ ?\ }$

    A. 6   **B.** 10
    C. 12   **D.** 24

13. $2 \times (1 \times 8) = \underline{\ ?\ }$

    A. 10   **B.** 16
    C. 17   **D.** 24

14. $4 \times (3 \times 3) = \underline{\ ?\ }$

    A. 9   **B.** 12
    C. 36   **D.** 49

15. $(5 \times 6) \times 1 = \underline{\ ?\ }$

    A. 30   **B.** 40
    C. 56   **D.** 60

16. $(3 \times 2) \times 2 = \underline{\ ?\ }$

    A. 8   **B.** 12   **C.** 18   **D.** 24

17. $2 \times (4 \times 2) = \underline{\ ?\ }$

    A. 8   **B.** 10   **C.** 16   **D.** 32

For questions 18–22, choose the number sentence that can be used to solve the problem.

18. Kip has 2 shelves in his room. There are 2 rows of 4 model airplanes on each shelf. How many airplanes are there?

    A. $(2 \times 1) \times 4 = \underline{\ ?\ }$
    B. $(2 \times 4) + 2 = \underline{\ ?\ }$
    C. $(2 \times 2) + 4 = \underline{\ ?\ }$
    D. $2 \times (2 \times 4) = \underline{\ ?\ }$

19. Rosa has a pumpkin patch. There are 6 rows with 3 pumpkins in each row. How many pumpkins are there in all?

    A. $6 + 3 = \underline{\ ?\ }$
    B. $6 \times 3 = \underline{\ ?\ }$
    C. $9 \times 3 = \underline{\ ?\ }$
    D. $6 - 3 = \underline{\ ?\ }$

20. Derek collected 6 stones on a class trip. Amy collected 4 stones. How many more stones did Derek collect?

    A. $6 \times 4 = \underline{\ ?\ }$
    B. $4 + 6 = \underline{\ ?\ }$
    C. $6 - 4 = \underline{\ ?\ }$
    D. $4 + \underline{\ ?\ } = 6$

21. A class took a walk. There were 5 groups of students. There were 5 students in each group. How many students were there in all?

    A. $5 \times 5 = \underline{\ ?\ }$
    B. $5 + 5 = \underline{\ ?\ }$
    C. $5 - 1 = \underline{\ ?\ }$
    D. $5 - 5 = \underline{\ ?\ }$

22. In the morning, Myra walked 4 mi. In the afternoon, she walked 2 mi. How many miles did she walk in all?

    A. $4 + 2 = \underline{\ ?\ }$
    B. $4 - 2 = \underline{\ ?\ }$
    C. $4 \times 2 = \underline{\ ?\ }$
    D. $2 + \underline{\ ?\ } = 4$

Choose the letter of the correct answer.

1. A softball team has 12 softballs. The team keeps the same number of balls in each of 4 boxes. How many softballs are in each box?

   A. 3 softballs   B. 6 softballs
   C. 8 softballs   D. 16 softballs

2. There are 25 students in a spelling bee. How many students are on each of 5 teams?

   A. 3 students   B. 5 students
   C. 10 students   D. 20 students

3. What operation is the inverse of division?

   A. addition   B. subtraction
   C. multiplication   D. not here

4. Which number sentence is in the same fact family as $4 \times 5 = 20$?

   A. $5 - 4 = 1$ B. $4 + 5 = 9$
   C. $20 \div 5 = 4$ D. $20 + 4 = 24$

For questions 5–6, use the multiplication fact to help you find the quotient.

5. $30 \div 5 = \underline{\ ?\ }$

   $5 \times 6 = 30$

   A. 5   B. 6
   C. 25   D. 35

6. $21 \div 7 = \underline{\ ?\ }$

   $3 \times 7 = 21$

   A. 3   B. 7
   C. 14   D. 28

For questions 7–8, use the model to find the quotient.

7. $18 \div 4 = \underline{\ ?\ }$

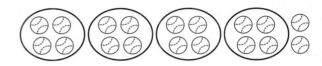

   A. 4   B. 4 r1
   C. 4 r2   D. 4 r3

8. $19 \div 3 = \underline{\ ?\ }$

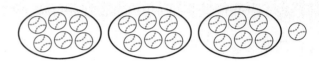

   A. 5 r4   B. 6
   C. 6 r1   D. 6 r2

9. There are 28 students in Miss Lo's class. She wants the students to work in small groups to make maps. How many students will be in each group if Miss Lo has 7 groups?

   A. 3 students   B. 4 students
   C. 5 students   D. 6 students

10. Vivian made 36 cookies to give away. She gave 6 cookies to each of her friends. How many friends got cookies?

   A. 4 friends   B. 6 friends
   C. 8 friends   D. 9 friends

Form A • Multiple-Choice   A11   **Go on.** ▶

For questions 11–14, use the multiplication table to find the quotient.

x	0	1	2	3	4	5
0	0	0	0	0	0	0
1	0	1	2	3	4	5
2	0	2	4	6	8	10
3	0	3	6	9	12	15
4	0	4	8	12	16	20
5	0	5	10	15	20	25

11. $20 \div 4 = $?

   A. 2   B. 3
   C. 5   D. 6

12. $16 \div 4 = $?

   A. 4   B. 5
   C. 8   D. 9

13. $3 \div 3 = $?

   A. 1   B. 3
   C. 4   D. 6

14. $15 \div 5 = $?

   A. 2   B. 3
   C. 5   D. 7

15. $6\overline{)42}$

   A. 5   B. 6
   C. 7   D. 8

16. $9\overline{)72}$

   A. 3   B. 4
   C. 6   D. 8

For questions 17–18, use the table.

Bake Sale Item	Cookies Sold
Chocolate-chip cookies	64
Oatmeal cookies	36
Peanut-butter cookies	24
Chocolate cookies	43

17. The oatmeal cookies were sold 4 cookies to a bag. How many bags were sold?

   A. 5 bags   B. 6 bags
   C. 7 bags   D. 9 bags

18. Four students each brought in the same number of peanut-butter cookies. How many cookies did each bring in?

   A. 4 cookies   B. 5 cookies
   C. 6 cookies   D. 9 cookies

For questions 19–20, solve each problem.

19. Gary earned $20 for walking his neighbor's dogs. He earned $5 each day. How many days did he walk the dogs?

   A. 2 days   B. 3 days
   C. 4 days   D. 5 days

20. Wanda was packing 32 glasses in boxes. She put 8 glasses in each box. How many boxes did Wanda pack?

   A. 4 boxes   B. 6 boxes
   C. 8 boxes   D. 12 boxes

Choose the letter of the correct answer.

1. $6 - 3 = 8 -$?

   A. 2　　B. 4　　C. 5　　D. 6

2.　　58
　　　16
　　$+ 45$

   A. 109
   B. 119
   C. 124
   D. not here

3. A rectangular table has a perimeter of 90 inches. The table is 20 inches wide. How long is it?

   A. 25 in.　　B. 30 in.
   C. 50 in.　　D. 70 in.

4. Which is the best estimate of this sum?

   489
   102
   $+ 276$

   A. 600
   B. 700
   C. 800
   D. 900

5.　$15.82
　$- 8.41$

   A. $6.41
   B. $7.23
   C. $7.41
   D. not here

6. Dan bought a burger for $4.29, salad for $1.29, and lemonade for $1.36. How much did he spend in all?

   A. $6.84　　B. $6.85
   C. $6.88　　D. $6.94

7. The perimeter of this figure is 96 yards. What is the missing length?

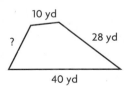
10 yd
?
28 yd
40 yd

   A. 18 yd　　B. 20 yd
   C. 24 yd　　D. 26 yd

8.　　700
　　$- 519$

   A. 181
   B. 191
   C. 201
   D. 291

9. There are 3,200 students at a high school and 1,450 students at a middle school. How many more students are at the high school?

   A. 1,650 more students
   B. 1,750 more students
   C. 1,850 more students
   D. not here

10. What is 565 rounded to the nearest hundred?

   A. 500　　B. 560　　C. 570　　D. 600

For questions 11–12, use the table.

SALES AT JOE'S BICYCLE SHOP	
Year	Sales
1994	1,414
1995	1,978
1996	2,036
1997	3,159

11. How many bicycles were sold in 1994 and 1995?

   A. 2,382 bicycles
   B. 2,392 bicycles
   C. 3,392 bicycles
   D. 3,402 bicycles

12. How many more bicycles were sold in 1997 than in 1996?

   A. 123 more bicycles
   B. 223 more bicycles
   C. 564 more bicycles
   D. 1,123 more bicycles

13. Which number sentence tells how many legs there are in all?

A. $4 + 3 = 7$ B. $3 \times 4 = 12$
C. $3 \times 3 = 9$ D. $4 - 3 = 1$

14. Which number sentence shows the Zero Property for Multiplication?

A. $6 \times 5 = 30$ B. $6 \times 1 = 1 \times 6$
C. $6 \times 0 = 0$ D. $6 \times 6 = 36$

15. $7 \times 4 = 28$, so $4 \times 7 = \underline{\ ?\ }$

A. 21   B. 24   C. 27   D. 28

16. $(5 \times 3) \times 4 = \underline{\ ?\ }$

A. 12   B. 32
C. 60   D. not here

17. Greg's school has 8 rows with 9 lockers in each row. How many lockers are there in all?

A. 17 lockers   B. 27 lockers
C. 63 lockers   D. 72 lockers

18. Choose the number sentence that can be used to solve the problem.

On Monday Cal read 4 pages. On Tuesday he read 8 pages. How many pages did he read in all?

A. $4 + 8 = \underline{\ ?\ }$
B. $4 \times 8 = \underline{\ ?\ }$
C. $8 \div 4 = \underline{\ ?\ }$
D. $4 + \underline{\ ?\ } = 8$

19. The tennis team has 18 tennis balls. The balls are kept in 6 cans. How many tennis balls are in each can?

A. 2 tennis balls
B. 3 tennis balls
C. 6 tennis balls
D. not here

20. Which number sentence is in the same fact family as $32 \div 8 = 4$?

A. $4 \times 8 = 32$
B. $32 - 18 = 14$
C. $8 + 4 = 12$
D. not here

21. Use the model to find the quotient.
$13 \div 2 = ?$

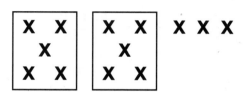

A. 2   B. 2 r3   C. 3 r2   D. 5 r3

22. A bookstore sold a total of 35 books to 5 customers. Each customer bought the same number of books. How many books did each customer buy?

A. 5 books   B. 6 books
C. 7 books   D. 30 books

23. $7\overline{)56}$

A. 6   B. 7   C. 8   D. 9

24. The P.E. class has 36 students. They are grouped in teams of 9 for baseball. How many teams are there?

A. 3 teams   B. 4 teams
C. 6 teams   D. 18 teams

Name _____

Choose the letter of the correct answer.

1. $2 + 5 = \underline{\ ?\ } + 3$

   A. 1   B. 3
   C. 4   D. 7

2. $9 - 4 = 6 - \underline{\ ?\ }$

   A. 1   B. 2
   C. 4   D. not here

3.   15   A. 45
     26   B. 55
   +14   C. 60
                 D. not here

4.   37   A. 147
     74   B. 151
   +56   C. 157
                 D. 167

5. What is 412 rounded to the nearest hundred?

   A. 300   B. 400
   C. 410   D. 500

6. Use the price list.

Movie	$4.25
Popcorn	$2.15
Soda	$1.65

Pete uses a $10 bill to pay for a movie, popcorn, and a soda. About how much change will he receive?

   A. about $1   B. about $2
   C. about $3   D. about $5

7. $8.19   A. $3.62
   − 3.57   B. $4.52
                    C. $4.62
                    D. not here

8. $3.89   A. $9.38
      1.12   B. $9.48
   + 4.37   C. $10.28
                    D. $10.68

9. At a baseball game, Tony bought a scorebook for $2.95, baseball cards for $4.75, and a bag of peanuts for $1.50. How much change should he get back from a $10 bill?

   A. $0.60   B. $0.70
   C. $0.80   D. not here

10. The perimeter of the figure is 1,168 feet. What is the missing length?

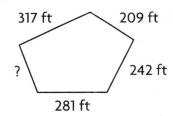

   A. 99 ft   B. 109 ft
   C. 117 ft   D. 119 ft

11. Mrs. Green put the flags of different countries on the classroom walls. Out of 212 flags, 41 were on the front wall, and the side walls had 57 on each. How many flags were on the back wall?

   A. 57 flags   B. 62 flags
   C. 67 flags   D. 77 flags

12. 900
     −387

A. 503
B. 513
C. 523
D. 613

13. 6,000
     −3,254

A. 2,536
B. 2,646
C. 2,736
D. 2,746

14. What is 383 rounded to the nearest hundred?

A. 400   B. 500
C. 800   D. 900

15. What is the best estimate of the sum?

9,789
+3,975

A. 10,000
B. 12,000
C. 13,000
D. 14,000

For questions 16–18, use the table.

PINTS OF MILK USED BY CAFETERIA	
August	1,881
September	1,957
October	2,112
November	1,925
December	1,949

16. How many pints were used in September and October?

A. 3,069 pints   B. 4,069 pints
C. 4,169 pints   D. 4,179 pints

17. How many fewer pints were used in August than in September?

A. 56 pints   B. 58 pints
C. 66 pints   D. 76 pints

18. How many fewer pints were used in November than in October?

A. 87 pints   B. 167 pints
C. 187 pints   D. 197 pints

19. Which number sentence tells how many rolls are on the plates?

A. 4 + 7   B. 7 − 4
C. 4 × 7   D. 7 ÷ 4

20. Which number sentence shows the Property of One for Multiplication?

A. 6 × 0 = 0
B. 6 × 3 = 3 × 6
C. 6 × 1 = 6
D. 6 × 6 = 36

Name_____

CUMULATIVE TEST PAGE 3

21. $7 \times 6 = 42$ so $6 \times 7 = \underline{\ ?\ }$

A. 42   **B.** 48
C. 49   **D.** not here

22. $(9 \times 1) \times 3 = \underline{\ ?\ }$

A. 0   **B.** 3
C. 9   **D.** 27

23. $5 \times (4 \times 4) = \underline{\ ?\ }$

A. 16   **B.** 40
C. 80   **D.** not here

24. Danny bought 3 packs of sports cards. Each pack had 6 cards. How many cards in all did Danny buy?

A. 8 cards   **B.** 12 cards
C. 15 cards   **D.** 18 cards

For questions 25–27, choose the number sentence that can be used to solve the problem.

25. In June, Ray read 7 books. In July, he read 9 books. How many books did he read in all?

A. $9 - 7 = \underline{\ ?\ }$
B. $9 \times 7 = \underline{\ ?\ }$
C. $7 + \underline{\ ?\ } = 9$
D. $9 + 7 = \underline{\ ?\ }$

26. There were 3 classes that took part in a school project. Each class was divided into 4 groups. How many groups were there in all?

A. $3 \times 4 = \underline{\ ?\ }$
B. $4 + 3 = \underline{\ ?\ }$
C. $3 + 4 = \underline{\ ?\ }$
D. $4 - 3 = \underline{\ ?\ }$

27. On a bird-watching trip, Mariah saw 5 kinds of birds. Jack saw 8 kinds of birds. How many more kinds of birds did Jack see?

A. $8 + 5 = \underline{\ ?\ }$
B. $8 \times 5 = \underline{\ ?\ }$
C. $5 \times 8 = \underline{\ ?\ }$
D. $8 - 5 = \underline{\ ?\ }$

28. A school band has 27 students. The band has 3 sections with an equal number of students in each section. How many students are in each section?

A. 6 students   **B.** 7 students
C. 9 students   **D.** 20 students

29. A zoo has 3 monkey pens. There are 6 monkeys in each pen. How many monkeys are there in all?

A. 6 monkeys   **B.** 12 monkeys
C. 18 monkeys   **D.** 24 monkeys

30. Which number sentence is in the same fact family as $3 \times 7 = 21$?

A. $7 - 3 = 4$ **B.** $3 + 7 = 10$
C. $21 - 7 = 14$ **D.** $21 \div 3 = 7$

Form A • Multiple-Choice   A17   **Chapters 1–4**   **Go on.** ▶

31. Use the multiplication fact
$5 \times 7 = 35$ to help you find the
quotient.

$$35 \div 7 = \underline{\ ?\ }$$

A. 5   **B.** 7   **C.** 25   **D.** 42

32. Use the model to find the quotient.

$$19 \div 5 = \underline{\ ?\ }$$

A. 3 r3   **B.** 3 r4
C. 4   **D.** 4 r4

33. Ms. Martin's art class was divided
into 5 groups. The groups got 58
markers to share equally. How
many markers did each group get?
How many markers were left over?

A. 10 markers; 3 left over
B. 10 markers; 4 left over
C. 11 markers; 3 left over
D. 12 markers; 3 left over

For questions 34–35, use the
multiplication table to find the quotient.

×	2	3	4	5
2	4	6	8	10
3	6	9	12	15
4	8	12	16	20
5	10	15	20	25

34. $12 \div 3 = \underline{\ ?\ }$

A. 3   **B.** 4   **C.** 5   **D.** 6

35. $10 \div 2 = \underline{\ ?\ }$

A. 2   **B.** 4   **C.** 5   **D.** 8

36. $8\overline{)64}$

A. 4   **B.** 5   **C.** 6   **D.** 8

37. $7\overline{)56}$

A. 8   **B.** 9   **C.** 10   **D.** 11

For questions 38–40, use the table.

CLASS TRIP	NUMBER OF STUDENTS
Museum	36
Library	24
Nature Trail	29
Zoo	32

38. On a trip to the library, 3 vans each
carried the same number of
students. How many students rode
in each van?

A. 6 students   **B.** 7 students
C. 8 students   **D.** 9 students

39. On a trip to the museum, students
rode in parents' cars that held 4
students each. How many cars
were needed?

A. 6 cars   **B.** 7 cars
C. 9 cars   **D.** 12 cars

40. Of the students who went to the
nature trail, 17 were girls. How
many boys went to the nature trail?

A. 3 boys   **B.** 12 boys
C. 15 boys   **D.** 18 boys

Name _____

Choose the letter of the correct answer.

1. Which is a *cardinal* number?

    A. 134 High Street
    B. 2 students
    C. Fifth in line
    D. Radio station 103.7

2. Which is an *ordinal* number?

 A.
 B.

 **C.**
 D.

For questions 3–6, use the grid.

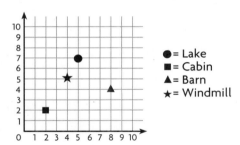

● = Lake
■ = Cabin
▲ = Barn
★ = Windmill

3. Which ordered pair shows the location of the lake?

    A. (5,7)   **B.** (7,5)
    C. (4,8)   **D.** not here

4. What is located at (2,2)?

    A. Lake   **B.** Cabin
    C. Barn   **D.** Windmill

5. Which ordered pair shows the location of the windmill?

    A. (4,8)   **B.** (5,4)
    C. (4,5)   **D.** (8,4)

6. What is located at (8,4)?

    A. Lake   **B.** Cabin
    C. Barn   **D.** Windmill

For questions 7–8, use the base-ten blocks.

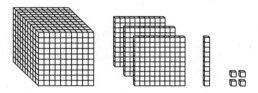

7. What does the large cube stand for?

    A. 1 thousand   **B.** 1 hundred
    C. 1 ten   **D.** 1 one

8. Which number is shown by all these base-ten blocks?

    A. 1,043   **B.** 1,314
    C. 1,433   **D.** 2,204

9. How many thousands are in 6,235?

    A. 2 thousands
    B. 3 thousands
    C. 5 thousands
    D. 6 thousands

10. How many tens are in 4,801?

    A. 0 tens   **B.** 1 ten
    C. 4 tens   **D.** 8 tens

11. Which number has a 5 in the hundreds place?

    A. 1,357   **B.** 3,715
    C. 5,731   **D.** not here

12. Which number has the comma in the correct place?

    A. 426,8   **B.** 42,68
    C. 4,268   **D.** not here

13. The engine is the first car of the train. The dining car is after the engine. The cattle car comes next. The freight car is next in line, and the caboose is the last car. Which car is fourth on this train?

A. freight car   B. dining car
C. cattle car   D. caboose

14. Cara has twice as many mystery books as her brother. Her brother has 9 books. How many books does Cara have?

A. 11 books   B. 16 books
C. 18 books   D. 20 books

15. Which benchmark number can you use to estimate the number of crackers in Box B?

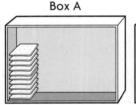

Box A   Box B

A. 3 crackers   B. 5 crackers
C. 10 crackers   D. 15 crackers

16. Which benchmark number can you use to estimate the number of squares on Quilt B?

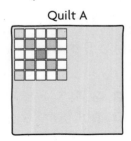

Quilt A   Quilt B

A. 10 squares   B. 15 squares
C. 20 squares   D. 25 squares

17. About how many marbles are in Jar B?

A   B

A. about 5 marbles
B. about 10 marbles
C. about 15 marbles
D. about 20 marbles

18. About how many tiles are on Floor B?

Floor A   Floor B

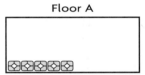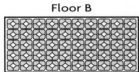

A. about 50 tiles
B. about 100 tiles
C. about 150 tiles
D. not here

19. A 6-inch sub costs $1.95. About how much should a 12-inch sub cost?

A. about $2.00   B. about $3.00
C. about $4.00   D. about $5.00

20. There are 100 jelly beans in the jar now. About how many could the jar hold?

A. about 120 jelly beans
B. about 150 jelly beans
C. about 200 jelly beans
D. not here

Name _____

Choose the letter of the correct answer.

1. What is the value of the digit 4 in the number 345?

   A. $4 \times 0 = 0$
   B. $4 \times 1 = 4$
   C. $4 \times 10 = 40$
   D. $4 \times 100 = 400$

2. In which number does the digit 5 have a value of 500?

   A. 155
   B. 3,851
   C. 5,048
   D. 7,521

3. Which number is written in expanded form?

   A. 5,364
   B. $5,000 + 300 + 60 + 4$
   C. fifty-three hundred, sixty-four
   D. five thousand, three hundred sixty-four

4. What is the standard form for the number shown in this place-value chart?

Thousands	Hundreds	Tens	Ones
2	1	3	6
$2 \times 1,000 = 2,000$	$1 \times 100 = 100$	$3 \times 10 = 30$	$6 \times 1 = 6$

   A. 2,136   B. 21,036
   C. 21,306   D. 21,360

5. What is *one hundred eighty-one* written in standard form?

   A. 180
   B. 181
   C. 800
   D. 80

6. What is *six thousand, two hundred two* written in standard form?

   A. 622
   B. 6,022
   C. 6,202
   D. 6,220

7. What is $3,000 + 70 + 4$ in written form?

   A. three thousand, seven
   B. three thousand, seventy-four
   C. three thousand, seven hundred four
   D. three thousand, seven hundred forty

8. What is 8,015 written in expanded form?

   A. $800 + 10 + 5$
   B. $8,000 + 10 + 5$
   C. $8,000 + 100 + 5$
   D. $8,000 + 100 + 50$

9. What is another name for 1,500?

   A. 15 hundreds
   B. 150 ones
   C. 150 hundreds
   D. 1,500 tens

10. Henri did the following addition problem. How should he write the sum in standard form?

    9 hundreds
    +8 hundreds
    17 hundreds

    A. 117
    B. 170
    C. 1,700
    D. 17,100

Form A • Multiple-Choice   A21   **Go on.** ▶

For questions 11–12, use mental math.

11.   600
     $+500$

A. 1,100
B. 1,110
C. 11,000
D. not here

12.   8,000
     $+7,000$

A. 1,500
B. 15,000
C. 150,000
D. not here

13. In which number are the commas correctly used to separate the periods?

A. 42,40,7216
B. 4,240,7216
C. 424,07,216
D. 42,407,216

14. Millions could be used to count the people in a ___?___.

A. school
B. neighborhood
C. state
D. movie theater

15. What is *one million, two hundred twenty thousand, three hundred fifteen* written in standard form?

A. 1,220,315
B. 1,313,220
C. 1,220,000,315
D. 1,220,315,000

16. What is *three hundred eight million, four hundred thousand, seven hundred nine* written in standard form?

A. 384,709   B. 3,084,709
C. 38,479,000   D. not here

17. Which shows how to write 11,345,867 with period names?

A. 11 thousand, 345 hundred, 867
B. 11 hundred thousand, 345 thousand, 867 hundred
C. 11 million, 345 thousand, 867
D. not here

18. Which shows how to write 107,006,200 with period names?

A. 1 million, 76 thousand
B. 107 million, 6 thousand, 200
C. 107 million, 60 thousand, 200
D. not here

For questions 19–20, use the table.

LEWIS COUNTY FAIR ATTENDANCE		
Year	Number of People	Increase from Previous Year
1994	14,370	–
1995	16,492	2,122
1996	19,058	2,566
1997	23,135	4,077

19. Between which two years did fair attendance increase the most?

A. 1994–1995   B. 1995–1996
C. 1996–1997   D. 1997–1998

20. How many more people attended the fair in 1996 than in 1994?

A. 2,122 more people
B. 2,566 more people
C. 4,077 more people
D. 4,688 more people

Choose the letter of the correct answer.

1. Use the number line to compare.

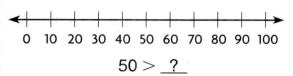

   0 10 20 30 40 50 60 70 80 90 100

   50 > _?_

   A. 40   B. 50   C. 60   D. 100

2. Use the number line to compare.

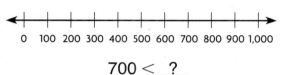

   0 100 200 300 400 500 600 700 800 900 1,000

   700 < _?_

   A. 400   B. 500   C. 700   D. 900

3. Choose the statement that is correct.
   A. 814 > 841   B. 340 < 304
   C. 125 = 251   D. 520 > 502

4. Choose the statement that is correct.
   A. 7,117 > 7,217
   B. 9,348 = 3,984
   C. 8,361 > 8,316
   D. 4,957 > 4,975

5. Choose the statement that is correct.
   A. 1,245 > 2,145
   B. 5,306 < 5,063
   C. 2,215 > 2,451
   D. 8,846 = 8,846

6. In which pair of numbers do the digits differ in the ones position?
   A. 243; 245   B. 132; 232
   C. 303; 313   D. 141; 151

7. In which pair of numbers do the digits differ in the hundreds position?
   A. 3,710; 1,710   B. 2,453; 2,455
   C. 2,235; 2,435   D. 3,846; 3,866

For questions 8–9, compare the numbers and choose the correct statement.

8. 483 ● 438
   A. 483 > 438   B. 483 = 438
   C. 483 < 438   D. not here

9. 6,912 ● 6,972
   A. 6,912 = 6,972
   B. 6,912 > 6,972
   C. 6,912 < 6,972
   D. not here

10. There are 27 children in Mrs. Enrique's class. There are 3 more girls than boys. How many boys are there?
    A. 12 boys   B. 13 boys
    C. 14 boys   D. 15 boys

11. Malcolm has 8 coins that total $1.02. He has at least 1 penny, 1 nickel, 1 dime, and 1 quarter. How many dimes does he have?
    A. 1 dime   B. 2 dimes
    C. 3 dimes   D. not here

12. Which numbers are written in order from the least to the greatest?

    600 610 620 630 640 650 660 670 680 690 700

    A. 680, 608, 688
    B. 608, 688, 680
    C. 680, 688, 608
    D. 608, 680, 688

13. Which numbers are written in order from the least to the greatest?

1,550   1,560   1,570   1,580   1,590

A. 1,557; 1,575; 1,570
B. 1,575; 1,557; 1,570
C. 1,570; 1,557; 1,575
D. 1,557; 1,570; 1,575

14. Which numbers are written in order from the least to the greatest?

A. 702, 678, 617
B. 617, 678, 702
C. 702, 617, 678
D. not here

15. Which numbers are written in order from the greatest to the least?

A. 2,742; 1,983; 2,344
B. 2,344; 1,983; 2,742
C. 2,742; 2,344; 1,983
D. 1,983; 2,344; 2,742

For questions 16–17, use the table.

LIBRARY BOOKS BORROWED	
Day of Week	Number of Books Borrowed
Monday	1,037
Tuesday	1,861
Wednesday	1,495
Thursday	1,019
Friday	1,798

16. On which day was the greatest number of books borrowed?

A. Monday   B. Tuesday
C. Thursday   D. Friday

17. On which day was the least number of books borrowed?

A. Monday   B. Tuesday
C. Thursday   D. Friday

For questions 18–20, use the Venn diagram.

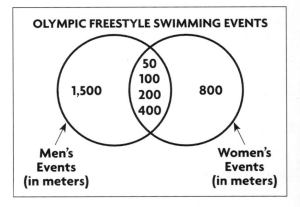

OLYMPIC FREESTYLE SWIMMING EVENTS

1,500   50 100 200 400   800

Men's Events (in meters)   Women's Events (in meters)

18. In which event do only women compete?

A. 50-meter freestyle
B. 400-meter freestyle
C. 800-meter freestyle
D. 1,500-meter freestyle

19. In which event do only men compete?

A. 50-meter freestyle
B. 400-meter freestyle
C. 800-meter freestyle
D. 1,500-meter freestyle

20. In which event do both men and women compete?

A. 100-meter freestyle
B. 800-meter freestyle
C. 1,000-meter freestyle
D. 1,500-meter freestyle

Choose the letter of the correct answer.

1. Which unit of time would you use to measure the time it takes to turn on a radio?

   A. seconds   B. minutes
   C. hours   D. days

2. Which unit of time would you use to measure how long you sleep at night?

   A. seconds   B. minutes
   C. hours   D. days

3. Which clock shows 4 minutes past five?

   A.  4:05   B.  4:50

   C. 5:04   D. 5:40

4. What time is shown on the clock?

   A. 1:05 and 9 seconds
   B. 1:15 and 45 seconds
   C. 1:45 and 15 seconds
   D. 3:05 and 9 seconds

5. Mr. Wong leaves for work at 8:05 every day. Which clock below shows the time Mr. Wong leaves?

   A.    B.

   C.   D.

6. Corinna gets on the school bus at 7:35 each morning. Which clock shows the time she gets on the bus?

   A.    B.

   C.   D.

7. Which time is closest to the time that the sun sets?

   A. 6:00 A.M.   B. 1:00 P.M.
   C. 6:00 P.M.   D. 1:00 A.M.

8. Which time is closest to the time that many people eat lunch?

   A. 12:30 P.M.   B. 7:30 P.M.
   C. 7:30 A.M.   D. 12:30 A.M.

9. Samuel walks his dog from 12:15 P.M. to 12:40 P.M. How many minutes pass from the beginning to the end of his walk?

   A. 15 minutes   B. 25 minutes
   C. 30 minutes   D. 35 minutes

10. Hannah's dance lesson begins at 4:30 P.M. and ends at 5:20 P.M. How many minutes pass from the beginning to the end of her dance lesson?

    A. 40 minutes   B. 45 minutes
    C. 50 minutes   D. 60 minutes

For questions 11–16, use the schedule.

BUS	LEAVES CHICAGO	ARRIVES MILWAUKEE
A	8:15 A.M.	9:45 A.M.
B	10:45 A.M.	?
C	12:15 P.M.	?
D	2:45 P.M.	?
Trip lasts 1 hour and 30 minutes.		

11. What time does Bus B arrive in Milwaukee?

A. 11:15 A.M.　　B. 11:45 A.M.
C. 12:30 A.M.　　D. 12:15 P.M.

12. What time does Bus C arrive in Milwaukee?

A. 1:00 P.M.　　B. 1:45 P.M.
C. 2:15 P.M.　　D. 2:45 P.M.

13. It takes Ms. Street 30 minutes to get to the bus station. She wants to take Bus A. What is the latest time she can leave her house?

A. 7:15 A.M.　　B. 7:45 A.M.
C. 8:00 A.M.　　D. 8:05 A.M.

14. Mr. Blum has a meeting in Milwaukee at 3:30 P.M. Which is the latest bus he could take to arrive at the meeting on time?

A. Bus A　　B. Bus B
C. Bus C　　D. Bus D

15. Janine plans to take Bus A to a band concert in Milwaukee. The concert begins at 12:05 P.M. Is there another bus on the schedule she can also take?

A. No, there is not.
B. Yes, she can take Bus B.
C. Yes, she can take Bus C.
D. Yes, she can take Bus D.

16. Kirk plans to leave Chicago on Bus D. It takes him 15 minutes to walk home after the bus arrives. At what time will he get home?

A. 3:30 P.M.　　B. 4:30 P.M.
C. 5:00 P.M.　　D. 5:15 P.M.

For questions 17–20, use the calendars.

June

Su	M	T	W	Th	F	Sa
1	2	3	4	5	6	7
8	9	10	11	12	13	14
15	16	17	18	19	20	21
22	23	24	25	26	27	28
29	30					

July

Su	M	T	W	Th	F	Sa
		1	2	3	4	5
6	7	8	9	10	11	12
13	14	15	16	17	18	19
20	21	22	23	24	25	26
27	28	29	30	31		

17. How many days is it from June 29 to July 3?

A. 3 days　　B. 4 days
C. 6 days　　D. 8 days

18. How many weeks is it from June 9 to July 28?

A. 7 weeks　　B. 8 weeks
C. 9 weeks　　D. 10 weeks

19. Ramon's family is going on a trip for 2 weeks. The trip will end on July 17. On what date will it begin?

A. June 30　　B. July 3
C. July 24　　D. July 31

20. Marion is going on a trip from June 27 until July 9. How many days will her trip last?

A. 9 days　　B. 11 days
C. 12 days　　D. 15 days

Name _____

Choose the letter of the correct answer.

For questions 1–2, use the grid.

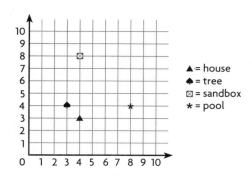

1. Which ordered pair shows the location of the tree?

A. (3,4)　　　B. (4,3)
C. (4,6)　　　D. (4,8)

2. What is located at (8,4)?

A. house　　　B. tree
C. sandbox　　D. pool

3. How many thousands are in 3,975?

A. 3 thousands　B. 5 thousands
C. 7 thousands　D. 9 thousands

4. Mark is 3 times as old as Kate. Kate is 3 years old. How old is Mark?

A. 3 years old　　B. 6 years old
C. 9 years old　　D. not here

5. Which benchmark number can you use to estimate the number of cookies on Tray A and Tray B?

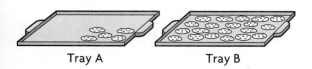

Tray A　　　　　　Tray B

A. 3 cookies　　　B. 5 cookies
C. 10 cookies　　D. 20 cookies

6. A 6-pack of juice costs $2.89. About how much should a 12-pack cost?

A. about $3.00　　B. about $4.00
C. about $8.00　　D. not here

7. What is *four hundred thirty* in standard form?

A. 340　B. 400　C. 403　D. 430

8. What is 2,035 in expanded form?

A. 200 + 30 + 5
B. 2,000 + 30 + 5
C. 2,000 + 300 + 5
D. 2,000 + 30 + 50

9. What is another name for 2,400?

A. 240 ones　　　B. 24 tens
C. 24 hundreds　D. 240 hundreds

For questions 10–11, use the table.

POPULATION OF OAK CITY	
Year	Population
1994	22,096
1995	22,608
1996	24,910
1997	25,999

10. Between which two years did the population increase the most?

A. 1994 and 1995
B. 1995 and 1996
C. 1996 and 1997

11. How many more people lived in Oak City in 1997 than in 1994?

A. 2,903 more people
B. 3,003 more people
C. 3,903 more people
D. not here

Form A • Multiple-Choice　　　　A27　　　　**Go on.** ▶

12. Choose the statement that is correct.

    A. $724 > 742$ **B.** $819 > 825$

    C. $259 < 261$ **D.** $102 = 120$

13. What is the greatest place-value position in which the digits differ in these numbers?

        6,405
        6,505

    A. ones   **B.** tens

    C. hundreds   **D.** thousands

14. Which numbers are in order from least to greatest?

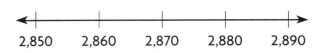

  2,850   2,860   2,870   2,880   2,890

    A. 2,884; 2,876; 2,887

    B. 2,876; 2,887; 2,884

    C. 2,876; 2,884; 2,887

    D. not here

For questions 15–16, use the Venn diagram.

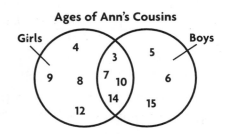

Ages of Ann's Cousins

15. Which is the age of a boy cousin only?

    A. 7 years old   **B.** 9 years old

    C. 14 years old   **D.** 15 years old

16. Which is the age of both a boy cousin and a girl cousin?

    A. 3 years old   **B.** 4 years old

    C. 5 years old   **D.** 12 years old

17. Which clock shows ten minutes past three?

  A.    **B.**

  C.    **D.**

18. A class lasts from 1:10 P.M. to 1:55 P.M. How many minutes pass from the beginning to the end of the class?

    A. 25 minutes   **B.** 35 minutes

    C. 45 minutes   **D.** not here

For questions 19–20, use the schedule.

Train	Leave Newark	Arrive New York
A	8:05 A.M.	8:55 A.M.
B	9:55 A.M.	?
C	11:05 A.M.	?
D	1:55 P.M.	?

The trip lasts 50 minutes.

19. What time does Train B arrive in New York?

    A. 10:45 A.M.   **B.** 11:05 P.M.

    C. 11:55 A.M.   **D.** not here

20. Mrs. Eng has to be in New York at 11:30 A.M. Which is the latest train she could take to arrive on time?

    A. Train A   **B.** Train B

    C. Train C   **D.** Train D

Name _____

Choose the letter of the correct answer.

1. $\begin{array}{r} 34 \\ 17 \\ + \ 29 \\ \hline \end{array}$
    A. 70
    B. 71
    C. 80
    D. 90

2. What is the best estimate of the difference?
    $\begin{array}{r} \$68.79 \\ - \ 19.57 \\ \hline \end{array}$
    A. $40.00
    B. $50.00
    C. $60.00
    D. $70.00

3. $\begin{array}{r} \$3.27 \\ 4.09 \\ + \ 1.25 \\ \hline \end{array}$
    A. $8.21
    B. $8.41
    C. $8.51
    D. $8.61

4. $\begin{array}{r} 600 \\ -312 \\ \hline \end{array}$
    A. 268
    B. 278
    C. 288
    D. not here

5. What is the best estimate of the difference?
    $\begin{array}{r} 717 \\ -513 \\ \hline \end{array}$
    A. 100
    B. 200
    C. 300
    D. 400

6. Ann has 3 fish tanks. There are 2 fish in each tank.

    Which number sentence shows how many fish there are in all?

    A. $2 + 3 = 5$ B. $3 - 2 = 1$
    C. $3 \times 3 = 9$ D. $2 \times 3 = 6$

7. Which number sentence shows the Order Property of Multiplication?
    A. $4 \times 7 = 7 \times 4$
    B. $4 \times 1 = 4$
    C. $7 \times 0 = 0$
    D. $4 \times 7 = 28$

8. $9 \times (2 \times 3) = \underline{\ ?\ }$
    A. 45   B. 54   C. 57   D. 64

9. Choose the number sentence that can be used to solve the problem.

    Kyle read 3 chapters every day for 5 days. How many chapters did he read in all?

    A. $5 - 3 = 2$ B. $3 \times 5 = 15$
    C. $3 + 2 = 5$ D. $3 + 5 = 8$

10. A P.E. class has 4 volleyball teams. There are 6 players on each team. How many players are there in all?

    A. 20 players   B. 22 players
    C. 24 players   D. 28 players

11. Which number sentence is in the same fact family as $18 \div 3 = 6$?

    A. $3 \times 6 = 18$ B. $3 + 6 = 9$
    C. $18 - 6 = 12$ D. $18 - 3 = 15$

12. Use the model to find the quotient.
$$16 \div 5 = \underline{\ ?\ }$$

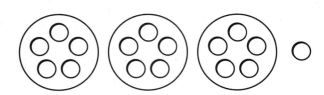

A. 2 r1   B. 3
C. 3 r1   D. not here

For questions 13–14, use the
multiplication table to find the quotient.

×	3	4	5
3	9	12	15
4	12	16	20
5	15	20	25

13. $12 \div 4 = \underline{\ ?\ }$

A. 1   B. 2   C. 3   D. 4

14. $16 \div 4 = \underline{\ ?\ }$

A. 2   B. 3   C. 4   D. 5

15. $8\overline{)48}$

A. 3   B. 4
C. 5   D. not here

16. Laura sold 42 boxes of cookies.
She sold 7 boxes each day. For
how many days did she sell
cookies?

A. 4 days   B. 5 days
C. 6 days   D. 7 days

17. Which shows a *cardinal* number?

A. 8 books
B. Channel 12
C. 3rd place
D. the number 6 on a shirt

18. What number is in the hundreds
place in the number 1,876?

A. 1   B. 6   C. 7   D. 8

19. There are 25 golf balls in a
container. About how many
could the container hold?

A. about 50 golf balls
B. about 75 golf balls
C. about 100 golf balls
D. about 150 golf balls

20. What is the value of the digit 2 in
the number 214?

A. $2 \times 100 = 200$
B. $2 \times 10 = 20$
C. $2 \times 1 = 2$
D. $2 \times 0 = 0$

21. What is *four hundred twenty-six* written in standard form?

   A. 46   **B.** 426
   C. 462   **D.** 4,260

22. What is *four million, three hundred twenty-seven thousand, four hundred twenty-four* written in standard form?

   A. 4,027,424   **B.** 4,273,424
   C. 4,307,424   **D.** 4,327,424

23. Which shows how to write 9,727,409 with period names?

   A. 9 thousand, 727 hundred, 409
   B. 9 million, 727 thousand, 409
   C. 9 hundred thousand, 727 hundred, 409
   D. not here

For questions 24–25, use mental math.

24.   500
     +700

   A. 200
   B. 1,100
   C. 1,200
   D. 3,500

25.   7,000
    +4,000

   A. 10,000
   B. 11,000
   C. 12,000
   D. not here

26. Use the number line to compare.

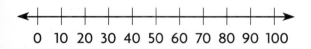

   0 10 20 30 40 50 60 70 80 90 100

      60 > ?

   A. 30   **B.** 60   **C.** 70   **D.** 90

27. Which statement is correct?

   A. 336 < 329
   B. 412 > 421
   C. 625 = 652
   D. 356 > 327

28. Compare the numbers. Which statement is correct?
         536 ● 563

   A. 536 > 563   **B.** 536 < 563
   C. 536 = 563   **D.** not here

For questions 29–30, use the table.

VISITORS TO THE ZOO	
Day of Week	**Number of Visitors**
Tuesday	1,282
Wednesday	1,104
Thursday	1,676
Friday	1,881
Saturday	1,890

29. On which day did the most visitors go to the zoo?

   A. Tuesday   **B.** Wednesday
   C. Friday   **D.** Saturday

30. On which day did the fewest visitors go to the zoo?

   A. Wednesday   **B.** Thursday
   C. Friday   **D.** Saturday

For questions 31–32, use the Venn diagram.

Scores On Math Test

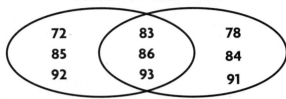

Mrs. Turner's Class   Mr. Nelson's Class

31. Which score was made only in Mr. Nelson's class?

   A. 83   **B.** 84   **C.** 85   **D.** 86

32. Which score was made in both Mr. Nelson's class and Ms. Turner's class?

   A. 84   **B.** 85   **C.** 86   **D.** 92

33. Which clock shows ten minutes before two?

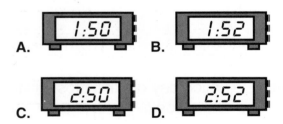

   A. 1:50   **B.** 1:52
   C. 2:50   **D.** 2:52

34. Which time is closest to the time that you arrive home from school?

   A. 11 A.M.   **B.** 11 P.M.
   C. 4 A.M.   **D.** 4 P.M.

For questions 35–36, use the schedule.

MOVIE SCHEDULE		
Movie	**Start Time**	**Finish Time**
A	4:30 P.M.	6:15 P.M.
B	5:00 P.M.	?
C	5:45 P.M.	?
All movies last 1 hour 45 minutes.		

35. At what time does Movie B end?

   A. 5:00 P.M.   **B.** 6:15 P.M.
   C. 6:30 P.M.   **D.** 6:45 P.M.

36. At what time does Movie C end?

   A. 7:15 P.M.   **B.** 7:30 P.M.
   C. 7:45 P.M.   **D.** 8:00 P.M.

For questions 37–38, use the calendars.

February

Su	M	T	W	Th	F	Sa
						1
2	3	4	5	6	7	8
9	10	11	12	13	14	15
16	17	18	19	20	21	22
23	24	25	26	27	28	

March

Su	M	T	W	Th	F	Sa
						1
2	3	4	5	6	7	8
9	10	11	12	13	14	15
16	17	18	19	20	21	22
23	24	25	26	27	28	29
30	31					

37. How many days is it from February 26 to March 4?

   A. 6 days   **B.** 8 days
   C. 9 days   **D.** 10 days

38. How many weeks is it from February 7 to March 14?

   A. 3 weeks   **B.** 4 weeks
   C. 5 weeks   **D.** 6 weeks

Choose the letter of the correct answer.

For questions 1–3, use the frequency table.

MAGAZINE SUBSCRIPTION DRIVE		
Week	Number Sold (Frequency)	Cumulative Frequency
1	111	111
2	97	208
3	74	?
4	105	?

1. During which week were the most subscriptions sold?

   A. Week 1   B. Week 2
   C. Week 3   D. Week 4

2. How many more subscriptions were sold in Week 2 than in Week 3?

   A. 14 more subscriptions
   B. 23 more subscriptions
   C. 74 more subscriptions
   D. 208 more subscriptions

3. What is the cumulative frequency for the magazine subscriptions sold in all 4 weeks?

   A. 111 magazines
   B. 209 magazines
   C. 248 magazines
   D. 387 magazines

4. For dessert, there are strawberries, blueberries, or raspberries. The berries can be served with ice cream, frozen yogurt, or whipped cream. How many dessert choices are there?

   A. 6 choices   B. 9 choices
   C. 10 choices   D. 12 choices

5. The copy center can make posters in small, regular, and large sizes. The paper for the posters can be blue, green, yellow, pink, or white. How many poster choices are there?

   A. 7 choices   B. 12 choices
   C. 14 choices   D. 15 choices

6. The school librarian will make a survey to find out what types of books students like to read. Which question would be the most useful?

   A. Do you like mysteries more than adventure stories?
   B. What is your favorite kind of book?
   C. Where do you look for books to read?
   D. What was the last book you read?

For questions 7–8, use the table.

FAVORITE SEASON	
Choice	Votes
Summer	ЖЖ ЖЖ III
Fall	ЖЖ I
Winter	ЖЖ III
Spring	ЖЖ ЖЖ II

7. Which season was chosen as the favorite by the greatest number of people?

   A. Summer   B. Fall
   C. Winter   D. Spring

8. Which season was the favorite choice of the fewest people?

   A. Summer   B. Fall
   C. Winter   D. Spring

For questions 9–12, use the graph.

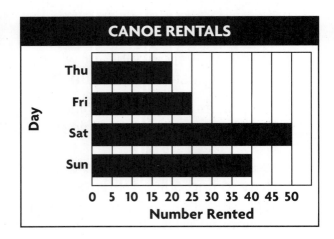

9. How many canoes were rented on Friday?

A. 15 canoes
B. 25 canoes
C. 40 canoes
D. 50 canoes

10. What interval is used in the scale of the graph?

A. 1   B. 5
C. 10   D. 25

11. How many more canoes were rented on Saturday than were rented on Friday?

A. 5 more canoes
B. 10 more canoes
C. 25 more canoes
D. 50 more canoes

12. How many canoes were rented on Friday, Saturday, and Sunday?

A. 115 canoes
B. 150 canoes
C. 175 canoes
D. 200 canoes

For questions 13–16, use the graph.

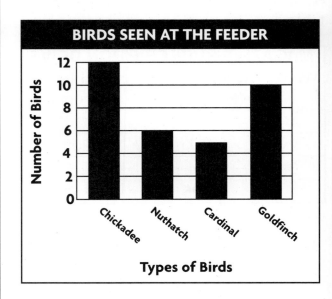

13. What interval is used in the scale of the graph?

A. 1   B. 2
C. 3   D. 4

14. How would the bars change if an interval of 3 were used in the graph?

A. The bars would be longer.
B. The bars would be exactly the same.
C. The bars would be wider.
D. The bars would be shorter.

15. How many more chickadees than cardinals were seen at the feeder?

A. 3 more   B. 5 more
C. 7 more   D. 9 more

16. How many birds were seen at the feeder altogether?

A. 5 birds   B. 15 birds
C. 25 birds   D. 33 birds

Choose the letter of the correct answer.

For questions 1–6, use the line graph.

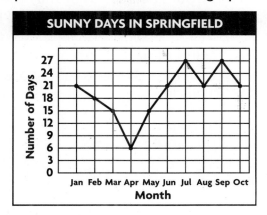

1. Why is a line graph a good choice for showing this information?

  A. It is easy to compare groups.
  B. It helps keep a count of the data as they are collected.
  C. It has a key.
  D. It shows how something changes over time.

2. What interval is used on the scale of this graph?

  A. 3   **B.** 5
  C. 10   **D.** 24

3. How many sunny days were there in January?

  A. 18 days   **B.** 21 days
  C. 22 days   **D.** 24 days

4. Which month had the fewest sunny days?

  A. March   **B.** April
  C. May   **D.** June

5. How many months had exactly 21 sunny days?

  A. 1 month   **B.** 2 months
  C. 3 months   **D.** 4 months

6. How many more sunny days were there in September than in February?

  A. 9 more days   **B.** 15 more days
  C. 18 more days   **D.** 21 more days

For questions 7–11, use the line plot. There is one X for each student.

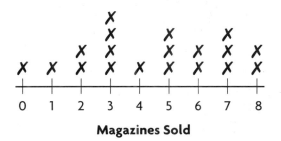

Magazines Sold

7. What do the numbers on the line plot represent?

  A. number of magazines sold
  B. number of students
  C. price of the magazines
  D. cost of the field trip

8. What is the range of data used in this line plot?

  A. 7   **B.** 8   **C.** 10   **D.** 12

9. How many students sold 8 magazines?

  A. 1 student   **B.** 2 students
  C. 3 students   **D.** 4 students

10. What was the greatest number of magazines sold by any student?

  A. 3 magazines   **B.** 7 magazines
  C. 8 magazines   **D.** 10 magazines

11. How many magazines were sold in all by students who sold 3?

  A. 4 magazines   **B.** 6 magazines
  C. 12 magazines **D.** 15 magazines

Form A • Multiple-Choice   **Go on.** ▶

For questions 12–16, use the stem-and-leaf plot.

HEIGHT OF MR. VICKER'S STUDENTS IN INCHES	
Stem	Leaves
4	8 9 9
5	0 1 3 4 4 4 5 7 8
6	0 0 1 2 3 3 4

12. How would you find the height of the shortest person?

   A. By looking at the first number in the plot
   B. By looking at the last number in the plot
   C. By finding the number that happens most
   D. By finding the middle number

13. What is the number that happens most often in this set of data called?

   A. stem   B. leaf
   C. mode   D. median

14. What is the mode for the data?

   A. 4 in.   B. 40 in.
   C. 54 in.   D. 55 in.

15. What is the median for the data?

   A. 48 in.   B. 50 in.
   C. 54 in.   D. 55 in.

16. What is the difference in height between the shortest member and the tallest member of the class?

   A. 12 in.   B. 16 in.
   C. 24 in.   D. 30 in.

For questions 17–20, choose the type of graph that would be best to display the data described.

17. What kind of graph or plot would be best to list the spelling test scores for 30 students?

   A. Bar graph
   B. Stem-and-leaf plot
   C. Line graph
   D. Double-bar graph

18. What kind of graph or plot would be best to show the favorite TV programs of 30 fourth-grade students?

   A. Bar graph
   B. Stem-and-leaf plot
   C. Line graph
   D. Line plot

19. What kind of graph or plot would be best to show how a bean plant has grown over time?

   A. Double-bar graph
   B. Stem-and-leaf plot
   C. Line graph
   D. Line plot

20. What kind of graph or plot would be best to display these data?

FAVORITE BOOKS OF FOURTH GRADERS		
Type	Mr. Bell's Class	Ms. Smith's Class
Mystery	15	14
Biography	3	8
Sports	6	2

   A. Double-bar graph
   B. Line plot
   C. Stem-and-leaf plot
   D. Line graph

Choose the letter of the correct answer.

1. An event is certain if it _?_ happens.

   A. always   **B.** sometimes
   C. usually   **D.** never

2. A bag contains quarters, dimes, and pennies. It is impossible to pull out a _?_ .

   A. quarter   **B.** dime
   C. nickel   **D.** penny

For questions 3–4, use the spinner.

3. Using this spinner, you are certain to spin a number less than _?_ .

   A. 2   **B.** 3   **C.** 4   **D.** 5

4. Using this spinner, it is impossible to spin a number greater than _?_ .

   A. 1   **B.** 2   **C.** 3   **D.** 4

For questions 5–6, use the tally table.

NUMBER OF BLOCKS IN A BAG	
White	𝍫𝍫𝍫 II
Black	III
Red	𝍫 II
Green	𝍫𝍫𝍫𝍫 III

5. Which outcome is most likely if a block is pulled from the bag?

   A. white   **B.** black
   C. red   **D.** green

6. Which block are you unlikely to pull?

   A. white   **B.** black
   C. red   **D.** green

For questions 7–8, use the spinner.

7. Which number are you most likely to spin on this spinner?

   A. 1   **B.** 2
   C. 3   **D.** All the numbers are equally likely.

8. Which number are you unlikely to spin?

   A. 1   **B.** 2
   C. 3   **D.** not here

For questions 9–10, use the bag.

9. If you pull a counter from the bag ten times, which color counter are you most likely to pull?

   A. blue
   B. green
   C. red
   D. Blue, green, and red are equally likely.

10. If you pull a counter from the bag ten times, which color counter are you unlikely to pull?

   A. blue
   B. green
   C. red
   D. Blue, green, and red are equally likely.

For questions 11–12, use a number cube that has 6 sides, labeled 1, 2, 3, 4, 5, and 6.

11. What is the probability of rolling a 4?

   A. $\frac{1}{6}$ B. $\frac{1}{4}$

   C. $\frac{1}{2}$ D. not here

12. What is the probability of rolling an odd number?

   A. $\frac{1}{6}$ B. $\frac{1}{5}$

   C. $\frac{1}{3}$ D. $\frac{1}{2}$

For questions 13–14, use the spinner.

13. What is the probability of spinning a 1 or a 2?

   A. $\frac{1}{3}$ B. $\frac{1}{2}$

   C. $\frac{2}{3}$ D. not here

14. What is the probability of spinning a 4?

   A. $\frac{0}{3}$ B. $\frac{1}{4}$

   C. $\frac{1}{3}$ D. $\frac{3}{3}$

15. A game is fair if each player has __?__.

   A. a good time playing
   B. an equal chance of winning
   C. the same number of turns
   D. the same final score

For questions 16–17, use the spinners.

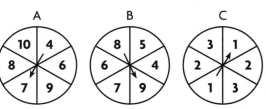

In this game, the "odd" player gets points for odd numbers and the "even" player gets points for even numbers.

16. Which spinner gives both players an equal chance to win?

   A. spinner A
   B. spinner B
   C. spinner C
   D. all of them

17. If you were the "odd" player, which spinner would give you the greatest probability of winning?

   A. spinner A
   B. spinner B
   C. spinner C
   D. none of them

18. Lane's spinner is divided into 6 equal sections. There are 2 red sections, 2 white sections, and 2 blue sections. Which is the best explanation of whether the spinner is fair or not fair?

   A. It is fair because there is an equal chance of spinning each color.
   B. It is not fair because there are two sections of each color.
   C. It is not fair because there is a greater chance of spinning red.
   D. It is not fair because there is no chance of spinning green.

Name _____

Choose the letter of the correct answer.

For questions 1–2, use the frequency table.

SCHOOL LUNCHES SOLD		
Day	Number Sold (Frequency)	Cumulative Frequency
Monday	136	136
Tuesday	101	237
Wednesday	98	335
Thursday	115	?
Friday	90	?

1. On which day were the most lunches sold?

   A. Monday **B.** Tuesday
   C. Wednesday **D.** Thursday

2. What is the cumulative frequency for the lunches sold on all 5 days?

   A. 335 lunches **B.** 450 lunches
   C. 550 lunches **D.** not here

For questions 3–4, use the table.

FAVORITE SPORT	
Choice	Votes
Baseball	ЖHT |||
Football	ЖHT ||
Basketball	ЖHT ЖHT	
Soccer	ЖHT ЖHT ||

3. Which sport was chosen as their favorite by the most people?

   A. baseball **B.** football
   C. basketball **D.** soccer

4. Which sport was the favorite of the fewest people?

   A. baseball **B.** football
   C. basketball **D.** soccer

For questions 5–6, use the bar graph.

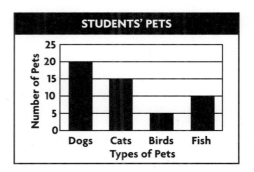

5. What interval is used on the scale?

   A. 1 **B.** 3 **C.** 5 **D.** 10

6. How would the bars change if an interval of 2 is used on the graph?

   A. The bars would be longer.
   B. The bars would be the same.
   C. The bars would be wider.
   D. The bars would be shorter.

For questions 7–8, use the line graph.

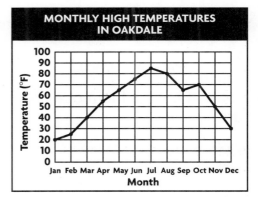

7. What interval is used on the scale of the graph?

   A. 5 **B.** 10 **C.** 20 **D.** 50

8. How many months had a high temperature of 65°F?

   A. 0 months **B.** 1 month
   C. 2 months **D.** 3 months

For questions 9–10, use the line plot. There is one X for each student.

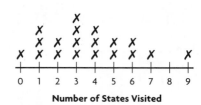

Number of States Visited

9. What is the range of data used in the line plot?

   A. 2   **B.** 5   **C.** 7   **D.** 9

10. What number of states was visited by the most students?

    A. 3 states   **B.** 4 states
    C. 6 states   **D.** 9 states

For questions 11–12, use the stem-and-leaf plot.

Stem	Leaves
6	8 8 9 9
7	1 2 2 3 5 7 7 7 7 9
8	2 5 5 6 8 9
9	1 1 2 2

Prices of Cameras

11. What number is the mode for the data?

    A. 69   **B.** 77
    C. 85   **D.** 91

12. What is the difference between the highest price and the lowest price?

    A. $21.00   **B.** $24.00
    C. $30.00   **D.** not here

For questions 13–14, use the box.

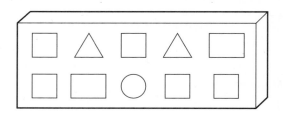

13. Which shape is it impossible for you to pull?

    A. circle   **B.** rectangle
    C. trapezoid   **D.** triangle

14. If you pull a shape from the box ten times, which of these are you unlikely to pull?

    A. circle   **B.** rectangle
    C. triangle   **D.** square

For questions 15–16, use the spinners.

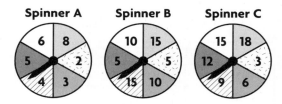

In this game, the "odd" player gets points for odd numbers and the "even" player gets points for even numbers.

15. Which spinner gives both players an equal chance to win?

    A. Spinner A   **B.** Spinner B
    C. Spinner C   **D.** all of them

16. If you were the "even" player, which spinner would give you the greatest probability of winning?

    A. Spinner A   **B.** Spinner B
    C. Spinner C   **D.** none of them

Name _____

Choose the letter of the correct answer.

1. Which is the best estimate of the sum?

318
289
+207

A. 600
B. 700
C. 800
D. 1,000

2.
  9,000
  −4,878

A. 4,022
B. 4,122
C. 4,222
D. 5,122

3. Diane has 3 music lessons each week. She has taken lessons for 4 weeks. How many music lessons has she taken in all?

A. 7 lessons
B. 8 lessons
C. 12 lessons
D. not here

4. $(5 \times 2) \times 6 =$ ___?___

A. 10
B. 16
C. 60
D. 106

5. There are 64 players in a soccer league. How many players are on each of 4 teams?

A. 16 players
B. 18 players
C. 20 players
D. not here

6. Which number sentence is in the same fact family as $3 \times 7 = 21$?

A. $7 - 3 = 4$
B. $7 - 4 = 3$
C. $7 + 3 = 10$
D. $21 \div 7 = 3$

7. $18 \div 4 =$ ___?___

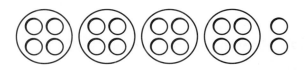

A. 3 r3
B. 4 r1
C. 4 r2
D. not here

For questions 8–9, use the multiplication table to find the quotient.

×	3	4	5
3	9	12	15
4	12	16	20
5	15	20	25

8. $25 \div 5 =$ ___?___

A. 2
B. 3
C. 4
D. 5

9. $12 \div 4 =$ ___?___

A. 3
B. 4
C. 6
D. not here

10. Mary earned a total of 10 extra credit points for her grade. She earned 2 extra credit points on each test. How many tests did she take?

A. 2 tests
B. 4 tests
C. 5 tests
D. not here

11. Which is a *nominal* number?

A. 110 pounds   B. 2 dollars
C. Third row   D. Channel 6

12. How many tens are in 3,658?

A. 3 tens   B. 5 tens
C. 6 tens   D. 8 tens

13. In the number 800, what is the value of 8?

A. 8 ones   B. 8 tens
C. 8 hundreds   D. not here

14. Which numbers are written in order from the least to the greatest?

A. 757, 765, 772
B. 765, 757, 772
C. 772, 765, 757
D. not here

For questions 15–16, use the Venn diagram.

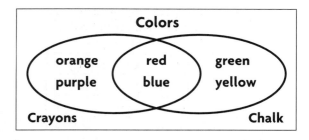

Colors

orange   red   green
purple   blue   yellow

Crayons   Chalk

15. Which color is used only for chalk?

A. red   B. yellow
C. blue   D. purple

16. Which color is used for both crayons and chalk?

A. orange   B. blue
C. green   D. purple

17. Which unit of time would you use to measure how long most people take to get dressed in the morning?

A. seconds   B. minutes
C. hours   D. days

18. Which time is closest to the time that a public library closes?

A. 8:00 A.M.   B. 1:00 P.M.
C. 8:00 P.M.   D. 1:00 A.M.

For questions 19–20, use the schedule.

TRAIN	LEAVE BALTIMORE	ARRIVE RICHMOND
A	9:00 A.M.	11:20 A.M.
B	9:40 A.M.	?
C	12:20 P.M.	?
D	3:50 P.M.	?
Trip lasts 2 hours and 20 minutes.		

19. At what time does Train B arrive in Richmond?

A. 11:20 A.M.   B. 11:40 A.M.
C. 12:00 noon   D. not here

20. If Mr. Ryan has a meeting in Richmond at 6:30 P.M., which is the latest train he can take?

A. Train A   B. Train B
C. Train C   D. Train D

For questions 21–22, use the table.

RAFFLE TICKETS SOLD		
Week	Number Sold (Frequency)	Cumulative Frequency
1	103	103
2	126	229
3	96	?
4	117	?

21. During which week were the most tickets sold?

A. Week 1 **B.** Week 2
C. Week 3 **D.** Week 4

22. By the end of Week 3, how many tickets had been sold?

A. 96 tickets **B.** 229 tickets
C. 325 tickets **D.** not here

23. Joey is making a survey to find out what season students like best. Which question would be the most useful for him to ask?

A. What did you do last winter?
B. Do you like spring best?
C. Did you go on a trip last fall?
D. What is your favorite time of year?

For questions 24–25, use the graph.

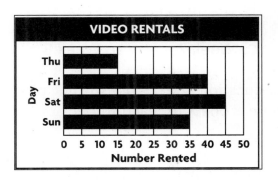

24. What interval is used in the scale of the graph?

A. 1 **B.** 5 **C.** 10 **D.** 25

25. How many more videos were rented on Sunday than on Thursday?

A. 5 more videos
B. 15 more videos
C. 20 more videos
D. not here

For questions 26–27, use the line graph.

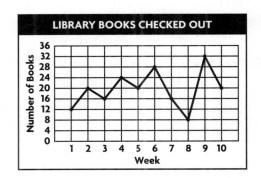

26. How many library books were checked out in Week 4?

A. 24 books **B.** 26 books
C. 28 books **D.** not here

27. During which week were the fewest books checked out?

   A. Week 1   **B.** Week 3
   C. Week 7   **D.** Week 8

For questions 28–29, use the line plot. There is one X for each student.

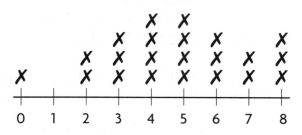

Shots Made During Basketball Game

28. How many students made 5 shots?

   A. 1 student   **B.** 3 students
   C. 4 students   **D.** 6 students

29. What was the greatest number of shots made by any student?

   A. 3 shots   **B.** 5 shots
   C. 7 shots   **D.** 8 shots

For questions 30–31, use the stem-and-leaf plot.

Points Scored by Basketball Team in 18 Games

Stem	Leaves
7	4 7 8 8
8	3 4 4 6 6 6 7
9	2 2 2 2 5 8 8

30. What number is the mode for the data?

   A. 86   **B.** 92   **C.** 95   **D.** 98

31. What number is the median for the data?

   A. 86   **B.** 87   **C.** 92   **D.** 98

32. What kind of graph would best show the changes in the time of sunrise for one month?

   A. double bar graph
   B. line graph
   C. stem-and-leaf plot
   D. line plot

For questions 33–36, use the spinner.

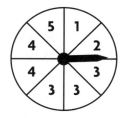

33. Using this spinner, you are certain to spin a number less than ___?___ .

   A. 2   **B.** 3   **C.** 5   **D.** 6

34. Using this spinner, it is impossible to spin a number greater than ___?___ .

   A. 2   **B.** 3   **C.** 4   **D.** 5

35. What is the probability of spinning a 1 or a 2?

   A. $\frac{2}{8}$ **B.** $\frac{3}{8}$
   C. $\frac{4}{8}$ **D.** not here

36. What is the probability of spinning a 3?

   A. $\frac{2}{8}$ **B.** $\frac{3}{8}$
   C. $\frac{4}{8}$ **D.** $\frac{3}{3}$

Name _____

Choose the letter of the correct answer.

1. Which figure is two-dimensional?

   A.   B.

   C. ▽   D. ～

2. Which of the following is a three-dimensional figure?

   A. square   B. rectangle
   C. circle   D. cylinder

3. Which unit could be used to measure the area of a basketball court?

   A. yards   B. feet
   C. square feet   D. cubic feet

4. Which unit could be used to measure the volume of a packing box?

   A. yards   B. feet
   C. square feet   D. cubic feet

For questions 5–6, use the figure.

5. How many faces are on this figure?

   A. 3 faces   B. 5 faces
   C. 6 faces   D. 8 faces

6. What two plane figures are the faces of this figure?

   A. rectangles and squares
   B. rectangles and pentagons
   C. triangles and rectangles
   D. triangles and squares

For questions 7–8, use the figure.

7. How many faces does this figure have?

   A. 4 faces   B. 5 faces
   C. 6 faces   D. 8 faces

8. Each face on this figure is a __?__.

   A. circle   B. triangle
   C. square   D. rectangle

For questions 9–11, use the figure.

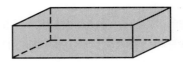

9. How many faces does this figure have?

   A. 4 faces   B. 6 faces
   C. 8 faces   D. 12 faces

10. How many edges does this figure have?

    A. 4 edges   B. 6 edges
    C. 8 edges   D. 12 edges

11. How many vertices does this figure have?

    A. 4 vertices   B. 6 vertices
    C. 8 vertices   D. 12 vertices

Form A • Multiple-Choice   A45   **Go on. ▶**

For questions 12–15, use the grid.

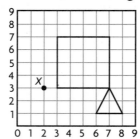

12. What is the ordered pair of point *X*?

   A. (2,3)   **B.** (3,2)
   C. (3,3)   **D.** not here

13. Which set of ordered pairs identifies the vertices of the square marked on the grid?

   A. (2,3), (2,7), (7,2), (7,7)
   B. (3,3), (3,7), (7,3), (7,7)
   C. (4,4), (4,8), (8,4), (8,8)
   D. not here

14. Which set of ordered pairs identifies the vertices of the triangle marked on the grid?

   A. (6,3), (7,3), (8,3)
   B. (3,6), (3,7), (3,8)
   C. (6,1), (6,7), (6,8)
   D. not here

15. Which ordered pair identifies the point that is a vertex of the square *and* the triangle?

   A. (3,7)   **B.** (7,3)
   C. (7,4)   **D.** not here

16. Mary placed a book, a cereal box, a shoe box, and a crayon box on the same shelf. Which term best describes these figures?

   A. triangular prism
   B. rectangular prism
   C. square pyramid
   D. sphere

17. Which list of items suggests the same shape?

   A. basketball, straw, drinking cup, football
   B. golf ball, party hat, box of candies, ice-cream cone
   C. balloon, baseball, globe, marbles
   D. book, feathered hat, tennis ball, building block

18. Which figure belongs in the overlapped section of this Venn diagram?

A.   **B.**

C.   **D.**

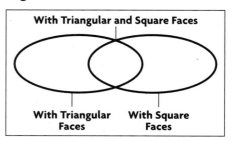

For questions 19–20, use the organized list.

Cylinders	Cubes	?
drinking glass	ice cubes	baseball
telescope	toy blocks	marble
?	dice	orange

19. Which heading is missing?

   A. Squares   **B.** Triangles
   C. Spheres   **D.** Pyramids

20. Which object should be listed under **Cylinders**?

   A. paint can   **B.** football
   C. textbook   **D.** poster paper

Choose the letter of the correct answer.

1. Which term names this figure?

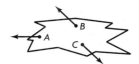

A. points   **B.** line
C. line segment **D.** plane

2. Which figure is a line segment?

 **A.**   **B.** A ⎯⎯⎯⎯ B

C. C **D.** G ⎯⎯ H

3. Which line segments are parallel?

A.   **B.**

C. 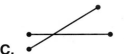   **D.**

4. Which term names these figures?

S•   •T

A. points   **B.** line
C. line segment **D.** plane

5. Which of the following is an obtuse angle?

A.   **B.**

C.    **D.**

6. What is the name of this figure?

S T

A. ray ST **B.** line ST
C. ray T **D.** line segment T

7. What kind of angles are formed when two lines are perpendicular?

A. acute angles **B.** obtuse angles
C. right angles   **D.** not here

8. Which pair of lines are perpendicular?

A.    **B.**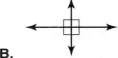

C.    **D.**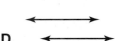

For questions 9–10, use the map.

Street A		

9. Which street is *not* perpendicular to Street 2?

A. Street A   **B.** Street B
C. Street C   **D.** Street D

10. Which street is parallel to Street B?

A. Street 2   **B.** Street 3
C. Street C   **D.** Street D

11. Which figure is a polygon?

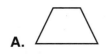

A.   B.

C.   D.

12. What is this figure called?

A. triangle   B. quadrilateral
C. hexagon   D. octagon

13. A hexagon has 6 sides. How many angles does it have?

A. 3 angles   B. 4 angles
C. 5 angles   D. 6 angles

14. Which figure is a quadrilateral?

A.   B.

C.   D.

15. All quadrilaterals have _?_.

A. 4 angles
B. parallel sides
C. acute angles
D. no parallel sides

16. Only 2 of my sides are parallel. What am I?

A. parallelogram
B. trapezoid
C. rectangle
D. rhombus

17. What is the name of this figure?

A. square
B. trapezoid
C. rectangle
D. rhombus

18. Which of these figures is *not* a parallelogram?

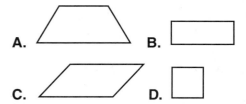

A.   B.

C.   D.

19. Ken brought a box of cookies and 5 extra cookies to share equally among 3 of his friends and himself. After sharing, he has 15 cookies. No cookies were left. How many cookies were in the box?

A. 15 cookies
B. 30 cookies
C. 40 cookies
D. 55 cookies

20. Five students are in a line. Al is third. Nan is next to Al. Bea is first. Ed is between Bea and Al. Where is Jim?

A. second
B. in the middle
C. fourth
D. last in line

Choose the letter of the correct answer.

1. Which tells how to find the perimeter of this figure?

- **A.** Add. $1 + 1 + 2 + 2 + 3 + 3$
- **B.** Add. $2 + 1 + 3$
- **C.** Multiply. 3×2
- **D.** Multiply. 6×3

2. Which tells how to find the perimeter of this figure?

- **A.** Multiply. 4×9
- **B.** Multiply. 9×3
- **C.** Add. $9 + 3$
- **D.** Add. $(2 \times 9) + (2 \times 3)$

For questions 3–4, find the perimeter.

3.

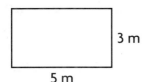

3 m

5 m

- **A.** 8 m
- **B.** 12 m
- **C.** 16 m
- **D.** 64 m

4.

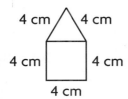

4 cm   4 cm

4 cm   4 cm

4 cm

- **A.** 16 cm
- **B.** 20 cm
- **C.** 24 cm
- **D.** 44 cm

5. A field is 84 yards long and 50 yards wide. How many yards of fencing are needed to go around the field?

- **A.** 134 yd
- **B.** 268 yd
- **C.** 420 yd
- **D.** 4,200 yd

6. Carlita is buying a wallpaper border for her room. Each wall is 12 feet long. How long does the border need to be?

- **A.** 24 ft
- **B.** 36 ft
- **C.** 48 ft
- **D.** 144 ft

For questions 7–8, find the area.

7.

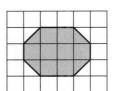

- **A.** 6 sq units
- **B.** 9 sq units
- **C.** 10 sq units
- **D.** 12 sq units

8.

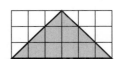

- **A.** 8 sq units
- **B.** 10 sq units
- **C.** 12 sq units
- **D.** 15 sq units

9. Estimate the area.

- **A.** about 2 sq units
- **B.** about 6 sq units
- **C.** about 10 sq units
- **D.** about 25 sq units

10. Estimate the area.

A. 5 sq units   B. 8 sq units
C. 12 sq units   D. 20 sq units

11. Find the area.

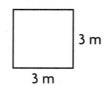

3 m

3 m

A. 6 sq m   B. 9 sq m
C. 12 sq m   D. 18 sq m

12. Find the area.

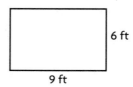

6 ft

9 ft

A. 15 sq ft   B. 30 sq ft
C. 42 sq ft   D. 54 sq ft

13. How many square yards of carpet do you need to cover a floor that is 5 yards long and 4 yards wide?

A. 9 sq yd   B. 18 sq yd
C. 20 sq yd   D. 81 sq yd

14. Lee's garden is 6 feet by 6 feet. To buy fertilizer for it, Lee needs to know its area. What is the area?

A. 24 sq ft   B. 36 sq ft
C. 48 sq ft   D. 66 sq ft

For questions 15–18, use the shaded figures below.

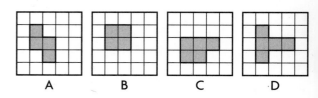

A   B   C   D

15. What is the perimeter of figure D?

A. 9 units   B. 12 units
C. 14 units   D. 18 units

16. What is the area of figure A?

A. 1 sq unit   B. 3 sq units
C. 4 sq units   D. 9 sq units

17. Which two figures have the same areas but different perimeters?

A. A and B   B. A and C
C. A and D   D. B and D

18. Which two figures have the same perimeters but different areas?

A. A and B   B. A and C
C. B and D   D. C and D

19. Tile costs $2.00 per square foot. The floor is 5 feet by 6 feet. How much does the tile cost?

A. $20.00   B. $30.00
C. $40.00   D. $60.00

20. A man has 32 feet of fencing for a dog pen. Which shape has the greatest area?

A. 8 ft by 8 ft   B. 9 ft by 7 ft
C. 10 ft by 6 ft   D. 12 ft by 4 ft

Name _____

Choose the letter of the correct answer.

1. A figure that has been flipped over a line is called a __?__.

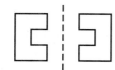

   A. translation   **B.** reflection
   C. rotation   **D.** slide

For questions 2–3, use the figures.

2. Which is a translation?

   A. A   **B.** B
   C. C   **D.** not here

3. Which is a rotation?

   A. A   **B.** B
   C. C   **D.** not here

4. Two figures are congruent if they have the same __?__.

   A. size and shape
   B. number of sides
   C. number of angles
   D. position on a page

5. Which figure is congruent with this figure?

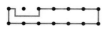

   A.    **B.**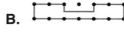

   C. 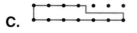   **D.**

6. Which pair of figures is congruent?

   A.   **B.**

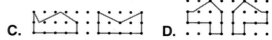

   C.   **D.**

7. Which figure has point symmetry?

   A.   **B.**

   C.   **D.**

8. Which figure shows a line symmetry?

   A.   **B.**

   C.   **D.**

9. Which figure has line symmetry?

   A. 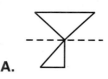   **B.**

   C.    **D.**

10. A pattern of repeated polygons is a tessellation if it has *no* __?__ .

   A. squares
   B. triangles
   C. gaps or overlaps
   D. lines of symmetry

11. What figure tessellates in this design?

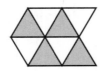

   A. circle
   B. square
   C. rectangle
   D. triangle

12. Which figure will tessellate?

   A.   B.

   C.   D.

13. This tessellation includes squares and __?__ .

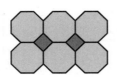

   A. circles
   B. rectangles
   C. octagons
   D. hexagons

14. A figure is drawn on 1-cm grid paper. If you copy the figure on 0.5-cm paper, it will be __?__ .

   A. similar but larger
   B. similar but smaller
   C. symmetrical
   D. congruent

For questions 15–17, use the pairs of figures.

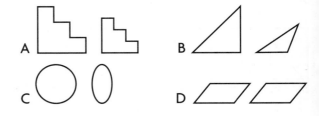

15. Which pair of figures is similar and congruent?

   A. A   B. B   C. C   D. D

16. Which pair of figures is similar but not congruent?

   A. A   B. B   C. C   D. D

17. Which best describes the pair of figures in B?

   A. similar and congruent
   B. similar but not congruent
   C. congruent but not similar
   D. neither similar nor congruent

18. You have a design on grid paper. How can you enlarge the design and be sure it is similar to the original design?

   A. Trace it.
   B. Copy a mirror image of it.
   C. Copy it onto smaller grid paper.
   D. Copy it onto larger grid paper.

Choose the letter of the correct answer.

1. Which of these is a two-dimensional figure?

   A. pyramid   B. triangle
   C. cube   D. prism

For questions 2–3, use the figure.

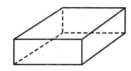

2. How many faces are on the figure?

   A. 4 faces   B. 6 faces
   C. 8 faces   D. 10 faces

3. What plane figures are the faces of the figure?

   A. rectangles   B. squares
   C. triangles   D. pentagons

For questions 4–6, use the grid.

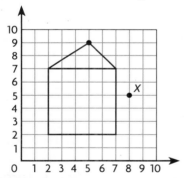

4. What is the ordered pair of point x?

   A. (2,7) B. (7,2) C. (5,8) D. (8,5)

5. Which set of ordered pairs identifies the vertices of the square marked on the grid?

   A. (2,2), (2,7), (7,7), (7,2)
   B. (2,3), (2,8), (8,2), (8,8)
   C. (3,3), (3,7), (7,3), (7,7)
   D. not here

6. Which ordered pair identifies the point that is a vertex of the triangle but not a vertex of the square?

   A. (2,7)   B. (7,7)
   C. (5,9)   D. (9,5)

7. The figure shows a __?__.

   A. point   B. line
   C. plane   D. line segment

For questions 8–9, use the map.

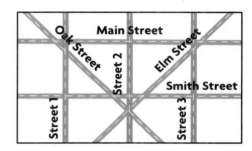

8. Which street is perpendicular to Oak Street?

   A. Street 1   B. Street 2
   C. Street 3   D. not here

9. Which street intersects Street 1 but is not perpendicular to it?

   A. Oak Street   B. Main Street
   C. Elm Street   D. Street 2

10. What is the figure called?

   A. hexagon   B. quadrilateral
   C. octagon   D. triangle

Form A • Multiple-Choice   A53   **Go on. ▶**

11. A square has a side 8 meters long. What is the perimeter of the square?

   A. 8 m   **B.** 16 m
   C. 32 m   **D.** 64 m

12. A frame is 28 inches long and 18 inches wide. How many inches of ribbon are needed to go around the frame?

   A. 46 in.   **B.** 64 in.
   C. 74 in.   **D.** 92 in.

13. What is the area of the shaded figure?

   A. 5 sq units
   B. 6 sq units
   C. 7 sq units
   D. not here

14. How many square meters are in a field that is 50 meters long and 25 meters wide?

   A. 1,000 sq m   **B.** 1,250 sq m
   C. 1,400 sq m   **D.** 1,500 sq m

For questions 15–16, use the shaded figures.

15. What is the perimeter of Figure B?

   A. 5 units   **B.** 10 units
   C. 12 units   **D.** 14 units

16. Which two figures have the same area but different perimeters?

   A. Figures A and B
   B. Figures A and C
   C. Figures B and C
   D. Figures C and D

17. To turn a figure around a point is called a __?__.

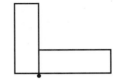

   A. flip
   B. slide
   C. translation
   D. rotation

18. Which figure is congruent to the figure shown?

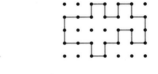

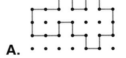
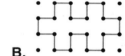

A.   **B.**

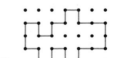

C.   **D.** not here

19. Which figure has line symmetry?

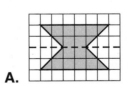

A.   **B.**

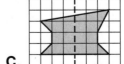

C.   **D.** not here

Name _____

Choose the letter of the correct answer.

1. $9 - 6 = 5 - \underline{\ ?\ }$

   A. 1   **B.** 2   **C.** 3   **D.** 4

2. The four sides of a store have 114 parking spaces. There are 27 spaces on one side. There are 32 on another side and 29 on the third side. How many spaces are on the fourth side?

   A. 21 spaces   **B.** 24 spaces
   C. 26 spaces   **D.** not here

3. Hal got 11 words right in the spelling bee. Michael got 9 words right. Which number sentence can you use to find how many more words Hal got right?

   A. $11 \times 9 = \underline{\ ?\ }$
   B. $11 + 9 = \underline{\ ?\ }$
   C. $11 - 9 = \underline{\ ?\ }$
   D. $9 + 11 = \underline{\ ?\ }$

4. $3\overline{)27}$

   A. 7   **B.** 8
   C. 9   **D.** not here

5. Which is a *cardinal* number?

   A. 4 tennis players   **B.** 6th floor
   C. 1510 Main Street **D.** Channel 5

6. An ice-cream cone with 1 dip costs $0.89. About how much should a cone with 2 dips cost?

   A. about $1.00   **B.** about $2.00
   C. about $3.00   **D.** about $4.00

7. In which number does the digit 2 have a value of 200?

   A. 327   **B.** 2,592
   C. 7,217   **D.** not here

8.   700
   $+600$

   A. 1,300
   B. 1,310
   C. 12,000
   D. 13,000

9. Compare the numbers. Which statement is correct?

   A. $5,217 > 5,712$
   B. $8,642 > 8,624$
   C. $4,327 = 4,372$
   D. $3,974 > 3,987$

10. Compare the numbers. Which statement is correct?
   389 ● 398

   A. $389 < 398$
   B. $389 = 398$
   C. $389 > 398$
   D. not here

11. A diner serves hot dogs, steak, fish, and chicken. With this, you can have french fries, baked potato, or cole slaw. How many choices are there?

   A. 7 choices   **B.** 9 choices
   C. 12 choices   **D.** 14 choices

12. Omar wanted to find out what type of movie his friends would prefer. Which question should he ask his friends?

   A. Do you like action movies?
   B. Where do you like to watch movies?
   C. What was the last movie you saw?
   D. What kind of movie do you like best?

For questions 13–14, use the graph.

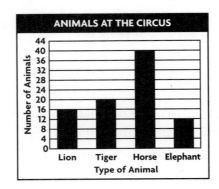

ANIMALS AT THE CIRCUS

13. What interval is used in the scale of the graph?

   A. 3   B. 4   C. 5   D. 6

14. How many more tigers than elephants were there?

   A. 4   B. 6   C. 8   D. 20

For questions 15–16, use the line plot. There is one X for each student.

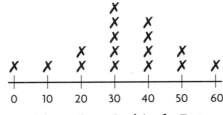

Minutes Spent Studying for Test

15. What is the range of data used in the line plot?

   A. 60   B. 70
   C. 80   D. not here

16. How many students studied for 40 minutes?

   A. 1 student   B. 2 students
   C. 3 students   D. 4 students

17. Which graph would be best to show the kinds of pets owned by a class of fourth-grade students?

   A. line graph
   B. line plot
   C. bar graph
   D. stem-and-leaf plot

18. Which graph would be best to show how many boys and how many girls are in 3 classes?

   A. line plot
   B. double-bar graph
   C. stem-and-leaf plot
   D. line graph

19. A bag contains jelly beans, gum drops, and lollipops. It is impossible to pull out a __?__ .

   A. gum drop   B. lollipop
   C. jelly bean   D. mint

20. Which unit would be used to measure the area of a page in a book?

   A. square inches
   B. cubic inches
   C. inches
   D. feet

For questions 21–22, use the figure.

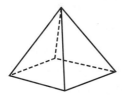

21. How many faces are on the figure?

A. 4 faces   B. 5 faces
C. 6 faces   D. 7 faces

22. Which two kinds of plane figures are the faces of the figure?

A. rectangles and square
B. rectangle and pentagons
C. triangles and pentagons
D. triangles and square

For questions 23–24, use the grid.

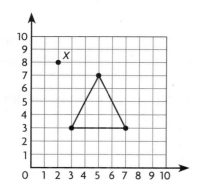

23. What are the coordinates of point *x*?

A. (2,7)   B. (3,3)
C. (8,2)   D. (2,8)

24. Which set of coordinates identifies the vertices of the triangle marked on the grid?

A. (2,3), (4,7), (6,3)
B. (3,7), (7,5), (3,4)
C. (3,3), (5,7), (7,3)
D. not here

25. What is the name of the figure?

A. ray *MP*
B. line *MP*
C. ray *M*
D. line segment *MP*

26. What is the name of the figure?

A. hexagon   B. octagon
C. quadrilateral   D. triangle

27. Which figure is a pentagon?

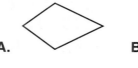

A.   B.

C.   D.

28. What is the name of the figure?

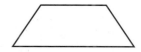

A. rhombus   B. square
C. trapezoid   D. not here

29. What is the perimeter?

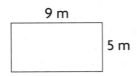

9 m

5 m

A. 14 m **B.** 21 m
C. 23 m **D.** 28 m

30. What is the area of the shaded figure?

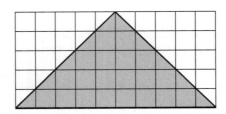

A. 25 sq units **B.** 27 sq units
C. 29 sq units **D.** not here

31. The roof of the shed is 9 feet by 8 feet. Shingles cost $3.00 per square foot. How much do the shingles cost?

A. $51.00 **B.** $102.00
C. $216.00 **D.** not here

32. What is a figure that has been flipped over a line called?

A. reflection **B.** translation
C. slide **D.** rotation

33. Two figures are congruent only if they have the same __?__ .

A. position
B. number of angles
C. number of sides
D. size and shape

34. Which figure has point symmetry?

A.   **B.**

C.   **D.**

35. This tessellation includes octagons and __?__ .

A. triangles **B.** pentagons
C. hexagons **D.** rectangles

36. Which pair of figures is similar and congruent?

A. 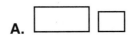 **B.**

C. 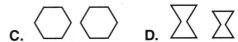 **D.**

Name _____

Choose the letter of the correct answer.

1. What number completes the pattern?

$3 \times 20 = 60$
$3 \times 200 = 600$
$3 \times \underline{\ ?\ } = 6,000$

A. 220
B. 2,000
C. 2,200
D. 20,000

2. What number completes the pattern?

$4 \times 40 = 160$
$4 \times 400 = 1,600$
$4 \times 4,000 = \underline{\ ?\ }$

A. 1,600
B. 4,400
C. 16,000
D. 160,000

3. $6 \times 50 = \underline{\ ?\ }$

A. 300   B. 3,000
C. 30,000   D. 300,000

4. 90
   $\times\ 4$
   _____

A. 36   B. 360
C. 3,600   D. 36,000

5. 800
   $\times\ \ 3$
   _____

A. 24   B. 240
C. 2,400   D. 24,000

6. $7 \times 2,000 = \underline{\ ?\ }$

A. 14   B. 140
C. 1,400   D. 14,000

For questions 7–8, use the model place-value chart.

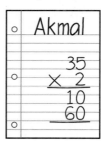

Tens	Ones

7. What multiplication sentence do the base-ten blocks show?

A. $3 + 14 = n$
B. $3 \times 14 = n$
C. $30 \times 4 = n$
D. not here

8. What should be written as the product?

A. 1 ten 4 ones
B. 3 tens 4 ones
C. 4 tens 2 ones
D. 4 tens 12 ones

For questions 9–10, use the student work.

Akmal
      35
   $\times\ \ 2$
   _____
      10
      60

9. How did Akmal get the partial product of 60?

A. multiplied 2 by 5
B. multiplied 2 by 30
C. added 10 and 60
D. multiplied 10 by 2

Form A • Multiple-Choice   A59   **Go on.** ▶

10. What should Akmal record as the product?

A. 45   **B.** 55
C. 60   **D.** 70

11.   123
      $\times$ 3

A. 369   **B.** 396
C. 409   **D.** 459

12.   316
      $\times$ 2

A. 622   **B.** 632
C. 722   **D.** 732

13.   405
      $\times$ 6

A. 2,403
B. 2,430
C. 2,610
D. 2,700

14.   528
      $\times$ 7

A. 3,546
B. 3,646
C. 3,696
D. 4,416

15. There are 144 pencils in a box of new pencils. How many pencils are there in 4 boxes?

A. 444 pencils
B. 466 pencils
C. 476 pencils
D. 576 pencils

16. A machine makes 525 pencils in 1 minute. How many pencils does it make in 5 minutes?

A. 2,525
B. 2,625
C. 2,705
D. 2,725

17. $3.05
      $\times$ 8

A. $24.40   **B.** $24.80
C. $28.00   **D.** $28.40

18. $3 \times \$4.95 = $ __?__

A. $12.95
B. $13.75
C. $13.95
D. $14.85

For questions 19–20, choose the number sentence that can be used to solve the problem.

19. Domingo walks dogs after school. He charges $2.25 for each dog. How much does he earn for walking 3 dogs?

A. $2.25 + $2.25 = $4.50
B. $3.00 − $2.25 = $0.75
C. 3 $\times$ $2.25 = $6.75
D. not here

20. Kari spent $3.50 for lunch. She paid with a $5.00 bill. How much change did she get?

A. 5 $\times$ $3.50 = $17.50
B. $5.00 + $3.50 = $8.50
C. 5 $\times$ $0.70 = $3.50
D. $5.00 − $3.50 = $1.50

Form A • Multiple-Choice   ▶ **Stop!**

Choose the letter of the correct answer.

For questions 1–3, find the product by using a basic fact and a pattern of zeros.

1. $5 \times 6 = 30$
    $5 \times 60 = 300$
    $50 \times 60 = 3,000$
    $50 \times 600 = n$

    A. 300
    B. 3,000
    C. 3,300
    D. 30,000

2. $90 \times 30 = n$

    A. 270
    B. 2,700
    C. 27,000
    D. 270,000

3. $70 \times 600 = n$

    A. 42,000   B. 420,000
    C. 4,200,000 D. 42,000,000

4. One box of paper contains 500 sheets. How many sheets are in 80 boxes?

    A. 400 sheets
    B. 4,000 sheets
    C. 40,000 sheets
    D. 400,000 sheets

5. Duane has a puzzle. When he says 10, the answer is 200. When he says 20, the answer is 400. When he says 50, the answer is 1,000. What is the pattern?

    A. Add 5.
    B. Add 10.
    C. Subtract 10.
    D. Multiply by 20.

6. To estimate the product of 29×42, which number sentence should you use?

    A. 20×40
    B. 25×40
    C. 30×40
    D. 30×50

For questions 7–8, choose the best estimate for each product.

7. $67 \times 52 = n$

    A. 3,000   B. 3,500
    C. 3,600   D. 4,200

8.   79
        $\times 19$

    A. 700   B. 800
    C. 1,400   D. 1,600

9. There are 29 students in each class. There are 21 classes in the school. Which is the best estimate of the number of students?

    A. 200 students
    B. 400 students
    C. 600 students
    D. 900 students

10. The school spends about $617 each month on paper. Which is the best estimate of how much the school spends on paper in 10 months?

    A. $6,000
    B. $8,000
    C. $12,000
    D. $14,000

Form A • Multiple-Choice   **Go on.** ▶

11. Suzanne is using the partial-products method to multiply 37 and 25. What should she do next?

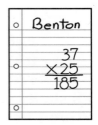

A. add 35 and 150
B. multiply 7 by 20
C. multiply 30 by 20
D. multiply 7 by 5

12. Benton is using a shorter way to multiply 37 and 25. What should he do next?

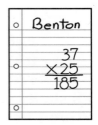

A. multiply 3 by 5
B. multiply 7 by 5
C. multiply 37 by 5
D. multiply 37 by 20

13. 94
$\times$45

A. 846
B. 3,760
C. 4,130
D. not here

14. $73
$\times$ 56

A. $4,088
B. $4,808
C. $4,888
D. not here

15. $87 \times 73 = n$

A. 5,861
B. 6,351
C. 6,391
D. not here

16. Lena is multiplying 102 by 13. What should she do next?

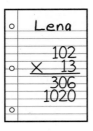

A. estimate the product
B. multiply by the ones
C. multiply by the tens
D. add the products

17. 367
$\times$ 24

A. 8,808
B. 8,888
C. 9,024
D. not here

18. $4.31
$\times$ 72

A. $31.32
B. $309.32
C. $310.32
D. $400.32

19. Maureen has 12 rolls of film. She can take 36 pictures with each roll. How many pictures can she take in all?

A. 432 pictures   **B.** 512 pictures
C. 720 pictures   **D.** 756 pictures

20. A carton of film holds 48 rolls. How many rolls are in 150 cartons?

A. 720 rolls   **B.** 2,400 rolls
C. 5,200 rolls   **D.** 7,200 rolls

Choose the letter of the correct answer.

1. To check the quotient for this division problem, first multiply 4 and 9, and then __?__ .

$$\frac{9\ r2}{4\overline{)38}}$$

   A. multiply by 2
   B. divide by 2
   C. subtract 2
   D. add 2

2. A number can always be divided by 5 with no remainder if the number __?__ .

   A. is even
   B. is odd
   C. ends with 0 or 5
   D. is greater than 5

3. $8\overline{)30}$

   A. 3 r6
   B. 3 r7
   C. 4
   D. not here

4. $5\overline{)27}$

   A. 4 r7
   B. 5
   C. 5 r2
   D. not here

5. When you divide by 9, what is the largest possible remainder?

   A. 3
   B. 8
   C. 9
   D. 10

6. Angela is solving the following problem. What should she do next?

   A. divide the 5 tens
   B. bring down the 3 ones
   C. multiply 2 by 2
   D. write the remainder

7. $3\overline{)72}$

   A. 20 r2   B. 23 r1
   C. 23 r3   D. not here

8. $6\overline{)86}$

   A. 11   B. 14 r2
   C. 16   D. not here

9. In which place should the first digit in the quotient be placed?

   $4\overline{)27}$

   A. ones place
   B. tens place
   C. hundreds place
   D. divisor

10. $7\overline{)58}$

   A. 6   B. 7 r1
   C. 8 r2   D. not here

Form A • Multiple-Choice   A63   **Go on.** ▶

11. The art teacher is dividing 96 sheets of colored paper among 8 groups of students. How many sheets will each group get?

   A. 11 sheets
   B. 12 sheets
   C. 16 sheets
   D. 17 sheets

12. There are 255 beads in a box. They will be divided equally to make 5 necklaces. How many beads will be on each necklace?

   A. 51 beads
   B. 53 beads
   C. 55 beads
   D. 56 beads

13. On a field trip, 100 students saw a play. They were in equal groups, and 4 students were left over. How many groups were formed?

   A. 10 groups
   B. 11 groups
   C. 12 groups
   D. 13 groups

14. Which problem shows where the first digit of the quotient should be placed?

   A. $3\overline{)577}$ B. $3\overline{)577}$

   C. $3\overline{)577}$ D. not here

15. $5\overline{)467}$

   A. 93 r2   B. 94 r2
   C. 95 r2   D. not here

16. $428 \div 7 = n$

   A. 60
   B. 60 r1
   C. 61
   D. not here

17. $305 \div 2 = n$

   A. 102 r1
   B. 150 r1
   C. 152 r1
   D. not here

18. A full bag holds 3 popcorn balls. There are 89 popcorn balls. How many bags are full?

   A. 29 full bags
   B. 30 full bags
   C. 31 full bags
   D. 33 full bags

19. Cans of juice come in six-packs. One store has 246 cans. How many six-packs are there?

   A. 40 six-packs
   B. 41 six-packs
   C. 42 six-packs
   D. 44 six-packs

20. Elize has 640 stamps from around the world. There is an equal number of stamps in each of 8 books. How many stamps are in each book?

   A. 60 stamps
   B. 70 stamps
   C. 80 stamps
   D. 90 stamps

Name _____

Choose the letter of the correct answer.

For questions 1–2, use a basic fact and a pattern of zeros to find the quotient.

1. $16 \div 8 = 2$
   $16,000 \div 8 = n$

   A. 200   **B.** 220
   C. 2,000   **D.** 2,200

2. $35 \div 5 = 7$
   $3,500 \div 5 = n$

   A. 70   **B.** 700
   C. 770   **D.** 7,700

For questions 3–4, estimate. Use a basic fact and a pattern of zeros to estimate the quotient.

3. $49,159 \div 7 = n$

   A. 600   **B.** 700
   C. 6,000   **D.** 7,000

4. $3,020 \div 6 = n$

   A. 5   **B.** 50   **C.** 55   **D.** 500

5. What number belongs in the tens place of the quotient?

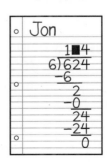

   A. 0   **B.** 1   **C.** 4   **D.** 7

6. $9\overline{)453}$

   A. 5 r3   **B.** 50
   C. 50 r3   **D.** 53

7. $3\overline{)609}$

   A. 23   **B.** 203   **C.** 230   **D.** 233

8. A baker makes 735 cakes in 7 days. How many cakes does he make each day?

   A. 15 cakes   **B.** 105 cakes
   C. 147 cakes   **D.** 150 cakes

9. There are 104 students on a field trip. The students are in groups of 8. How many groups are there?

   A. 10 groups   **B.** 12 groups
   C. 13 groups   **D.** 15 groups

10. Which shows the correct quotient?

    A. $4\overline{)\$5.00}$ with quotient $\$1.25$ **B.** $4\overline{)\$5.00}$ with quotient $\$12.5$

    C. $4\overline{)\$5.00}$ with quotient $\$.125$ **D.** $4\overline{)\$5.00}$ with quotient $\$125.00$

11. $2\overline{)\$12.08}$

    A. $0.64   **B.** $6.04
    C. $6.40   **D.** $64.00

12. $8\overline{)\$6.48}$

    A. $0.81   **B.** $0.88
    C. $8.10   **D.** $8.80

13. Movie tickets cost $22.50 for 5. What is the cost for each ticket?

    A. $0.45   **B.** $4.05
    C. $4.10   **D.** $4.50

14. Mrs. Ho buys 6 pounds of apples for $5.70. What is the cost for each pound of apples?

    A. $0.95   **B.** $0.99
    C. $9.05   **D.** $9.50

Form A • Multiple-Choice   A65   **Go on.** ▶

For questions 15–16, tell how you interpret the remainder.

15. Mr. Sal needs 129 sheets of poster paper. There are 8 sheets in a package. How many packages does he need to buy?

   A. Round the quotient to the next greater whole number.
   B. Drop the remainder.
   C. Use the remainder as part of your answer.
   D. Not enough information is given.

16. Mrs. Haley has 304 pennies and 6 grandchildren. She wants to give each child an equal share of the pennies. How many pennies can each child get?

   A. Round the quotient to the next greater whole number.
   B. Drop the remainder.
   C. Use the remainder in the answer.
   D. Not enough information is given.

17. Lea has 157 inches of ribbon. How many bows can she make if she uses 9 inches of ribbon in each bow?

   A. 13 bows   B. 15 bows
   C. 17 bows   D. 18 bows

18. Jack has to read 126 pages. How many pages should he plan to read each day to be sure he finishes in 5 days?

   A. 18 pages   B. 20 pages
   C. 24 pages   D. 26 pages

19. Mia can paint 1 T-shirt in 8 minutes. How many T-shirts can she paint in 140 minutes?

   A. 14 T-shirts B. 17 T-shirts
   C. 18 T-shirts D. 22 T-shirts

20. Al plays the piano. He plays each song for 10 minutes. How many songs can he play in 115 minutes?

   A. 11 songs   B. 12 songs
   C. 15 songs   D. 16 songs

For questions 21–24, solve. Name the operation you used.

21. Ed's family drove 157 miles on Monday, 223 miles on Tuesday, and 118 miles on Wednesday. How many miles did they drive in all?

   A. 498 miles, addition
   B. 105 miles, subtraction
   C. 18,526 miles, multiplication
   D. 166 miles, division

22. The school play lasts 90 minutes. Each of the 3 acts takes the same amount of time. How long is each act?

   A. 93 minutes; addition
   B. 87 minutes; subtraction
   C. 270 minutes; multiplication
   D. 30 minutes; division

23. Vin is reading a book with 221 pages. He has read 118 pages. How many more pages does he have to read?

   A. 339 pages; addition
   B. 103 pages; subtraction
   C. 3,000 pages; multiplication
   D. 2 pages; division

24. Jessica travels 13 miles round trip to school. How many miles does she travel to school and back in 21 days?

   A. 34 miles; addition
   B. 8 miles; subtraction
   C. 273 miles; multiplication
   D. 2 miles; division

Name _____

Choose the letter of the correct answer.

1. What number completes the pattern?
   $4 \times 80 = 320$
   $4 \times 800 = 3,200$
   $4 \times \underline{\ ?\ } = 32,000$

   A. 800
   B. 880
   C. 888
   D. 8,000

2. $\begin{array}{r} 600 \\ \times\ \ 7 \\ \hline \end{array}$
   A. 420
   B. 4,200
   C. 42,000
   D. 420,000

3. $\begin{array}{r} 306 \\ \times\ \ 5 \\ \hline \end{array}$
   A. 153
   B. 1,503
   C. 1,530
   D. 15,030

4. There are 126 crayons in a box of new crayons. How many crayons are in 6 boxes?

   A. 626 crayons
   B. 656 crayons
   C. 726 crayons
   D. 756 crayons

5. $5 \times \$5.35 = \underline{\ ?\ }$

   A. $25.55
   B. $25.75
   C. $26.65
   D. not here

6. Choose the number sentence that can be used to solve the problem.

   Earlene sells her drawings. She charges $3.25 for each drawing. How much does she earn for 4 drawings?

   A. $\$3.25 \times 4 = n$
   B. $\$3.25 + \$4.00 = n$
   C. $\$4.00 - \$3.25 = n$
   D. $\$3.25 \div 4 = n$

7. $50 \times 700 = n$

   A. 3,500
   B. 35,000
   C. 350,000
   D. 3,500,000

8. On Earth Day 10 groups of volunteers planted new trees. Each group planted 50 trees. What was the total number of trees planted?

   A. 50 trees
   B. 500 trees
   C. 550 trees
   D. 5,000 trees

9. James sleeps about 8 hours per night. Which of these is the best estimate of the number of hours he sleeps in 12 nights?

   A. about 50 hours
   B. about 60 hours
   C. about 100 hours
   D. about 160 hours

10. $\begin{array}{r} 92 \\ \times 53 \\ \hline \end{array}$
    A. 955
    B. 4,776
    C. 4,876
    D. not here

11. $\begin{array}{r} \$5.12 \\ \times\ \ \ 17 \\ \hline \end{array}$
    A. $40.96
    B. $86.94
    C. $97.04
    D. not here

12. There are 70 chocolate chip cookies in a bag. Each cookie has 18 chocolate chips. How many chocolate chips are in the bag?

    A. 700 chocolate chips
    B. 1,180 chocolate chips
    C. 1,260 chocolate chips
    D. 1,560 chocolate chips

13. $7\overline{)46}$

   A. 6 r4   **B.** 6 r6
   C. 7 r4   **D.** 8 r2

14. When you divide by 7, what is the largest possible remainder?

   A. 3   **B.** 4   **C.** 6   **D.** 8

15. $5\overline{)63}$

   A. 10 r3   **B.** 11 r2
   C. 12 r2   **D.** 12 r3

16. Larry set up 70 chairs. They were in equal rows with 6 chairs left over. How many rows were formed?

   A. 8 rows   **B.** 9 rows
   C. 11 rows   **D.** 12 rows

17. $538 \div 7 = n$

   A. 76 r5   **B.** 76 r6
   C. 78 r2   **D.** not here

18. A carton contains 336 small toys. Inside the carton, there are 2 toys in each box. How many boxes are in the carton?

   A. 118 boxes   **B.** 158 boxes
   C. 168 boxes   **D.** 169 boxes

19. Use a basic fact and a pattern of zeros to find the quotient.
$28 \div 7 = 4$
$280 \div 7 = 40$
$2{,}800 \div 7 = 400$
$28{,}000 \div 7 = n$

   A. 40   **B.** 400
   C. 440   **D.** 4,000

20. $6\overline{)364}$

   A. 6 r4   **B.** 60
   C. 60 r4   **D.** not here

21. $4\overline{)850}$

   A. 212 r2   **B.** 213 r3
   C. 214 r2   **D.** 215 r2

22. $9\overline{)\$7.38}$

   A. \$0.80   **B.** \$0.82
   C. \$8.00   **D.** not here

23. Val has 242 baseball cards. It takes 16 cards to fill a page. How many album pages can he fill? How many baseball cards will be left over?

   A. 14 pages; 2 baseball cards
   B. 15 pages; 2 baseball cards
   C. 15 pages; 3 baseball cards
   D. 16 pages; 2 baseball cards

24. Solve, and name the operation you used.

A game lasts 36 minutes. Each of the 4 periods takes the same amount of time. How long is each period?

   A. 9 minutes; division
   B. 32 minutes; subtraction
   C. 40 minutes; addition
   D. 144 minutes; multiplication

Choose the letter of the correct answer.

1. The perimeter of the figure is 642 feet. What is the missing length?

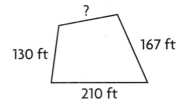

   A. 100 ft   **B.** 125 ft
   C. 135 ft   **D.** 507 ft

2. Use the multiplication fact to help you find the quotient.
$$5 \times 8 = 40$$
$$40 \div 8 = \underline{\ ?\ }$$

   A. 5   **B.** 8   **C.** 16   **D.** 40

3. How many tens are in 5,263?

   A. 2 tens   **B.** 3 tens
   C. 5 tens   **D.** 6 tens

4. Which numbers are written in order from the greatest to the least?

   A. 3,745; 3,459; 2,973
   B. 2,973; 3,459; 3,745
   C. 2,973; 3,745; 3,459
   D. 3,459; 2,973; 3,745

For questions 5–7, use the graph.

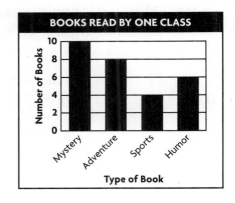

5. What interval is used in the scale of the graph?

   A. 1   **B.** 2   **C.** 3   **D.** 4

6. How many more mystery books than sports books did the class read?

   A. 2   **B.** 4   **C.** 6   **D.** 8

7. How many books did the class read in all?

   A. 10 books   **B.** 22 books
   C. 24 books   **D.** 28 books

For questions 8–9, use the stem-and-leaf-plot.

Scores on a Science Test

Stem	Leaves
7	5 7 9
8	0 1 2 3 3 3 4 8 9
9	0 1 2 2 3 3 4

8. What number is the mode for the data?

   A. 79   **B.** 83   **C.** 92   **D.** 93

9. What is the difference between the lowest score and the highest score on the test?

   A. 19   **B.** 20   **C.** 22   **D.** 24

For questions 10–11, use the tally table.

NUMBER OF BLOCKS IN A BAG	
White	HHT HHT HHT
Black	HHT HHT
Red	HHT II
Green	HHT HHT HHT III

10. Which outcome is most likely if a block is pulled from the bag?

A. pulling a white block
B. pulling a black block
C. pulling a red block
D. pulling a green block

11. Which color block are you least likely to pull?

A. white   B. black
C. red   D. green

12. Which unit would be used to measure the area of a floor?

A. feet   B. square feet
C. yards   D. cubic yards

For questions 13–14, use the organized list.

Cylinders	?	Spheres
can flashlight pencil holder	boxes dice blocks	ball globe ?

13. Which heading is missing?

A. Cubes   B. Triangles
C. Squares   D. Pyramids

14. Which object should be listed under *Spheres*?

A. toy block   B. pencil
C. marble   D. telescope

15. What is a flat surface with no end called?

A. line   B. line segment
C. angle   D. plane

16. I am a 4-sided polygon. None of my sides are parallel. What am I?

A. parallelogram
B. trapezoid
C. rectangle
D. general quadrilateral

17. What is the area of the shaded figure?

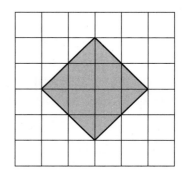

A. 4 sq units   B. 6 sq units
C. 8 sq units   D. 12 sq units

18. Ross has 24 feet of rope to make a border around his garden. Which shape has the greatest area?

A. 6 ft by 6 ft   B. 8 ft by 4 ft
C. 10 ft by 2 ft   D. 5 ft by 7 ft

19. Which pair of figures is congruent?

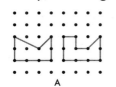

A.   A   **B.**   B

C.   C   **D.**   D

20. Which figure will *not* tessellate?

A. 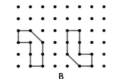   **B.**

C.   **D.**

21. $5 \times 80 =$ ___?___

A. 400   **B.** 4,000
C. 40,000   **D.** 400,000

22. $4 \times 6,000 =$ ___?___

A. 24   **B.** 240
C. 2,400   **D.** 24,000

For questions 23–24, use the model place-value chart.

Tens	Ones
	▫ ▫
	▫ ▫
	▫ ▫

23. Which multiplication sentence do the base-ten blocks show?

A. $3 \times 2 = n$ **B.** $3 \times 6 = n$
C. $3 \times 10 = n$ **D.** $3 \times 12 = n$

24. What should Anna record as the product?

A. 1 ten 2 ones
B. 3 tens 2 ones
C. 3 tens 6 ones
D. 4 tens 6 ones

25. $4 \times \$2.95 =$ ___?___

A. \$5.90   **B.** \$11.80
C. \$18.80   **D.** \$38.80

26. $20 \times 70 = n$

A. 140   **B.** 14,000
C. 140,000   **D.** not here

27. What is the best estimate of the product?

$$\begin{array}{r} 58 \\ \times 21 \\ \hline \end{array}$$

A. about 210   **B.** about 1,160
C. about 1,200   **D.** about 12,000

28.
$$\begin{array}{r} 72 \\ \times 48 \\ \hline \end{array}$$
A. 1,200
B. 3,456
C. 7,248
D. 8,496

29.
$$\begin{array}{r} \$5.49 \\ \times \quad 23 \\ \hline \end{array}$$
A. \$26.27
B. \$124.07
C. \$126.27
D. \$226.27

30. Philip has 11 boxes of cookie mix. He can make 24 cookies with each box. How many cookies can he make in all?

A. 264 cookies   B. 360 cookies
C. 480 cookies   D. 512 cookies

31. $7\overline{)60}$

A. 8   B. 8 r2
C. 8 r6   D. not here

32. $5\overline{)64}$

A. 12 r1   B. 12 r4
C. 12 r6   D. not here

33. A total of 83 students went to a park. They were in equal groups with 2 students left over. How many equal groups were there?

A. 9 groups   B. 10 groups
C. 11 groups   D. 12 groups

34. $364 \div 6 = n$

A. 60   B. 60 r1
C. 60 r4   D. not here

For questions 35–36, use a basic fact and a pattern of zeros to find the quotient.

35. $20 \div 4 = 5$
$20,000 \div 4 = n$

A. 50   B. 500
C. 5,000   D. 50,000

36. $63 \div 9 = 7$
$6,300 \div 9 = n$

A. 70   B. 700
C. 770   D. 7,700

37. $3\overline{)217}$

A. 72 r1   B. 72 r2
C. 72 r7   D. 80

38. $8\overline{)\$16.08}$

A. $0.20   B. $2.01
C. $2.10   D. $20.10

39. How would you interpret the remainder?

Mrs. Jenks has 38 cookies. She wants to give an equal number of cookies to each of 9 children. How many cookies should she give each child?

A. Drop the remainder.
B. Use the remainder as part of your answer.
C. Round the quotient to the next greater whole number.
D. not here

40. Solve and name the operation you used.

Lynn jogs 14 miles each week. How many miles does she jog in 52 weeks?

A. 3 miles; division
B. 38 miles; subtraction
C. 66 miles; addition
D. 728 miles; multiplication

Name _____

Choose the letter of the correct answer.

1. What fraction of the bar is shaded?

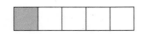

A. $\frac{1}{5}$ B. $\frac{1}{4}$ C. $\frac{1}{3}$ D. $\frac{1}{2}$

2. What fraction of the circle is shaded?

A. $\frac{2}{5}$ B. $\frac{2}{3}$ C. $\frac{3}{4}$ D. $\frac{7}{8}$

3. Which figure is one-sixth shaded?

A.

B.

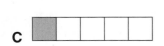

C

D.

4. Which fraction means the same as four out of five?

A. $\frac{4}{5}$ B. $\frac{5}{4}$ C. $\frac{5}{9}$ D. $\frac{9}{10}$

For questions 5–6, use this figure.

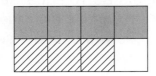

5. What fraction of the figure is striped?

A. $\frac{1}{8}$ B. $\frac{3}{8}$ C. $\frac{5}{8}$ D. $\frac{7}{8}$

6. What fraction of the figure is NOT striped or shaded?

A. $\frac{1}{8}$ B. $\frac{3}{8}$

C. $\frac{5}{8}$ D. $\frac{7}{8}$

For questions 7–10, choose the fraction that represents the group that is shaded.

7.

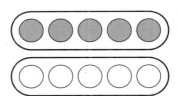

A. $\frac{1}{5}$ B. $\frac{1}{4}$

C. $\frac{1}{3}$ D. $\frac{1}{6}$

8.

A. $\frac{1}{10}$ B. $\frac{1}{5}$

C. $\frac{1}{3}$ D. $\frac{1}{2}$

9.

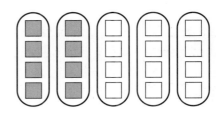

A. $\frac{2}{5}$ B. $\frac{3}{5}$

C. $\frac{2}{3}$ D. $\frac{3}{4}$

Form A • Multiple-Choice   A73   **Go on.** ▶

10.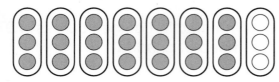

A. $\frac{1}{8}$ B. $\frac{5}{10}$

C. $\frac{7}{8}$ D. $\frac{7}{24}$

11. Small cans of juice come in four-packs. The Hennessey twins share a four-pack equally. What fraction of a four-pack does each twin drink?

A. $\frac{1}{4}$ B. $\frac{2}{4}$

C. $\frac{3}{4}$ D. $\frac{4}{2}$

12. Terry takes 5 books out of the library. Of the books, 2 are mystery stories. What fraction of the books are mystery stories?

A. $\frac{2}{5}$ B. $\frac{3}{5}$

C. $\frac{2}{7}$ D. $\frac{5}{2}$

For questions 13–14, use the fraction bars to compare the fractions. Choose $<$, $>$, or $=$ for each ●.

13.

| $\frac{1}{8}$ | $\frac{1}{8}$ | $\frac{1}{8}$ | $\frac{1}{8}$ | $\frac{1}{8}$ | $\frac{1}{8}$ | $\frac{1}{8}$ | $\frac{1}{8}$ |

| $\frac{1}{4}$ | $\frac{1}{4}$ | $\frac{1}{4}$ | $\frac{1}{4}$ |

$\frac{6}{8}$ ● $\frac{3}{4}$

A. $<$

B. $>$

C. $=$

14.

| $\frac{1}{5}$ | $\frac{1}{5}$ | $\frac{1}{5}$ | $\frac{1}{5}$ | $\frac{1}{5}$ |

| $\frac{1}{3}$ | $\frac{1}{3}$ | $\frac{1}{3}$ |

$\frac{4}{5}$ ● $\frac{2}{3}$

A. $<$ B. $>$ C. $=$

15. Which group of fractions is in order from least to greatest?

A. $\frac{2}{3}, \frac{1}{6}, \frac{5}{6}$ B. $\frac{1}{6}, \frac{5}{6}, \frac{2}{3}$

C. $\frac{5}{6}, \frac{2}{3}, \frac{1}{6}$ D. $\frac{1}{6}, \frac{2}{3}, \frac{5}{6}$

16. Which group of fractions is in order from greatest to least?

A. $\frac{1}{4}, \frac{3}{8}, \frac{3}{4}$ B. $\frac{1}{4}, \frac{3}{4}, \frac{3}{8}$

C. $\frac{3}{4}, \frac{3}{8}, \frac{1}{4}$ D. $\frac{3}{8}, \frac{3}{4}, \frac{1}{4}$

17. A muffin recipe calls for $\frac{3}{4}$ cup coconut, $\frac{1}{4}$ cup nuts, and $\frac{1}{2}$ cup dates. Which shows the ingredients listed in order from least to greatest?

A. coconut, nuts, dates
B. nuts, dates, coconut
C. nuts, coconut, dates
D. dates, nuts, coconut

18. A spinner has 10 equal sections. Of the sections, 2 are blue, 3 are yellow, 1 is white, and 4 sections are red. Which two colors together cover more than $\frac{1}{2}$ the spinner?

A. blue and yellow
B. yellow and white
C. red and white
D. blue and red

Form A • Multiple-Choice   A74   **Go on.** ▶

For questions 19–20, choose the mixed number that matches the picture.

19.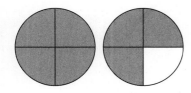

A. $1\frac{1}{4}$ B. $1\frac{3}{4}$

C. $3\frac{1}{4}$ D. $4\frac{1}{3}$

20.

A. $1\frac{2}{3}$ B. $2\frac{1}{3}$

C. $2\frac{2}{3}$ D. $3\frac{1}{3}$

For questions 21–24, rename each fraction as a mixed number.

21. $\frac{13}{8} = $ ___?___

A. $\frac{8}{13}$ B. $1\frac{1}{8}$

C. $1\frac{3}{8}$ D. $1\frac{5}{8}$

22. $\frac{11}{4} = $ ___?___

A. $2\frac{3}{4}$ B. $3\frac{1}{4}$

C. $3\frac{1}{2}$ D. $3\frac{3}{4}$

23. $\frac{7}{3} = $ ___?___

A. $\frac{3}{7}$ B. $1\frac{2}{3}$

C. $2\frac{1}{3}$ D. $3\frac{1}{2}$

24. $\frac{9}{5} = $ ___?___

A. $\frac{5}{9}$ B. $1\frac{4}{5}$

C. $2\frac{1}{5}$ D. $2\frac{1}{4}$

Choose the letter of the correct answer.

1. Which number sentence matches the model?

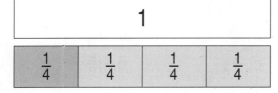

1

$\frac{1}{4}$	$\frac{1}{4}$	$\frac{1}{4}$	$\frac{1}{4}$

A. $\frac{1}{4} + \frac{3}{4} = 1$ B. $\frac{1}{5} + \frac{4}{5} = 1$

C. $\frac{1}{2} + \frac{1}{2} = 1$ D. $\frac{4}{8} + \frac{4}{8} = 1$

2. Use the fraction bars to help you find the sum.

1

$\frac{1}{3}$	$\frac{1}{3}$	$\frac{1}{3}$	$\frac{1}{3}$

$\frac{2}{3} + \frac{2}{3} = \underline{\ ?\ }$

A. $\frac{4}{6}$ B. 1

C. $1\frac{1}{3}$ D. $1\frac{2}{3}$

3. Which is the number sentence for this problem?

four tenths plus five tenths

A. $\frac{4}{10} + \frac{5}{10} = \underline{\ ?\ }$

B. $\frac{10}{4} + \frac{10}{5} = \underline{\ ?\ }$

C. $4 + \frac{5}{10} = \underline{\ ?\ }$

D. $410 + 510 = \underline{\ ?\ }$

4. Which sum is greater than 1?

A. $\frac{1}{5} + \frac{2}{5} = \underline{\ ?\ }$ B. $\frac{5}{7} + \frac{4}{7} = \underline{\ ?\ }$

C. $\frac{3}{8} + \frac{3}{8} = \underline{\ ?\ }$ D. $\frac{7}{10} + \frac{1}{10} = \underline{\ ?\ }$

5. $\frac{1}{6} + \frac{4}{6} = \underline{\ ?\ }$

A. $\frac{5}{12}$ B. $\frac{1}{2}$

C. $\frac{5}{6}$ D. $1\frac{1}{6}$

6. $\frac{3}{8} + \frac{4}{8} = \underline{\ ?\ }$

A. $\frac{7}{16}$ B. $\frac{7}{8}$

C. $\frac{11}{12}$ D. $\frac{15}{16}$

7. Jerome ate $\frac{1}{4}$ cup of cereal before school. He ate $\frac{2}{4}$ cup of cereal after school. How much cereal did Jerome eat?

A. $\frac{3}{4}$ cup   B. $\frac{7}{8}$ cup

C. 1 cup   D. $1\frac{1}{4}$ cup

8. Using a ruler, Dottie draws a line that is $\frac{5}{8}$-inch long. Then she makes the line $\frac{3}{8}$-inch longer. How long is the line now?

A. $\frac{8}{16}$ in.   B. $\frac{7}{8}$ in.

C. $\frac{15}{16}$ in.   D. $\frac{8}{8}$, or 1 in.

9. Which number sentence matches the model?

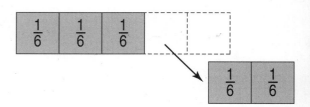

$\frac{1}{6}$	$\frac{1}{6}$	$\frac{1}{6}$

$\frac{1}{6}$	$\frac{1}{6}$

A. $\frac{3}{6} - \frac{1}{6} = \underline{\ ?\ }$

B. $\frac{6}{3} - \frac{4}{2} = \underline{\ ?\ }$

C. $\frac{5}{6} - \frac{3}{6} = \underline{\ ?\ }$

D. $\frac{5}{6} - \frac{2}{6} = \underline{\ ?\ }$

10. Use the model to help you find the difference.

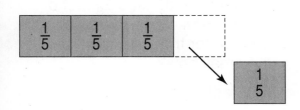

$\frac{4}{5} - \frac{1}{5} = \underline{\ ?\ }$

A. $\frac{1}{5}$

B. $\frac{2}{5}$

C. $\frac{3}{5}$

D. $\frac{5}{5}$

11. Kyle ate $\frac{1}{4}$ of a blueberry pie. How much of the pie is left?

A. $\frac{1}{4}$ of the pie

B. $\frac{2}{4}$ of the pie

C. $\frac{5}{8}$ of the pie

D. $\frac{3}{4}$ of the pie

12. Frederico and Danielle each ate $\frac{3}{8}$ of a large pizza. What fraction of the pizza is left?

A. $\frac{1}{8}$ of the pizza

B. $\frac{2}{8}$ of the pizza

C. $\frac{3}{8}$ of the pizza

D. $\frac{5}{8}$ of the pizza

13. Use the model to help you find the sum.

$2\frac{1}{3}$
$+1\frac{1}{3}$
_____

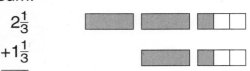

A. $2\frac{2}{3}$

B. $3\frac{1}{3}$

C. $3\frac{2}{3}$

D. $4\frac{1}{3}$

14.
$3\frac{1}{5}$
$+2\frac{3}{5}$
_____

A. $4\frac{4}{5}$

B. $5\frac{4}{5}$

C. $6\frac{1}{5}$

D. $6\frac{3}{5}$

15.
$4\frac{3}{8}$
$+2\frac{5}{8}$
_____

A. 6

B. $6\frac{5}{8}$

C. $6\frac{7}{8}$

D. $6\frac{8}{8}$, or 7

16. $6\frac{3}{10} + 2\frac{4}{10} = \underline{\ ?\ }$

A. $8\frac{7}{10}$

B. $8\frac{9}{10}$

C. 9

D. $9\frac{1}{10}$

17. A bread recipe calls for $1\frac{1}{4}$ cups whole wheat flour and $2\frac{3}{4}$ cups white flour. How many cups of flour are used in the recipe?

A. 3 cups flour

B. $3\frac{4}{8}$ cups flour

C. $3\frac{4}{4}$, or 4 cups flour

D. $4\frac{1}{4}$ cups flour

18. Moira and Kelly made cookies for a bake sale. Moira made $2\frac{2}{6}$ dozen cookies. Kelly made $3\frac{3}{6}$ dozen cookies. How many dozen cookies did they make in all?

A. $5\frac{5}{6}$ dozen

B. 6 dozen

C. $6\frac{1}{6}$ dozen

D. $6\frac{5}{6}$ dozen

Form A • Multiple-Choice   A77   **Go on. ▶**

19.

$3\frac{2}{3}$
$-1\frac{1}{3}$
___

A. $1\frac{1}{3}$ B. $1\frac{2}{3}$

C. 2 D. $2\frac{1}{3}$

20.

$6\frac{2}{4}$
$-2\frac{1}{4}$
___

A. $4\frac{1}{4}$ B. $4\frac{2}{4}$, or $4\frac{1}{2}$

C. $4\frac{3}{4}$ D. $4\frac{7}{8}$

21.

$8\frac{7}{8}$
$-6\frac{5}{8}$
___

A. $2\frac{1}{8}$ B. $2\frac{2}{8}$, or $2\frac{1}{4}$

C. $2\frac{3}{8}$ D. $2\frac{3}{4}$

22. $7\frac{3}{5} - 4\frac{1}{5} = \underline{\ ?\ }$

A. $2\frac{4}{5}$ B. $3\frac{1}{5}$

C. $3\frac{2}{5}$ D. $3\frac{4}{5}$

23. The bow for a large holiday wreath uses $4\frac{5}{8}$ feet of ribbon. The bow for a small wreath uses $2\frac{4}{8}$ feet of ribbon. How much more ribbon is needed for the large bow than for the small bow?

A. 2 feet

B. $2\frac{1}{8}$ feet

C. $2\frac{3}{8}$ feet

D. $3\frac{1}{8}$ feet

24. The Scouts hiked $5\frac{6}{10}$ miles. They stopped for lunch. Then they hiked $2\frac{3}{10}$ miles. How many miles did they hike in all?

A. $3\frac{3}{10}$ miles

B. $3\frac{9}{10}$ miles

C. $7\frac{3}{10}$ miles

D. $7\frac{9}{10}$ miles

Name _____

Choose the letter of the correct answer.

1. The model shows 0.8. How is this written as a fraction?

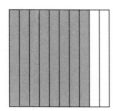

A. $\frac{8}{10}$ **B.** $\frac{8}{100}$

C. $\frac{18}{100}$ **D.** $\frac{88}{100}$

2. The model shows $\frac{25}{100}$. How is this written as a decimal?

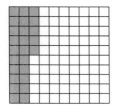

A. 0.25   **B.** 0.3   **C.** 0.4   **D.** 0.52

3. What is $\frac{3}{10}$ written as a decimal?

A. 0.03   **B.** 0.3   **C.** 0.33   **D.** 3.10

4. What is 0.15 written as a fraction?

A. $\frac{15}{100}$ **B.** $\frac{1}{15}$ **C.** $\frac{1}{5}$ **D.** $\frac{10}{15}$

5. What is the decimal name for the shaded part of the model?

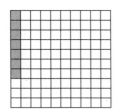

A. seven tenths
B. seventy-two hundredths
C. seventy tenths
D. seven hundredths

6. What is the decimal for the shaded part of the model?

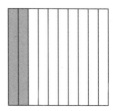

A. 0.02   **B.** 0.2   **C.** 2.0   **D.** 2.2

7. What is 9 dimes written as a money amount?

A. $0.09   **B.** $0.90
C. $0.99   **D.** $9.00

8. What is 5 pennies written as a money amount?

A. $0.05   **B.** $0.50
C. $0.55   **D.** $5.00

9. Sandi has 76 pennies in a jar. What part of a dollar is that?

A. 1.60   **B.** 1.76
C. 0.76   **D.** 76

10. Marco has $\frac{50}{100}$ of a dollar. How many pennies is that?

A. 5 pennies   **B.** 15 pennies
C. 50 pennies   **D.** 150 pennies

For questions 11–12, use the number line.

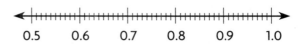

11. The number line has small ticks and large ticks. What do the small ticks show?

A. hundredths   **B.** tenths
C. ones   **D.** tens

Form A • Multiple-Choice   A79   **Go on.** ▶

12. Which pair of decimal numbers would be at the same place on the number line?

   A. 0.8 and 0.88   **B.** 0.7 and 0.8
   C. 0.79 and 0.80   **D.** 0.8 and 0.80

For questions 13–14, compare the decimals.

13. Which number is less than 0.4?

   A. 0.24   **B.** 0.42
   C. 0.8   **D.** not here

14. Which number is less than 0.05?

   A. 0.06   **B.** 0.14
   C. 0.04   **D.** not here

15. Which group of decimals is written in order from least to greatest?

   A. 0.5, 0.45, 0.6
   B. 0.5, 0.6, 0.45
   C. 0.45, 0.5, 0.6
   D. 0.6, 0.5, 0.45

16. Which group of decimals is written in order from greatest to least?

   A. 0.14, 0.8, 0.09
   B. 0.14, 0.09, 0.8
   C. 0.09, 0.8, 0.14
   D. 0.8, 0.14, 0.09

17. What mixed decimal is shown by the model?

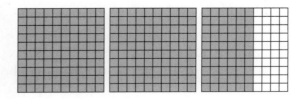

   A. 0.26   **B.** 2.00
   C. 2.60   **D.** 2.62

18. Which mixed decimal is equivalent to 2.60?

   A. 2.0   **B.** 2.6
   C. 6.0   **D.** 6.2

19. What is an equivalent mixed decimal for 5.90?

   A. 0.59   **B.** 5.9
   C. 5.09   **D.** 9.50

20. What is $10\frac{1}{10}$ written as a decimal?

   A. 1.01   **B.** 1.10
   C. 10.01   **D.** 10.1

21. What is $3\frac{5}{100}$ written as a decimal?

   A. 0.35   **B.** 3.05
   C. 3.50   **D.** not here

22. What is 6.33 written as a mixed number?

   A. $6\frac{3}{100}$ **B.** $6\frac{3}{10}$
   C. $6\frac{33}{100}$ **D.** $6\frac{33}{10}$

23. At a gymnastics meet, Dee scored 9.43, Meg scored 8.95, Val scored 9.50, and Wendy scored 9.38. Who had the highest score?

   A. Dee   **B.** Meg
   C. Val   **D.** Wendy

24. Dan has $4.94. Ed has $4.49. Ben has $4.69. Tom has $4.96. Which boy has the least amount of money?

   A. Dan   **B.** Ed
   C. Ben   **D.** Tom

Choose the letter of the correct answer.

For questions 1–2, use the decimal-square model.

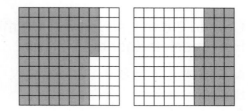

1. Which number sentence matches the model?

   A. $0.7 + 0.3 = n$
   B. $0.75 + 0.36 = n$
   C. $0.76 + 0.35 = n$
   D. $7.5 + 3.6 = n$

2. What is the sum of the shaded parts of the model?

   A. 0.95   **B.** 1.00
   C. 1.05   **D.** 1.11

3.   0.9   **A.** 0.15
   $+0.6$ **B.** 0.96
              C. 1.15
              D. 1.5

4.   0.85   **A.** 1.19
   $+0.34$ **B.** 0.119
              C. 1.91
              D. 11.9

5.   1.42   **A.** 0.113
   $+0.71$ **B.** 1.03
              C. 2.13
              D. 21.3

6. Lil has 1.3 pounds of grapes and 2.2 pounds of oranges. How many pounds of fruit does she have?

   A. 3.3 lb   **B.** 3.32 lb
   C. 3.4 lb   **D.** 3.5 lb

7. Ricky swims the first half of a race in 1.53 minutes and the second half in 1.51 minutes. What is his total time?

   A. 2.04 minutes
   B. 2.4 minutes
   C. 3.04 minutes
   D. 3.4 minutes

8. Use the model to find the difference.

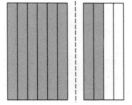

   $0.8 - 0.2 = n$

   A. 0.06   **B.** 0.6
   C. 0.66   **D.** 6.0

9. Use the model to find the difference.

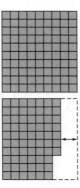

   $0.90 - 0.67 = n$

   A. 0.15   **B.** 0.23
   C. 1.05   **D.** 1.57

10.   1.3   **A.** 0.7
    -0.6 **B.** 1.7
              C. 1.9
              D. not here

11. 0.73
−0.32

A. 1.05
B. 0.41
C. 0.49
D. not here

12. 1.05
−0.29

A. 0.86
B. 1.24
C. 1.34
D. not here

13. Myra is 1.56 meters tall. Phil is 1.34 meters tall. What is the difference in their heights?

A. 0.22 m
C. 1.22 m
B. 0.90 m
D. 2.90 m

14. Dewey walks 2.4 miles. Xavier walks 0.9 miles. How many miles farther does Dewey walk?

A. 0.5 mi
C. 2.3 mi
B. 1.5 mi
D. 3.3 mi

15. 0.89
+0.39

A. 0.50
B. 1.18
C. 1.28
D. not here

16. 0.70
−0.25

A. 0.45
B. 0.50
C. 0.95
D. not here

17. 1.60
−0.04

A. 1.20
B. 1.24
C. 1.56
D. not here

18. $0.23 + 0.3 = n$

A. 0.233
C. 0.5
B. 0.26
D. not here

For questions 19–20, choose the number sentence that shows how to solve the problem.

19. Cal ran 2.6 miles. Ben ran 1.3 miles. How much farther did Cal run?

A. $2.6 + 1.3 = 3.9$
B. $2.6 - 1.3 = 1.3$
C. $2.6 \times 1.3 = 3.38$
D. $2.6 \div 1.3 = 2$

20. Eva played soccer for 1.2 hours on Saturday and 4.5 hours on Sunday. How many hours did she play in all?

A. $1.2 + 4.5 = 5.7$
B. $4.5 - 1.2 = 3.3$
C. $1.2 \times 4.5 = 5.40$
D. $4.5 \div 1.2 = 3.75$

21. What is 6.7 rounded to the nearest whole number?

A. 2   B. 5   C. 7   D. 8

For questions 22–24, estimate the sum or difference by rounding to the nearest whole number.

22. 3.9
+1.7

A. 4
B. 5
C. 6
D. 7

23. 8.8
−1.2

A. 6
B. 7
C. 8
D. 9

24. Mel ran 2.8 miles on Monday, 2.9 miles on Tuesday, and 3.1 miles on Wednesday. About how many miles did he run those 3 days?

A. about 6 mi
C. about 8 mi
B. about 7 mi
D. about 9 mi

Name _____

Choose the letter of the correct answer.

1. Which fraction of the rectangle is shaded?

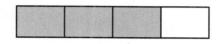

A. $\frac{1}{4}$ B. $\frac{3}{8}$

C. $\frac{5}{8}$ D. $\frac{3}{4}$

2. Which fraction represents the group that is shaded?

A. $\frac{1}{4}$ B. $\frac{2}{4}$

C. $\frac{2}{3}$ D. $\frac{3}{4}$

3. Lisa went out for 7 hours. She spent 3 hours at the park. What fraction of her time was spent at the park?

A. $\frac{3}{7}$ of her time   B. $\frac{4}{7}$ of her time

C. $\frac{7}{3}$ of her time   D. not here

4. Which group of fractions is in order from greatest to least?

A. $\frac{1}{4}, \frac{3}{8}, \frac{3}{4}$ B. $\frac{1}{4}, \frac{3}{4}, \frac{3}{8}$

C. $\frac{3}{8}, \frac{3}{4}, \frac{1}{4}$ D. $\frac{3}{4}, \frac{3}{8}, \frac{1}{4}$

5. Which mixed number matches the picture?

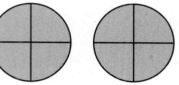

A. $2\frac{1}{4}$ B. $2\frac{3}{4}$

C. $3\frac{1}{4}$ D. $3\frac{3}{4}$

6. $\frac{4}{6} + \frac{3}{6} = \underline{\ ?\ }$

A. $\frac{1}{12}$ B. $1\frac{1}{6}$

C. $1\frac{1}{3}$ D. $1\frac{5}{12}$

7. $2\frac{2}{9} + 6\frac{4}{9} = \underline{\ ?\ }$

A. $8\frac{6}{9}$ B. 9

C. $9\frac{2}{9}$ D. $12\frac{2}{3}$

8. A recipe for hot sauce uses $3\frac{2}{5}$ ounces of red pepper and $4\frac{2}{5}$ ounces of black pepper. How many ounces of pepper are needed in all?

A. $1\frac{4}{5}$ oz   B. $7\frac{4}{10}$ oz

C. $7\frac{4}{5}$ oz   D. $8\frac{1}{5}$ oz

9. Mike rode his bike $3\frac{2}{8}$ miles. Then he rode $2\frac{5}{8}$ miles. How many miles did he ride in all?

A. $1\frac{3}{8}$ mi   B. $5\frac{5}{16}$ mi

C. $5\frac{3}{8}$ mi   D. $5\frac{7}{8}$ mi

10. $8\frac{6}{7} - 5\frac{2}{7} = \underline{\ ?\ }$

   A. $3\frac{3}{7}$ **B.** $3\frac{4}{7}$

   C. $3\frac{5}{7}$ **D.** $4\frac{4}{7}$

11. Steve fed his dog $\frac{2}{5}$ of a can of dog food. How much of the can is left?

   A. $\frac{2}{3}$ of the can **B.** $\frac{4}{5}$ of the can

   C. $\frac{5}{3}$ of the can **D.** not here

12. What is $\frac{56}{100}$ written as a decimal?

   A. 0.44 **B.** 0.56
   C. 0.6 **D.** 5.60

13. What is 34 pennies written as a money amount?

   A. $0.03 **B.** $0.33
   C. $0.34 **D.** not here

14. What is 4.24 written as a mixed number?

   A. $4\frac{14}{100}$ **B.** $4\frac{2}{10}$

   C. $4\frac{24}{100}$ **D.** not here

15. Which group of decimals is in order from greatest to least?

   A. 0.4, 0.55, 0.6
   B. 0.6, 0.55, 0.4
   C. 0.6, 0.4, 0.55
   D. 0.55, 0.6, 0.4

16. Which mixed decimal is equivalent to 4.70?

   A. 4.7 **B.** 4.77
   C. 7.0 **D.** 7.4

17. Mickey's spelling average is 0.95, Ted's is 0.90, Jon's is 0.89, and Robby's is 0.96. Who has the highest average?

   A. Mickey **B.** Jon
   C. Robby **D.** Ted

18. Which number sentence matches the model?

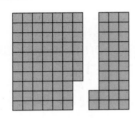

   A. $0.67 + 0.32 = n$
   B. $0.68 + 0.31 = n$
   C. $0.77 + 0.33 = n$
   D. $6.6 + 3.4 = n$

19. $\begin{array}{r} 1.59 \\ +0.87 \\ \hline \end{array}$

   A. 2.46
   B. 2.56
   C. 2.66
   D. not here

20. $\begin{array}{r} 2.5 \\ -0.6 \\ \hline \end{array}$

   A. 1.4
   B. 1.8
   C. 1.9
   D. not here

21. What is 4.3 rounded to the nearest whole number?

   A. 2 **B.** 3 **C.** 4 **D.** 7

22. Linda read her book for 2.8 hours at home, 5.7 hours at the library, and 3.1 hours at Abby's house. About how many hours did she read?

   A. about 8 hr **B.** about 10 hr
   C. about 12 hr **D.** about 14 hr

Choose the letter of the correct answer.

1. Which number sentence shows the Zero Property for Multiplication?

   A. $8 \times 5 = 40$ **B.** $8 \times 0 = 0$
   C. $8 \times 7 = 7 \times 8$ **D.** $8 \times 1 = 8$

2. Which is a *cardinal* number?

   A. third quarter   **B.** 477-4146
   C. 104.5 FM   **D.** 15 minutes

3. A 5-lb bag of potatoes costs $1.45. About how much should a 10-lb bag of potatoes cost?

   A. about $2.00   **B.** about $3.00
   C. about $4.00   **D.** about $5.00

4. What is *two hundred eleven million, four hundred thirty–two thousand, one hundred sixty–five* written in standard form?

   A. 2,132,165   **B.** 21,432,165
   C. 211,032,165   **D.** 211,432,165

5. A bicycle can be red, blue, or white. It can have 3, 10, or 15 speeds. How many bicycle choices are there?

   A. 9 choices   **B.** 11 choices
   C. 12 choices   **D.** 18 choices

For questions 6–7, use the line plot. There is one X for each student.

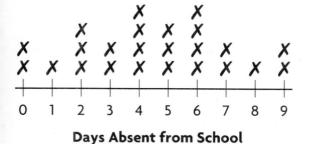

Days Absent from School

6. What is the range of data used in the line plot?

   A. 7   **B.** 8   **C.** 9   **D.** 10

7. How many students were absent on 5 days?

   A. 1 student   **B.** 2 students
   C. 3 students   **D.** 4 students

8. A cookie jar contains oatmeal, lemon, and chocolate chip cookies. It is impossible to pull out ___?___ .

   A. a chocolate chip cookie
   B. a lemon cookie
   C. an oatmeal cookie
   D. an almond cookie

For questions 9–10, use the spinners.

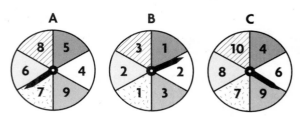

In this game, the "odd" player gets points for odd numbers and the "even" player gets points for even numbers.

9. Which spinner gives the "even" player the greatest probability of winning?

   A. Spinner A   **B.** Spinner B
   C. Spinner C   **D.** all of them

10. Which spinner gives the "odd" player the greatest probability of winning?

A. Spinner A   **B.** Spinner B
C. Spinner C   **D.** none of them

11. Use the figure.

How many faces are on the figure?

A. 3 faces   **B.** 5 faces
C. 6 faces   **D.** 8 faces

12. What angle is formed when two intersecting lines that are not perpendicular cross?

A. acute angle   **B.** obtuse angle
C. right angle   **D.** both A and B

13. What is the perimeter?

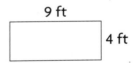
9 ft
4 ft

A. 22 ft   **B.** 26 ft
C. 32 ft   **D.** 36 ft

14. A figure that has been moved to a new location as shown is called a ___?___ .

A. translation   **B.** reflection
C. rotation   **D.** flip

15. Which figure has point symmetry?

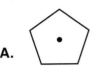
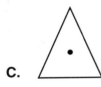

A.   **B.**

C.   **D.**

16.
$$\begin{array}{r} 70 \\ \times\ 6 \\ \hline \end{array}$$

A. 4.2
B. 42
C. 420
D. 4,200

17. Use the model place-value chart.

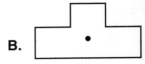

Tens	Ones

Which multiplication sentence do the base-ten blocks show?

A. $3 \times 10 = n$ **B.** $3 \times 11 = n$
C. $30 \times 1 = n$ **D.** not here

18.
$$\begin{array}{r} \$4.19 \\ \times\ \ \ \ 7 \\ \hline \end{array}$$

A. $22.33
B. $27.33
C. $28.03
D. $29.33

19. Choose the best estimate for the product.

$$88 \times 31 = n$$

A. about 2,200   **B.** about 2,400
C. about 2,700   **D.** about 2,800

20.
$$229 \times 38$$

A. 8,502
B. 8,702
C. 8,802
D. not here

21. $4\overline{)71}$

A. 17 r3
B. 18
C. 18 r3
D. not here

22. $255 \div 3 = n$

A. $n = 85$
B. $n = 85$ r2
C. $n = 86$
D. not here

23. Use a basic fact and a pattern of zeros to estimate the quotient.
$$2,816 \div 7 = n$$

A. about 4
B. about 40
C. about 44
D. about 400

24. $7\overline{)\$5.25}$

A. $0.71
B. $0.75
C. $7.50
D. $7.70

25. Which fraction means the same as *one out of nine*?

A. $\frac{1}{9}$
B. $\frac{2}{7}$
C. $\frac{7}{9}$
D. $\frac{9}{7}$

26. Which fraction represents the group that is shaded?

A. $\frac{1}{4}$
B. $\frac{2}{6}$
C. $\frac{1}{2}$
D. $\frac{2}{3}$

27. What is the fraction renamed as a mixed number?
$$\frac{12}{7} = \underline{\quad?\quad}$$

A. $\frac{7}{12}$
B. $1\frac{2}{7}$
C. $1\frac{4}{7}$
D. $1\frac{5}{7}$

28. Use the fraction bars to help you find the sum.

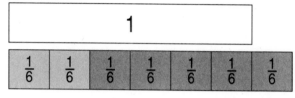

$$\frac{2}{6} + \frac{5}{6} = \underline{\quad?\quad}$$

A. $\frac{4}{6}$
B. $\frac{5}{6}$
C. $1\frac{1}{6}$
D. $\frac{17}{18}$

29. $\frac{2}{9} + \frac{5}{9} = \underline{\quad?\quad}$

A. $\frac{7}{18}$
B. $\frac{3}{9}$
C. $\frac{7}{9}$
D. $\frac{17}{18}$

30. Clara spent $\frac{1}{8}$ of her allowance on a notebook. What fraction of her allowance is left?

A. $\frac{1}{4}$
B. $\frac{4}{8}$
C. $\frac{5}{8}$
D. $\frac{7}{8}$

31. $2\frac{5}{7}$
    $+6\frac{1}{7}$
    _____

    A. $8\frac{6}{7}$ B. $8\frac{7}{7}$

    C. $9\frac{4}{7}$ D. $9\frac{6}{7}$

32. $9\frac{5}{7}$
    $-7\frac{2}{7}$
    _____

    A. $2\frac{2}{7}$ B. $2\frac{3}{7}$

    C. $2\frac{5}{7}$ D. $2\frac{6}{7}$

33. What is 0.37 written as a fraction?

    A. $\frac{37}{1,000}$ B. $\frac{3}{10}$

    C. $\frac{37}{100}$ D. $\frac{7}{10}$

34. What is 8 nickels written as a money amount?

    A. $0.08   B. $0.40
    C. $0.44   D. $0.80

35. Which number is less than 0.09?

    A. 0.07   B. 0.11
    C. 0.44   D. not here

36. What is 5.79 written as a mixed number?

    A. $5\frac{7}{100}$ B. $5\frac{7}{10}$

    C. $5\frac{79}{100}$ D. $5\frac{79}{10}$

37. Jake worked on his science project for 1.8 hours on Tuesday, 2.2 hours on Thursday, and 4.7 hours on Saturday. On which day did he work on his project the longest?

    A. Tuesday
    B. Thursday
    C. Saturday
    D. He worked about the same amount of time each day.

38. 0.79
    $+0.22$
    _____

    A. 0.67
    B. 0.91
    C. 0.97
    D. 1.01

39. 0.86
    -0.39
    _____

    A. 0.45
    B. 0.47
    C. 1.25
    D. not here

40. What is 8.9 rounded to the nearest whole number?

    A. 1   B. 7   C. 8   D. 9

Choose the letter of the correct answer.
For some items, an inch ruler may be needed.

1. Which of the following is a linear unit?

A. mile   **B.** gallon
C. ton   **D.** ounce

2. Use a ruler to measure the length of this string.

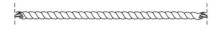

A. 1 in.   **B.** 2 in.   **C.** 3 in.   **D.** 4 in.

For questions 3–4, choose the reasonable unit of measure.

3. Bess is in fourth grade. She is 4 _?_ tall.

A. inches   **B.** feet
C. yards   **D.** miles

4. The width of a doorway is about 1 _?_.

A. inch   **B.** foot   **C.** yard   **D.** mile

5. A Scout troop hiked all day. Which unit is best for describing the distance they hiked?

A. inches   **B.** feet
C. yards   **D.** miles

6. Mrs. Weston is sewing a dress. Which unit is best for describing the amount of material she needs?

A. yards   **B.** miles
C. cups   **D.** pounds

For questions 7–9, find the equivalent measurement.

7. 4 ft = _?_ in.

    A. 12   **B.** 36   **C.** 48   **D.** not here

8. 12 ft = _?_ yd

A. 1   **B.** 2
C. 3   **D.** not here

9. 5 ft = _?_ in.

A. 50   **B.** 60
C. 70   **D.** not here

For questions 10–11, use the diagram.

Mr. Rodgers's Garden

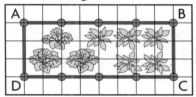

1 square = 1 yard

10. How many fence posts are in Mr. Rodgers's garden?

A. 10 fence posts
B. 20 fence posts
C. 30 fence posts
D. 40 fence posts

11. How far is it from the fence post at A to the fence post at B?

A. 8 in.   **B.** 8 ft   **C.** 8 yd   **D.** 8 mi

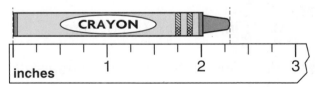

12. How long is the crayon to the nearest $\frac{1}{4}$ in.?

A. 2 in.   **B.** $2\frac{1}{4}$ in.

C. $2\frac{1}{2}$ in.   **D.** $2\frac{3}{4}$ in.

13. How long is the string to the nearest $\frac{1}{2}$ in.?

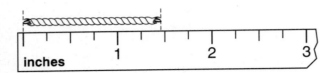

A. 1 in.   **B.** $1\frac{1}{2}$ in.

C. 2 in.   **D.** $2\frac{1}{2}$ in.

For questions 14–16, use an inch ruler to measure length.

14. How long is this nail to the nearest $\frac{1}{2}$ in.?

A. $2\frac{1}{2}$ in.   **B.** $2\frac{3}{4}$ in.

C. 3 in.   **D.** not here

15. How long is this pencil to the nearest $\frac{1}{4}$ in.?

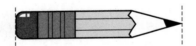

A. $1\frac{1}{4}$ in.   **B.** $1\frac{1}{2}$ in.

C. $1\frac{3}{4}$ in.   **D.** not here

16. How long is this line to the nearest $\frac{1}{4}$ in.?

_____

A. $2\frac{3}{4}$ in.   **B.** $2\frac{1}{4}$ in.

C. $3\frac{1}{2}$ in.   **D.** not here

17. To change pounds to ounces, ___.

A. multiply by 16
B. divide by 16
C. multiply by 2,000
D. divide by 2,000

18. Which is the best estimate of the weight of a pair of jeans?

A. about 1 ounce
B. about 1 pound
C. about 10 pounds
D. about 1 ton

19. Which is the best estimate of the weight of a large dog?

A. about 80 ounces
B. about 8 pounds
C. about 80 pounds
D. about 8 tons

20. Find the equivalent measure.

3 tons = __?__ lb

A. 48   **B.** 60
C. 600   **D.** 6,000

21. Mr. Kim hauls boxes that weigh 50 lb each. His truck can carry 200 boxes. How many pounds can he haul at a time?

A. 10,000 lb   **B.** 20,000 lb
C. 30,000 lb   **D.** 40,000 lb

22. Jan is making fish stew for 8 people. The recipe calls for 6 oz of fish per person. How many ounces of fish should Jan use?

A. 16 oz   **B.** 24 oz
C. 36 oz   **D.** 48 oz

Choose the letter of the correct answer.

1. Which shows metric units in order from smallest to largest?

   A. dm, cm, m
   B. m, dm, cm
   C. cm, m, dm
   D. cm, dm, m

2. 1 dm = _?_ m

   A. 0.01   **B.** 0.1
   C. 10   **D.** 100

3. 1 cm = _?_ m

   A. 0.01   **B.** 0.1
   C. 10   **D.** 100

4. 1 dm = _?_ cm

   A. 0.01   **B.** 0.1
   C. 10   **D.** not here

5. 2 m = _?_ dm

   A. 0.02   **B.** 0.2
   C. 20   **D.** not here

6. 3 m = _?_ cm

   A. 0.03   **B.** 0.3
   C. 30   **D.** not here

7. Doreen has 1 m of blue ribbon and 10 cm of red ribbon. Doreen's blue ribbon is _?_ as the red ribbon.

   A. the same length
   B. 0.1 times as long
   C. 10 times as long
   D. 100 times as long

8. Sam needs 1 m of string. He has 50 cm of string. How much more string does he need?

   A. 25 cm   **B.** 50 cm
   C. 60 cm   **D.** 75 cm

9. Which number sentence shows how to change 5 m to dm?

   A. $5 \times 10 = 50$
   B. $5 \times 100 = 500$
   C. $5 \div 10 = 0.5$
   D. $5 \div 100 = 0.05$

10. How do you change 4 m to cm?

    A. multiply 4 by 0.1
    B. multiply 4 by 10
    C. multiply 4 by 100
    D. not here

For questions 11–14, find the equivalent measurement.

11. 6 dm = _?_ cm

    A. 6   **B.** 60
    C. 600   **D.** 6,000

12. 7 m = _?_ dm

    A. 70   **B.** 700
    C. 770   **D.** 7,000

13. 12 m = _?_ cm

    A. 12   **B.** 120
    C. 1,200   **D.** not here

14. 18 m = _?_ dm

    A. 180   **B.** 1,800
    C. 18,000   **D.** not here

For questions 15–16, use the diagram.

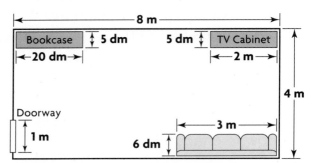

Floor Plan of Amy's Family Room

15. About how far is it from the doorway to the edge of the sofa?

    A. 3 m   B. 5 m
    C. 8 m   D. 9 m

16. Which of these are the same size in length?

    A. doorway and sofa
    B. sofa and TV cabinet
    C. TV cabinet and bookcase
    D. bookcase and doorway

17. Which is a unit of measure of capacity?

    A. meter   B. liter
    C. millimeter   D. gram

18. Which is the most reasonable measurement of the amount of water in the glass?

    A. 2 mL   B. 20 mL
    C. 200 mL   D. 2 L

19. Which is the most reasonable measurement of the amount of soup in the large spoon?

    A. 1 mL   B. 10 mL
    C. 500 mL   D. 1 L

For questions 20–21, find the equivalent measure.

20. 2 liters = __?__ milliliters

    A. 20   B. 200
    C. 2,000   D. 4,000

21. 4 metric cups = __?__ L

    A. 1   B. 2
    C. 4   D. 8

22. If 8 cups of water are needed each day, what is a reasonable estimate of the number of liters of water a person should drink in a day?

    A. 0.2 L   B. 2 L
    C. 20 L   D. 200 L

23. A 3-L bottle of soda costs $1.59. How much would 12 L of soda cost?

    A. $3.82   B. $5.25
    C. $5.41   D. $6.36

24. A hiker's canteen holds 750 mL. How many liters are needed to fill the canteens of 8 hikers?

    A. 6 L   B. 60 L
    C. 12 L   D. 125 L

Name _____

Choose the letter of the correct answer.

For questions 1–2, choose the correct clock.

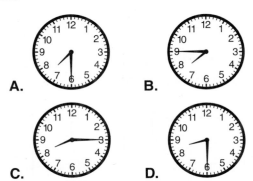

A. **B.** **C.** **D.**

1. Which clock shows a quarter to eight?

    A. A   **B.** B   **C.** C   **D.** D

2. Which clock shows half past eight?

    A. A   **B.** B   **C.** C   **D.** D

3. What is another way to write *a quarter past ten*?

    A. 9:45   **B.** 10:15
    C. 10:30   **D.** 10:45

4. What is another way to write *half past three*?

    A. 2:30 **B.** 2:45 **C.** 3:15 **D.** 3:30

5. What is another way to write 6:45?

    A. half past six
    B. a quarter to six
    C. a quarter past six
    D. a quarter to seven

6. What is another way to write 9:15?

    A. a quarter to nine
    B. a quarter past nine
    C. a quarter to ten
    D. half past nine

7. The perimeter of a square is 20 in. If the same square is measured in cm, the number of units would be __?__.

    A. less than 20   **B.** exactly 20
    C. greater than 20   **D.** 0

8. Which is the most reasonable estimate for the length of this line?

    A. 5 cm   **B.** 10 in.
    C. 50 cm   **D.** 50 in.

9. Which is the most reasonable estimate for the length of the insect?

    A. 1.2 cm   **B.** 2 in.
    C. 12 cm   **D.** 12 in.

10. Which is the most reasonable estimate of the length of the ribbon?

    A. 2 cm   **B.** 8 cm
    C. 15 cm   **D.** 60 cm

11. Use the ruler to find the perimeter of the square in inches.

    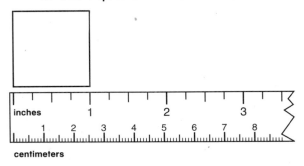

    A. 1 in. **B.** 2.5 in. **C.** 4 in. **D.** 10 in.

Form A • Multiple-Choice   A93   **Go on.** ▶

12. Al's pen is 5 in. long. His pencil is 5 cm long. Which is longer?

   A. the pen
   B. the pencil
   C. They are the same length.
   D. More information is needed.

13. Carrie's thumb is 2 cm shorter than her ring finger. Her ring finger is 7 cm long. How long is Carrie's thumb?

   A. 2 cm   B. 5 cm
   C. 7 cm   D. 9 cm

14. Les wants 3 CDs that cost $8 each. He has a coupon for $3 off the price of 1 CD. What price will he pay for all 3 CDs?

   A. $5   B. $15   C. $21   D. $24

15. Mariko puts ribbon around a picture. Two sides are 50 cm long, and 2 sides are 25 cm long. How many meters of ribbon does she need?

   A. 0.75 meters   B. 1 meter
   C. 1.25 meters   D. 1.50 meters

16. What temperature does this thermometer show?

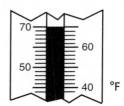

   A. ⁻10°F
   B. 0°F
   C. 70°F
   D. 90°F

17. Which of the following temperatures is the coldest?

   A. ⁻5°F   B. 0°F
   C. 5°F   D. 10°F

18. What is the difference between the two temperatures?

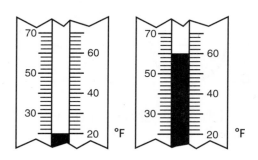

   A. 20°F   B. 40°F
   C. 60°F   D. 80°F

19. What is the difference between the two temperatures?

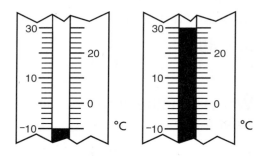

   A. 10°C   B. 20°C
   C. 30°C   D. 40°C

20. At sunrise the temperature was 62°F. At noon it was 18 degrees warmer. By six o'clock in the evening it had cooled off 10 degrees. What was the evening temperature?

   A. 52°F   B. 70°F
   C. 72°F   D. 80°F

Name _____

Choose the letter of the correct answer.

For some items, you may need an inch ruler.

1. Which of the following is a linear unit?

   A. quart   **B.** yard
   C. gallon   **D.** pound

2. What is the reasonable unit of measure?
   Joe's new puppy is 8 __?__ long.

   A. inches   **B.** feet
   C. yards   **D.** miles

3. 6 ft = __?__ in.

   A. 24   **B.** 36   **C.** 72   **D.** 96

4. How long is the chalk to the nearest $\frac{1}{4}$ in.?

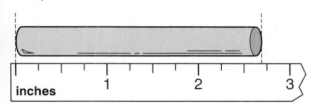

   A. 2 in.   **B.** $2\frac{1}{4}$ in.
   C. $2\frac{1}{2}$ in.   **D.** $2\frac{3}{4}$ in.

5. How long is the nail to the nearest $\frac{1}{2}$ in.?

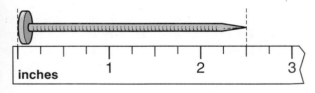

   A. 1 in.   **B.** $1\frac{1}{2}$ in.
   C. 2 in.   **D.** $2\frac{1}{2}$ in.

6. To change tons to pounds, __?__ .

   A. multiply by 16
   B. divide by 16
   C. multiply by 2,000
   D. divide by 2,000

7. A school uses 80 bags of potatoes in one month. One bag weighs 20 pounds. How many pounds does the school use in a month?

   A. 160 lb   **B.** 1,600 lb
   C. 2,400 lb   **D.** 16,000 lb

8. Julie is making hot chocolate for 9 people. She uses 3 oz of chocolate per person. How many ounces of chocolate should Julie use?

   A. 27 oz   **B.** 32 oz
   C. 36 oz   **D.** not here

9. 10 cm = __?__ dm

   A. 0.01   **B.** 0.1   **C.** 1   **D.** 10

10. The teacher's desk is 2 meters wide. A student desk is 10 decimeters wide. The teacher's desk is __?__ as the student desk.

    A. the same width
    B. 0.5 times as wide
    C. 2 times as wide
    D. not here

11. Which number sentence shows how to change 30 dm to meters?

    A. 30 × 1.0 = 30
    B. 30 × 10 = 300
    C. 30 ÷ 3 = 10
    D. 30 ÷ 10 = 3

Form A • Multiple-Choice   A95   **Go on.** ▶

12. 5 m = _?_ dm

    A. 50   **B.** 500   **C.** 550   **D.** 5,000

For questions 13–14, use the diagram.

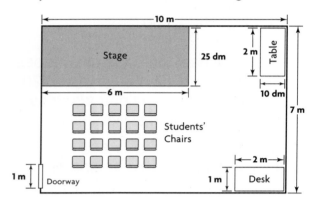

13. About how far is it from the edge of the table to the edge of the desk?

    A. 2 m   **B.** 3 m
    C. 4 m   **D.** not here

14. Which of these are the same length?

    A. doorway and stage
    B. stage and table
    C. table and desk
    D. not here

15. Which of these is a reasonable measurement of the amount of milk in a jug?

    A. 100 mL   **B.** 1 L
    C. 10 L   **D.** 50 L

16. After baseball practice, Jason drinks 500 mL of water. What is the amount of water Jason will drink after 7 practices?

    A. 350 mL   **B.** 2 L 50 mL
    C. 2 L 200 mL   **D.** 3 L 50 mL

17. What is another way to write a quarter to three?

    A. 2:15   **B.** 2:45
    C. 3:15   **D.** 3:45

18. What is another way to write 3:15?

    A. a quarter to 3
    B. a quarter past 3
    C. a quarter to 4
    D. a quarter past 4

19. Anne is sewing lace around a place mat she made. The place mat has 2 sides 15 inches long and 2 sides 10 inches long. How many inches of lace does Anne need?

    A. 40 inches   **B.** 50 inches
    C. 60 inches   **D.** 70 inches

20. At sunrise the temperature was 43°F. At noon it was 15 degrees warmer. By six o'clock in the evening, it had cooled 9 degrees. What was the evening temperature?

    A. 40°F   **B.** 45°F
    C. 47°F   **D.** 49°F

Name _____

Choose the letter of the correct answer.

1.
```
  76
  44
+ 52
```
A. 168
B. 171
C. 172
D. 182

2. There are 32 runners at the track meet. How many runners are on each of 8 relay teams?

A. 3 runners B. 4 runners
C. 6 runners D. not here

3. How many thousands are in 3,654?

A. 3 thousands B. 4 thousands
C. 5 thousands D. 6 thousands

4. In which number does the digit 7 have a value of 700?

A. 217 B. 4,871
C. 7,452 D. 8,738

5. In which pair of numbers do the digits differ in the hundreds position?

A. 4,629; 3,692
B. 2,756; 2,657
C. 5,312; 6,321
D. 7,832; 8,823

For questions 6–7, use the frequency table.

SCOUT MEMBERSHIP DRIVE		
Week	Number Joined (Frequency)	Cumulative Frequency
1	12	12
2	9	21
3	7	?
4	3	?

6. How many more Scouts joined in Week 2 than in Week 3?

A. 2 more Scouts
B. 3 more Scouts
C. 4 more Scouts
D. 9 more Scouts

7. What is the cumulative frequency for the number of Scouts who joined in all 4 weeks?

A. 12 Scouts B. 22 Scouts
C. 28 Scouts D. 31 Scouts

For questions 8–9, use the stem-and-leaf plot.

Scores in the Bowling Tournament

Stem	Leaves
9	4 6 7
10	3 3 5 6 6 6 9
11	2 3 4 7 8

8. What number is the mode for the data?

A. 97 B. 103
C. 106 D. not here

9. What is the difference between the highest and the lowest score?

A. 6 points B. 15 points
C. 24 points D. not here

For questions 10–11, use the grid.

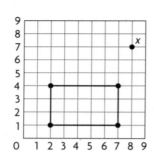

10. What are the coordinates of point x?

    A. (7,8)   **B.** (7,7)
    C. (8,8)   **D.** (8,7)

11. Which set of coordinates identifies the vertices of the rectangle marked on the grid?

    A. (1,2), (4,2), (1,7), (4,7)
    B. (2,1), (2,4), (7,4), (7,1)
    C. (3,2), (3,5), (8,2), (8,8)
    D. not here

12. Susie's dining room table is 4 feet by 7 feet. What is the area of the table?

    A. 11 sq ft   **B.** 24 sq ft
    C. 28 sq ft   **D.** 49 sq ft

13. Which figure shows a line of symmetry?

A. 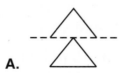   **B.**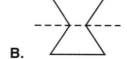

C. 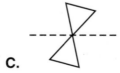   **D.**

14.
$$\begin{array}{r} 637 \\ \times\ \ 8 \\ \hline \end{array}$$

    A. 4,996
    B. 5,016
    C. 5,096
    D. 5,104

15. Find the product by using a basic fact and a pattern of zeros.
$$20 \times 900 = n$$

    A. $n = 18,000$
    B. $n = 180,000$
    C. $n = 1,800,000$
    D. $n = 18,000,000$

16.
$$\begin{array}{r} \$59 \\ \times\ \ 46 \\ \hline \end{array}$$

    A. \$2,414
    B. \$2,654
    C. \$2,655
    D. \$2,714

17. In which place should the first digit in the quotient be placed?
$$5\overline{)74}$$

    A. ones place
    B. tens place
    C. hundreds place
    D. divisor

18. $5\overline{)325}$

    A. 61   **B.** 63
    C. 65   **D.** not here

19. A basketball team needs to score 87 points to equal its season average. How many points should the team score in each of the game's 4 quarters to be sure it reaches its season average?

    A. 19 points   **B.** 20 points
    C. 21 points   **D.** 22 points

20. Sharon scored 6 of her volleyball team's 18 points. What fraction of the team's points did Sharon score?

A. $\frac{6}{24}$ B. $\frac{6}{18}$

C. $\frac{12}{18}$ D. $\frac{2}{3}$

21. What is the fraction renamed as a mixed number?

$$\frac{13}{7} = \underline{\quad?\quad}$$

A. $1\frac{5}{7}$ B. $1\frac{6}{7}$

C. $2\frac{1}{7}$ D. $2\frac{3}{7}$

22. Use the fraction bars to help you find the sum.

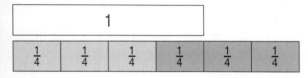

$$\frac{3}{4} + \frac{3}{4} = \underline{\quad?\quad}$$

A. $\frac{3}{8}$ B. $\frac{3}{4}$

C. $1\frac{2}{4}$ D. $1\frac{3}{4}$

23. Which number sentence matches the model?

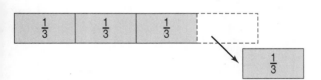

A. $\frac{3}{3} - \frac{1}{3} = \underline{\quad?\quad}$ B. $\frac{3}{4} - \frac{1}{3} = \underline{\quad?\quad}$

C. $\frac{4}{3} - \frac{3}{3} = \underline{\quad?\quad}$ D. $\frac{4}{3} - \frac{1}{3} = \underline{\quad?\quad}$

24. What is 0.47 written as a fraction?

A. $\frac{1}{47}$ B. $\frac{10}{47}$

C. $\frac{1}{4}$ D. $\frac{47}{100}$

25. Which group of decimals is written in order from least to greatest?

A. 0.6, 0.75, 0.8
B. 0.75, 0.6, 0.8
C. 0.75, 0.8, 0.6
D. 0.8, 0.75, 0.6

26.
$$\begin{array}{r} 2.96 \\ +1.37 \\ \hline \end{array}$$

A. 3.33
B. 4.23
C. 4.33
D. 4.35

27.
$$\begin{array}{r} 2.12 \\ -0.07 \\ \hline \end{array}$$

A. 2.05
B. 2.06
C. 2.19
D. not here

28. A reasonable unit of measure for the diameter of a soccer ball is about 1 __?__ .

A. inch   B. foot
C. yard   D. mile

29. How long is the string to the nearest $\frac{1}{4}$ in.?

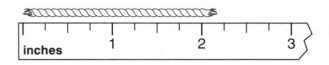

A. $1\frac{1}{2}$ in.   B. $1\frac{3}{4}$ in.

C. 2 in.   D. $2\frac{1}{4}$ in.

30. 36 in. = ___?___ ft

    A. 1   **B.** 3

    C. 12   **D.** not here

For questions 31–32, use the diagram.

Stars in the Sky

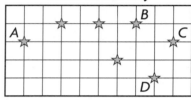

1 square = 1 light year

31. How many stars are in the diagram?

    A. 7 stars   **B.** 8 stars

    C. 9 stars   **D.** 10 stars

32. How far is it from the star at *A* to the star at *C*?

    A. 8 miles   **B.** 80 miles

    C. 8 light years   **D.** 80 light years

33. 4,000 lb = ___?___ tons

    A. 2   **B.** 3   **C.** 4   **D.** 5

34. 8 dm = ___?___ cm

    A. 0.08   **B.** 0.8

    C. 8   **D.** 80

35. 18 dm = ___?___ cm

    A. 18   **B.** 180

    C. 1,800   **D.** not here

36. 7 liters = ___?___ milliliters

    A. 70   **B.** 700

    C. 1,400   **D.** 7,000

37. What is another way to write *a quarter to twelve*?

    A. 11:30   **B.** 11:45

    C. 12:15   **D.** 12:30

38. Which is the most reasonable measure for the length of the ribbon?

    A. 1 mm   **B.** 1 cm

    C. 3 cm   **D.** 3 in.

39. A hamburger costs $2.00. Ralph buys a dozen. He uses a coupon to save $4.00. How much will Ralph pay?

    A. $8   **B.** $20   **C.** $24   **D.** $28

40. What is the difference between the temperatures on the thermometers?

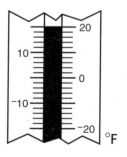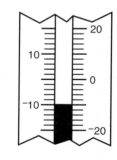

    A. 10°   **B.** 20°

    C. 30°   **D.** 40°

Choose the letter of the correct answer.

1. Which numbers should you use to estimate the quotient for this division problem?

   $82 \div 18 = n$

   A. $80 \div 10 = n$
   B. $80 \div 20 = n$
   C. $90 \div 10 = n$
   D. $90 \div 20 = n$

2. What basic fact helps find these quotients?

   | $280 \div 70 = n$ |
   | $2,800 \div 70 = n$ |
   | $28,000 \div 70 = n$ |

   A. $28 \div 7 = 4$ B. $28 \div 4 = 7$
   C. $28 \times 4 = 7$ D. not here

For questions 3–4, find the best estimate of the quotient.

3. $598 \div 19 = n$

   A. 20   B. 30   C. 40   D. 150

4. $309 \div 54 = n$

   A. 4   B. 3   C. 6   D. 7

For questions 5–6, choose the best estimate.

5. There are 217 books. About 39 books fit in a carton. About how many cartons are needed to pack the books?

   A. about 5 cartons
   B. about 7 cartons
   C. about 9 cartons
   D. about 10 cartons

6. For a field trip, 192 students are divided into groups of 11 each. About how many groups are there?

   A. about 10 groups
   B. about 12 groups
   C. about 15 groups
   D. about 20 groups

7. Which box shows where the first digit of the quotient should be placed?

   A. $50\overline{)785}^{\blacksquare}$ B. $50\overline{)785}^{\quad\blacksquare}$

   C. $50\overline{)785}^{\;\blacksquare}$ D. not here

8. Where should the first digit in the quotient be placed?

   $60\overline{)488}$

   A. thousands place
   B. hundreds place
   C. tens place
   D. ones place

9. $30\overline{)364}$

   A. 10 r24   B. 11 r14
   C. 12 r4   D. 13 r4

10. $50\overline{)412}$

    A. 8 r12   B. 8 r42
    C. 80 r12   D. 82 r2

11. $80\overline{)580}$

    A. 7   B. 7 r20
    C. 8   D. 8 r40

Form A • Multiple-Choice   A101   **Go on. ▶**

12. During one month 20 volunteers at a soup kitchen worked 440 hours. Each volunteer worked the same number of hours. How many hours did each volunteer work?

   A. 20 hours   B. 21 hours
   C. 22 hours   D. 23 hours

13. Florence must solve the division problem below. She starts by estimating. What is the next step?

   27)306

   A. Check the estimate by multiplying.
   B. Divide the hundreds.
   C. Write the remainder.
   D. Decide where to place the first digit in the quotient.

14. Roger started doing the problem below. What should he do next?

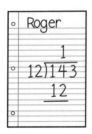

   A. Divide the tens.
   B. Divide the ones.
   C. Write the remainder.
   D. Subtract 12 from 14.

15. 13)167

   A. 10 r37   B. 11 r4
   C. 12 r11   D. 13 r2

16. 24)180

   A. 5   B. 6 r16
   C. 7 r2   D. 7 r12

17. 46)756

   A. 16   B. 16 r20
   C. 17 r14   D. 17 r24

18. 33)689

   A. 20 r29   B. 21 r16
   C. 22 r29   D. 23

19. A movie video is 118 minutes long. How many hours and minutes is this?

   A. 1 hour 18 minutes
   B. 1 hour 58 minutes
   C. 2 hours 18 minutes
   D. 2 hours 38 minutes

20. Corinna walked on her hands for a distance of 105 inches. How far is this in feet and inches?

   A. 8 feet 9 inches
   B. 9 feet 8 inches
   C. 9 feet 9 inches
   D. 10 feet 5 inches

For questions 21–24, decide if each estimate is too high, too low, or just right.

21. $\overset{8}{17)158}$ A. too high
                      B. too low
                      C. just right

22. $\overset{5}{31)184}$ A. too high
                      B. too low
                      C. just right

23. $\overset{6}{53)314}$ A. too high
                      B. too low
                      C. just right

24. $\overset{7}{78)575}$ A. too high
                      B. too low
                      C. just right

Name _____

Choose the letter of the correct answer.

For questions 1–2, use the circle graph.

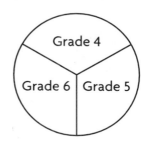

1. What does the whole circle represent?

   A. the whole school
   B. all the students in grade 4, grade 5, and grade 6
   C. the 24 members of the school band
   D. high school students in the school band

2. By looking at the graph, what do you know about the number of students in each grade?

   A. There are not many students.
   B. There are fewer students in sixth grade than in other grades.
   C. There are more fourth-graders than fifth-graders.
   D. The number of students from each grade is the same.

For questions 3–6, use the circle graph.

Favorite Fruit Choices of 30 Students

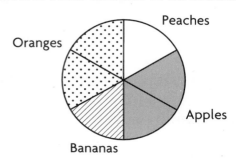

3. What fraction of the 30 students chose peaches as their favorite fruit?

   A. $\frac{1}{6}$ B. $\frac{2}{6}$ C. $\frac{3}{6}$ D. $\frac{4}{6}$

4. What fraction of the 30 students chose apples as their favorite?

   A. $\frac{1}{6}$ B. $\frac{2}{6}$ C. $\frac{3}{6}$ D. $\frac{4}{6}$

5. What fraction represents all the students in the survey?

   A. $\frac{6}{30}$ B. $\frac{4}{6}$ C. $\frac{5}{6}$ D. $\frac{6}{6}$

6. Which two fruits were chosen by the most students?

   A. apples and peaches
   B. bananas and peaches
   C. oranges and apples
   D. bananas and oranges

For questions 7–8, use the circle.

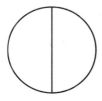

7. What decimal represents 1 part of the circle?

   A. 0.25   B. 0.50
   C. 0.75   D. 1.00

8. What is the sum of the decimals that represent the 2 parts of the circle?

   A. 0.50   B. 0.80
   C. 1.00   D. 2.00

For questions 9–12, use the graph.

Seasons When Students Were Born

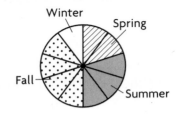

9. What decimal tells how many students were born in the spring?

    A. 0.1   **B.** 0.2   **C.** 0.3   **D.** 0.4

10. What decimal tells how many students were born in the summer?

    A. 0.1   **B.** 0.2   **C.** 0.3   **D.** 0.4

11. What decimal tells how many students were born in the fall?

    A. 0.1   **B.** 0.2   **C.** 0.3   **D.** 0.4

12. What decimal tells how many students were born in the winter?

    A. 0.1   **B.** 0.2   **C.** 0.3   **D.** 0.4

For questions 13–14, use the circles.

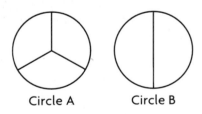

Circle A   Circle B

13. Which circle can be used to show that $\frac{1}{2}$ the members of a chorus are boys and $\frac{1}{2}$ are girls?

    A. only Circle A
    B. only Circle B
    C. Circle A or Circle B
    D. neither Circle A nor Circle B

14. Which circle can be used to show that $\frac{1}{2}$ the school band are sixth graders, $\frac{1}{4}$ are fifth graders and $\frac{1}{3}$ are fourth graders?

    A. only Circle A
    B. only Circle B
    C. either Circle A or Circle B
    D. neither Circle A nor Circle B

For questions 15–18, choose the graph that matches the data.

Weather for 24 Days in May

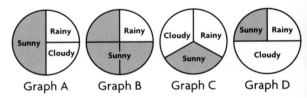

Graph A   Graph B   Graph C   Graph D

15. Which graph shows that $\frac{1}{2}$ of the days were cloudy, $\frac{1}{4}$ were sunny, and $\frac{1}{4}$ were rainy?

    A. Graph A   **B.** Graph B
    C. Graph C   **D.** Graph D

16. Which graph shows that $\frac{1}{2}$ of the days were sunny, $\frac{1}{4}$ were rainy, and $\frac{1}{4}$ were cloudy?

    A. Graph A   **B.** Graph B
    C. Graph C   **D.** Graph D

17. Which graph shows that $\frac{1}{4}$ of the days were rainy and $\frac{3}{4}$ were sunny?

    A. Graph A   **B.** Graph B
    C. Graph C   **D.** Graph D

18. Which graph shows that $\frac{1}{3}$ of the days were sunny, $\frac{1}{3}$ were cloudy, and $\frac{1}{3}$ were rainy?

    A. Graph A   **B.** Graph B
    C. Graph C   **D.** Graph D

Choose the letter of the correct answer.

1. Which numbers should you use to estimate the quotient for this problem?
$$56 \div 31 = n$$

   A. $50 \div 40 = n$ **B.** $70 \div 30 = n$
   C. $60 \div 40 = n$ **D.** $60 \div 30 = n$

2. Find the best estimate of the quotient.
$$411 \div 9 = n$$

   A. 20 **B.** 30 **C.** 40 **D.** 360

3. A librarian packed 309 books in boxes, with 32 books in each box. About how many boxes were there?

   A. about 10 boxes
   B. about 12 boxes
   C. about 15 boxes
   D. about 30 boxes

4. $50\overline{)860}$

   A. 17 r10 **B.** 17 r11
   C. 18 r2 **D.** 18 r10

5. Lenny must solve this problem. He starts by estimating. What is the next step?
$$32\overline{)908}$$

   A. Write the remainder.
   B. Divide the hundreds.
   C. Check the estimate by multiplying.
   D. Decide where to place the first digit in the quotient.

6. $15\overline{)231}$

   A. 15 **B.** 15 r6
   C. 16 **D.** not here

7. A school play is 105 minutes long. How many hours and minutes is this?

   A. 1 hour 5 minutes
   B. 1 hour 45 minutes
   C. 2 hours 5 minutes
   D. 2 hours 25 minutes

8. A rug is 110 inches long. How long is this in feet and inches?

   A. 8 feet 10 inches
   B. 8 feet 11 inches
   C. 9 feet 2 inches
   D. 9 feet 6 inches

For questions 9–10, decide whether the estimate is *too high, too low,* or *just right.*

9. $75\overline{)480}^{\,5}$

   A. too high
   B. too low
   C. just right

10. $45\overline{)390}^{\,8}$

   A. too high
   B. too low
   C. just right

For questions 11–12, use the circle graph.

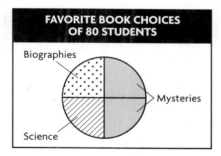

FAVORITE BOOK CHOICES OF 80 STUDENTS

Biographies
Mysteries
Science

11. What fraction of the 80 students chose biographies as their favorite books?

   A. $\frac{1}{4}$ **B.** $\frac{2}{4}$
   C. $\frac{3}{4}$ **D.** not here

12. What fraction of the 80 students chose mysteries as their favorite?

A. $\frac{1}{4}$ B. $\frac{2}{4}$

C. $\frac{2}{3}$ D. $\frac{3}{4}$

For questions 13–14, use the circle.

13. What decimal represents 1 part of the circle?

A. 0.25   B. 0.50
C. 0.75   D. 1.00

14. What is the sum of the decimals that represent the 4 parts of the circle?

A. 0.150   B. 0.75
C. 0.80   D. 1.00

For questions 15–16, use the circle graph.

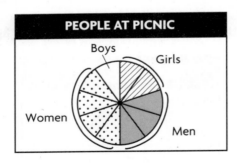

PEOPLE AT PICNIC

15. What decimal tells how many people at the picnic were men?

A. 0.1   B. 0.2   C. 0.3   D. 0.4

16. What decimal tells how many people were girls?

A. 0.2   B. 0.25   C. 0.3   D. 0.4

For questions 17–18, use the circle graphs.

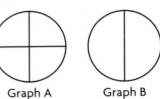

Graph A   Graph B

17. Which graph can be used to show that $\frac{1}{2}$ of the students in a class are boys and $\frac{1}{2}$ are girls?

A. only Graph A
B. only Graph B
C. Graph A or Graph B
D. neither Graph A nor Graph B

18. Which graph can be used to show that $\frac{1}{2}$ of the cookies are chocolate, $\frac{1}{4}$ are peanut butter, and $\frac{1}{4}$ are oatmeal?

A. only Graph A
B. only Graph B
C. either Graph A or Graph B
D. neither Graph A nor Graph B

For questions 19–20, choose the graph that matches the data.

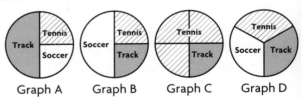

Graph A   Graph B   Graph C   Graph D

19. Which graph shows that $\frac{1}{2}$ of the students played soccer, $\frac{1}{4}$ played tennis, and $\frac{1}{4}$ ran track?

A. Graph A   B. Graph B
C. Graph C   D. Graph D

20. Which graph shows that $\frac{1}{3}$ of the students played soccer, $\frac{1}{3}$ played tennis, and $\frac{1}{3}$ ran track?

A. Graph A   B. Graph B
C. Graph C   D. Graph D

Choose the letter of the correct answer.

1. Choose the best estimate of the sum or difference.

8,762
−1,197

A. 6,000
B. 7,000
C. 8,000
D. 9,000

2. Use the model to find the quotient.

23 ÷ 4 = _?_

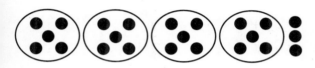

A. 5 r2
C. 6

B. 5 r3
D. 6 r1

3. What is the value of the digit 8 in the number 892?

A. $8 \times 0 = 0$
C. $8 \times 10 = 80$

B. $8 \times 1 = 8$
D. $8 \times 100 = 800$

4. Compare the numbers and choose the correct statement.

787 ● 778

A. $787 > 778$
C. $787 < 778$

B. $787 = 778$
D. not here

5. Which time is closest to the time that a cafeteria serves breakfast?

A. 1:00 A.M.
C. 1:00 P.M.

B. 7:00 A.M.
D. 7:00 P.M.

For questions 6–7, use the calendars.

June

Su	M	T	W	Th	F	Sa
1	2	3	4	5	6	7
8	9	10	11	12	13	14
15	16	17	18	19	20	21
22	23	24	25	26	27	28
29	30					

July

Su	M	T	W	Th	F	Sa
		1	2	3	4	5
6	7	8	9	10	11	12
13	14	15	16	17	18	19
20	21	22	23	24	25	26
27	28	29	30	31		

6. How many days is it from June 25 to July 5?

A. 5 days
C. 9 days

B. 7 days
D. 10 days

7. Paul is going to visit his cousin for 8 days. His visit will end on June 15. On what day will it begin?

A. June 6
C. June 8

B. June 7
D. June 9

8. What kind of graph would be best to compare the number of home runs hit by different players on a baseball team?

A. Bar graph
B. Stem-and-leaf plot
C. Line graph
D. Double-bar graph

For questions 9–10, use the spinner.

9. What is the probability of spinning a 3 or a 4?

A. $\frac{1}{4}$ B. $\frac{2}{4}$

C. $\frac{3}{4}$ D. not here

10. What is the probability of spinning a 4?

A. $\frac{0}{4}$ B. $\frac{1}{4}$ C. $\frac{2}{4}$ D. $\frac{3}{4}$

11. Which line segments are parallel?

    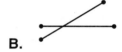

A.   B.

C.   D.

12. A figure is drawn on 1-in. grid paper. If you copy the figure on 1.5-in. paper, it will be __?__.

A. similar but larger
B. similar but smaller
C. symmetric
D. congruent

13. 217   A. 651
   × 4   B. 858
                C. 868
                D. 908

14. $6\overline{)35}$

A. 5 r3   B. 5 r5
C. 7   D. not here

15. $3\overline{)\$14.55}$

A. $4.53   B. $4.79
C. $4.85   D. $5.83

16. Which group of fractions is in order from greatest to least?

A. $\frac{1}{4}, \frac{3}{8}, \frac{5}{8}$ B. $\frac{3}{8}, \frac{1}{4}, \frac{5}{8}$

C. $\frac{3}{8}, \frac{5}{8}, \frac{1}{4}$ D. $\frac{5}{8}, \frac{3}{8}, \frac{1}{4}$

17. $\frac{2}{7} + \frac{3}{7} = $ __?__

A. $\frac{1}{7}$ B. $\frac{5}{14}$

C. $\frac{5}{7}$ D. $1\frac{6}{7}$

18.   0.64   A. 0.17
    −0.47   B. 0.27
                C. 1.11
                D. not here

19. Find the equivalent measurement.
8 yd = __?__ ft

A. 16   B. 20   C. 22   D. 24

20. To change ounces to pounds, __?__.

A. multiply by 16
B. divide by 16
C. multiply by 2,000
D. divide by 2,000

21. 4 dm = __?__ cm

A. 40   B. 4
C. 0.4   D. not here

For questions 22–23, use the diagram.

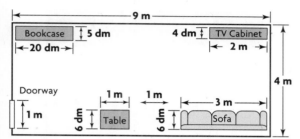

Floor Plan of Nathan's Family Room

22. About how far is it from the TV cabinet to the sofa?

   A. 1 m   **B.** 2 m
   C. 3 m   **D.** 4 m

23. Which of these are the same size in width?

   A. doorway and sofa
   B. sofa and TV cabinet
   C. TV cabinet and bookcase
   D. table and sofa

24. Jean's tennis racket is 33 in. long. Her dog is 33 cm long. Which is longer?

   A. the tennis racket
   B. the dog
   C. They are the same length.
   D. More information is needed.

25. Which of the following temperatures is the warmest?

   A. ⁻30°F   **B.** 5°F
   C. 15°F   **D.** 25°F

For questions 26–27, find the best estimate of the quotient.

26. $409 \div 9 = n$

   A. 20   **B.** 30
   C. 40   **D.** 80

27. $493 \div 49 = n$

   A. 8   **B.** 9
   C. 10   **D.** 11

28. $40\overline{)299}$

   A. 6 r19   **B.** 6 r29
   C. 7 r9   **D.** 7 r19

29. $70\overline{)814}$

   A. 11 r44   **B.** 11 r54
   C. 12 r10   **D.** 12 r34

30. $17\overline{)219}$

   A. 12 r5   **B.** 12 r13
   C. 12 r15   **D.** 13 r5

For questions 31–32, decide if each estimate is *too high, too low,* or *just right.*

31. $13\overline{)128}^{9}$

   A. too high
   B. too low
   C. just right

32. $27\overline{)520}^{20}$

   A. too high
   B. too low
   C. just right

33. A baseball game is 144 minutes long. How many hours and minutes is this?

    A. 1 hour 44 minutes
    B. 2 hours 4 minutes
    C. 2 hours 14 minutes
    D. 2 hours 24 minutes

34. A camel is 117 inches tall. How high is this in feet and inches?

    A. 8 feet 7 inches
    B. 9 feet 3 inches
    C. 9 feet 9 inches
    D. 10 feet 2 inches

For questions 35–36, use the circle graph.

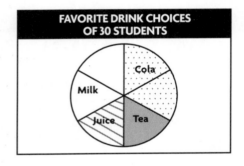

FAVORITE DRINK CHOICES OF 30 STUDENTS

35. What fraction of the 30 students chose cola as their favorite drink?

    A. $\frac{1}{6}$ **B.** $\frac{2}{6}$
    C. $\frac{3}{6}$ **D.** $\frac{4}{6}$

36. What fraction of the 30 students chose juice as their favorite?

    A. $\frac{1}{6}$ **B.** $\frac{2}{6}$
    C. $\frac{3}{6}$ **D.** $\frac{4}{6}$

For questions 37–38, use the graph.

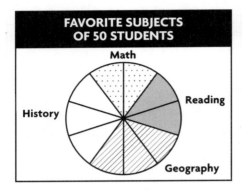

FAVORITE SUBJECTS OF 50 STUDENTS

37. What decimal tells how many students like history best?

    A. 0.1   **B.** 0.2   **C.** 0.3   **D.** 0.4

38. What decimal tells how many students like math best?

    A. 0.1   **B.** 0.2   **C.** 0.3   **D.** 0.4

For questions 39–40, choose the graph that matches the data on cars in 4 lots.

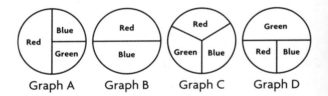

Graph A   Graph B   Graph C   Graph D

39. Which graph shows that $\frac{1}{4}$ of the cars were red and $\frac{2}{4}$ were green?

    A. Graph A   **B.** Graph B
    C. Graph C   **D.** Graph D

40. Which graph shows that $\frac{1}{4}$ of the cars were blue, $\frac{1}{4}$ were green, and $\frac{1}{2}$ were red?

    A. Graph A   **B.** Graph B
    C. Graph C   **D.** Graph D

Choose the letter of the correct answer.

1. 6
    +3
    A. 3
    B. 9 ✓
    C. 10
    D. not here
1-A.1

2. Which subtraction fact is related to this addition fact?

$8 + 6 = 14$

A. $14 - 6 = 8$ **B.** $8 - 6 = 2$
C. $14 + 6 = 20$ **D.** $14 + 8 = 22$
1-A.2

For question 3, estimate the sum by rounding.

3. 22
    +51
    A. 70 ✓
    B. 80
    C. 90
    D. 100
2-A.3

4. Mike has 16 stickers in his pocket and 25 stickers in his book. How many stickers does he have in all?

A. 31 stickers **B.** 35 stickers
C. 39 stickers **D.** 41 stickers ✓
2-A.4

5. 51
    −18
    A. 33 ✓
    B. 43
    C. 47
    D. 49
3-A.1

For questions 6–7, tell what time it is.

6.
`2:36`
    A. 6 minutes after 2
    B. 6 minutes after 3
    C. 23 minutes after 6
    D. not here ✓
5-A.3

7.

A. 7:20 **B.** 7:25
C. 8:24 ✓ **D.** 8:30
5-A.3

8. Mr. Clark spent $11.50 for a shirt and $21.00 for slacks. He gave the clerk $50.00. How much change did he receive?

A. $15.00 **B.** $17.50 ✓
C. $17.60 **D.** not here
7-A.3

For questions 9–10, use the calendar.

April						
Su	M	T	W	Th	F	Sa
		1	2	3	4	5
6	7	8	9	10	11	12
13	14	15	16	17	18	19
20	21	22	23	24	25	26
27	28	29	30			

9. How many Fridays are there in the month?

A. 2 Fridays **B.** 3 Fridays
C. 4 Fridays ✓ **D.** 5 Fridays
8-A.1

10. What is the date of the second Monday?

A. April 14 ✓ **B.** April 15
C. April 21 **D.** April 29
8-A.1

Form A • Multiple-Choice   A1   **Go on.** ▶

For question 11, round the number to the nearest hundred.

11. 780

A. 800 ✓ **B.** 700
C. 600 **D.** 500
10-A.3

12. A cabinet had 5 shelves with 6 glasses on each shelf. How many glasses were there in all?

A. 11 glasses **B.** 20 glasses
C. 30 glasses ✓ **D.** 40 glasses
11-A.1

13. $1 \times 7 = \underline{\ ?\ }$

A. 0 **B.** 1 **C.** 7 ✓ **D.** 17
11-A.2

14. 8
    ×4
    A. 12
    B. 16
    C. 28
    D. 32 ✓
11-A.2

15. $28 \div 4 = \underline{\ ?\ }$

A. 4 **B.** 5 **C.** 6 **D.** 7 ✓
13-A.3

16. Ann bought 15 goldfish. She placed an equal number of fish in each of 3 bowls. How many fish were in each bowl?

A. 2 fish **B.** 5 fish ✓
C. 6 fish **D.** 9 fish
13-A.4

For questions 17–18, use the table.

STUDENTS' FAVORITE VACATION	
Place	**Votes**
Beach	IIII IIII III
Theme Park	IIII IIII
Campground	IIII II
Home with Friends	IIII I

17. How many students answered the survey?

A. 24 students **B.** 28 students
C. 30 students **D.** 35 students ✓
15-A.2

18. How many more students liked a theme park than liked a campground?

A. 1 more student
B. 2 more students ✓
C. 3 more students
D. 4 more students
15-A.2

For questions 19–20, identify the solid figure that is like the object shown.

19.

A. sphere ✓ **B.** cone
C. cube **D.** cylinder
18-A.1

20.
CRAYONS

A. cylinder **B.** sphere
C. cone **D.** rectangular prism ✓
18-A.1

Form A • Multiple-Choice   A2   **Go on.** ▶

---

21. Chen drew this figure. She matched it to make the other half. What does the complete figure look like?

A. ✓ **B.**

C. **D.**
20-A.3

For questions 22–23, use the picture.

22. How many parts make up the whole?

A. 4 parts **B.** 6 parts ✓
C. 8 parts **D.** 10 parts
21-A.1

23. How many parts are shaded?

A. 1 part ✓ **B.** 2 parts
C. 6 parts **D.** not here
21-A.1

For question 24, find the words that name the part of the group that is shaded.

24.
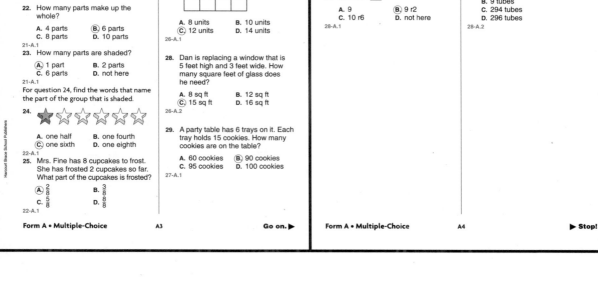

A. one half **B.** one fourth
C. one sixth ✓ **D.** one eighth
22-A.1

25. Mrs. Fine has 8 cupcakes to frost. She has frosted 2 cupcakes so far. What part of the cupcakes is frosted?

A. $\frac{2}{8}$ ✓ **B.** $\frac{3}{8}$
C. $\frac{5}{8}$ **D.** $\frac{8}{8}$
22-A.1

For question 26, measure the length to the nearest half-inch.

26.

A. 1 in. **B.** $1\frac{1}{2}$ in.
C. 2 in. ✓ **D.** not here
24-A.2

For question 27, find the perimeter of the figure.

27.

A. 8 units **B.** 10 units
C. 12 units ✓ **D.** 14 units
26-A.1

28. Dan is replacing a window that is 5 feet high and 3 feet wide. How many square feet of glass does he need?

A. 8 sq ft **B.** 12 sq ft
C. 15 sq ft ✓ **D.** 16 sq ft
26-A.2

29. A party table has 6 trays on it. Each tray holds 15 cookies. How many cookies are on the table?

A. 60 cookies **B.** 90 cookies ✓
C. 95 cookies **D.** 100 cookies
27-A.1

Form A • Multiple-Choice   A3   **Go on.** ▶

---

30. 23
    × 6
    A. 123
    B. 129
    C. 138 ✓
    D. 139
27-A.1

31. $9 \times 71 = \underline{\ ?\ }$

A. 161 **B.** 169
C. 638 **D.** 639 ✓
27-A.1

32. $56 \div 6 = \underline{\ ?\ }$

A. 9 **B.** 9 r2 ✓
C. 10 r6 **D.** not here
28-A.1

33. Mrs. Flynn had 50 party prizes. She gave the same number to 8 children at the party. How many prizes did each child get and how many prizes were left over?

A. 5 prizes each; 0 left over
B. 5 prizes each; 8 left over
C. 6 prizes each; 2 left over ✓
D. 7 prizes each; 6 left over
28-A.2

34. A paint box has 42 tubes of paint. If 7 children share the paints, how many tubes will each child have?

A. 6 tubes ✓
B. 9 tubes
C. 294 tubes
D. 296 tubes
28-A.2

Form A • Multiple-Choice   A4   ▶ **Stop!**

Multiple Choice • Test Answers

Harcourt Brace School Publishers

Solve. Then choose the letter of the correct answer.

1. $5 + 4 = \underline{\ ?\ } + 3$
   A. 3   B. 4   C. 5   (D) 6

2. $8 - 2 = 7 - \underline{\ ?\ }$
   (A) 1   B. 2   C. 3   D. 6

3. $\underline{\ ?\ } + 0 = 9 - 1$
   (A) 8   B. 9   C. 10   D. 11

4. $11 - 5 = \underline{\ ?\ } + 2$
   A. 3   (B) 4   C. 5   D. 6

5. Find the perimeter.

   | 24 in. |
   9 in. [   ] 9 in.
   | 24 in. |

   A. 56 in.   (B) 66 in.
   C. 68 in.   D. 156 in.

6. Find the perimeter.

   44 in.   44 in.
   42 in.   42 in.
   36 in.

   A. 104 in.   B. 198 in.
   (C) 208 in.   D. 214 in.

7. 16
   22
   +13
   (A) 51
   B. 59
   C. 61
   D. 69

8. 25
   15
   +65
   A. 95
   (B) 105
   C. 110
   D. 115

9. 57
   36
   +71
   A. 154
   B. 163
   (C) 164
   D. 173

10. 98
    34
    + 17
    A. 135
    B. 139
    C. 145
    (D) 149

11. A rectangular garden has a perimeter of 80 ft. The garden is 25 ft long. How wide is it?
    (A) 15 ft   B. 25 ft
    C. 30 ft   D. 55 ft

12. Leila made a rectangular dog pen. She used 12 fence sections each for the long sides, and 8 sections each for the short sides of the pen. How many fence sections did she use in all?
    A. 20 sections   B. 32 sections
    (C) 40 sections   D. 48 sections

13. What is 319 rounded to the nearest hundred?
    (A) 300   B. 320
    C. 400   D. 500

Form A • Multiple-Choice   A5   **Go on.** ▶

---

14. What is $67.25 rounded to the nearest $10.00?
    A. $60.00   B. $67.00
    C. $68.00   (D) $70.00

15. Which is the best estimate of this sum?
    209
    187
    +326
    A. 500   (B) 700
    C. 800   D. 1,000

16. What is the best estimate of this difference?
    $52.99
    − 29.53
    A. $10.00   (B) $20.00
    C. $40.00   D. $50.00

For questions 17–18, use the price list.

Corn	$2.89 a dozen
Potatoes	$3.19 a bag
Lettuce	$1.09 a head

17. About how much change will Jere receive from a $10.00 bill if he buys a dozen ears of corn and a bag of potatoes?
    A. about $2.00   (B) about $4.00
    C. about $6.00   D. about $7.00

18. Felicia bought 2 heads of lettuce and 2 bags of potatoes. About how much did she spend?
    A. about $4.00
    B. about $6.00
    (C) about $8.00
    D. about $10.00

19. $6.34
    − 2.78
    (A) $3.56
    B. $4.44
    C. $4.56
    D. $4.66

20. $2.45
    1.79
    + 4.11
    A. $7.25
    B. $7.35
    (C) $8.35
    D. $9.25

21. $11.75
    − 6.64
    A. $4.11
    B. $4.89
    C. $4.99
    (D) $5.11

22. $14.55
    + 18.25
    A. $22.70
    B. $23.80
    (C) $32.80
    D. $33.70

23. Valerie bought a salad for $3.49, juice for $1.19, and pie for $1.50. How much did she spend in all?
    A. $4.68   B. $5.08
    C. $6.08   (D) $6.18

24. Alan uses a $5.00 bill to buy lunch. He buys a sandwich for $1.75, lemonade for $1.25, and a cookie for $0.50. How much change should he get?
    A. $0.50   (B) $1.50
    C. $2.50   D. $3.50

Form A • Multiple-Choice   A6   ▶ **Stop!**

Solve. Then choose the letter of the correct answer.

1. The perimeter of this figure is 542 ft. Find the missing length.

   ?
   142 ft   105 ft
   185 ft

   A. 100 ft   (B) 110 ft
   C. 200 ft   D. 432 ft

2. The perimeter of this figure is 1,260 ft. Find the missing length.

   387 ft   307 ft
   ?   166 ft

   A. 373 ft   B. 387 ft
   (C) 400 ft   D. 473 ft

3. The city planted 170 plants on the four sides of a parking lot. There are 48 plants on one side. There are 35 on another side and 53 on the third side. How many plants are on the fourth side?
   (A) 34 plants   B. 36 plants
   C. 44 plants   D. 136 plants

4. A rectangular field has a perimeter of 624 yd. The field has 2 sides that are each 212 yd. What is the length of each of the other two sides?
   A. 50 yd   (B) 100 yd
   C. 200 yd   D. 212 yd

5. Which place-value positions should be regrouped to solve this problem?
   3,000
   −1,000
   A. Regroup all places.
   B. Regroup hundreds.
   C. Regroup 3 thousands.
   (D) Do not regroup.

6. 800
   −428
   A. 228
   (B) 372
   C. 382
   D. 482

7. 300
   −106
   (A) 194
   B. 196
   C. 204
   D. 294

8. 8,000
   −6,917
   (A) 1,083
   B. 2,083
   C. 2,093
   D. 2,183

9. 40,000
   −29,195
   A. 1,915
   B. 9,105
   (C) 10,805
   D. 11,195

Form A • Multiple-Choice   A7   **Go on.** ▶

---

10. Salmon swim 6,000 mi when they migrate. Dogfish swim 2,500 mi. How much farther do salmon swim?
    A. 2,500 mi   (B) 3,500 mi
    C. 4,500 mi   D. 8,500 mi

11. The zoo planted 3,400 red tulip bulbs and 1,850 yellow tulip bulbs. How many more red tulip bulbs were planted?
    A. 850 bulbs   B. 1,050 bulbs
    C. 1,150 bulbs   (D) 1,550 bulbs

12. The soccer team has won 5 games, lost 4 games, and tied 2 games. Their season has a total of 16 games. How many games does the team have left to play?
    A. 3 games   (B) 5 games
    C. 7 games   D. 9 games

13. Tori chose a number. She added 6. Then, she subtracted 8. Last, she added 5. The result was 13. What number did Tori start with?
    (A) 10   B. 16
    C. 22   D. 27

14. What is 377 rounded to the nearest hundred?
    A. 300   B. 370
    C. 380   (D) 400

15. What is 5,298 rounded to the nearest thousand?
    (A) 5,000   B. 5,200
    C. 5,300   D. 6,000

For questions 16–18, choose the best estimate of the sum or difference.

16. 192
    313
    +267
    A. 500
    B. 700
    (C) 800
    D. 900

17. 7,384
    −3,871
    A. 2,000
    (B) 3,000
    C. 5,000
    D. 9,000

18. 5,688
    +1,924
    A. 4,000
    B. 7,000
    (C) 8,000
    D. 9,000

For questions 19–20, use the table.

| VISITORS TO BAXTER STATE PARK | |
Month	Visitors
May	1,279
June	1,872
July	2,943
August	3,295
September	1,061

19. How many people visited the park in May and June?
    A. 1,593 people   B. 1,607 people
    C. 2,007 people   (D) 3,151 people

20. How many more people visited the park in August than in September?
    A. 2,154 more   (B) 2,234 more
    C. 4,256 more   D. 4,356 more

Form A • Multiple-Choice   A8   ▶ **Stop!**

Harcourt Brace School Publishers

Choose the letter of the correct answer.

1. Which answer choice tells how many times Carla walks her dog in 5 days?

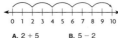

  0 1 2 3 4 5 6 7 8 9 10

  A. 2 + 5   B. 5 − 2
  C. 5 × 2   D. 5 + 2

2. Which answer choice tells how many sticks of gum Tonya bought?

  A. 5 × 5   B. 4 × 5
  C. 4 + 5   D. 5 − 4

3. Which answer choice tells how many flowers there are?

  A. 3 × 6   B. 6 × 6
  C. 6 + 3   D. 6 − 3

4. Elaine bought 2 packages of film. Each package held 3 rolls of film. How many rolls of film did Elaine buy in all?

  A. 3 rolls   B. 6 rolls
  C. 7 rolls   D. 9 rolls

5. Ali feeds his cat 2 times a day. In one week, how many times does he feed his cat?

  A. 2 times   B. 9 times
  C. 12 times   D. 14 times

6. Which number sentence shows the Order Property of Multiplication?

  A. 3 × 1 = 3
  B. 3 × 3 = 9
  C. 3 × 2 = 2 × 3
  D. 3 × 0 = 0

7. Which number sentence shows the Zero Property for Multiplication?

  A. 5 × 6 = 6 × 5
  B. 5 × 1 = 5
  C. 5 × 5 = 25
  D. 5 × 0 = 0

8. Which number sentence shows the Property of One?

  A. 4 × 1 = 4
  B. 4 × 0 = 0
  C. 4 × 2 = 2 × 4
  D. 4 × 4 = 16

9. 120 × 0 = _?_

  A. 0   B. 1
  C. 12   D. 120

10. 1 × 7 = _?_

  A. 0   B. 1
  C. 7   D. 8

Form A • Multiple-Choice   A9   Go on. ▶

---

11. 8 × 4 = 32   4 × 8 = _?_

  A. 24   B. 32
  C. 48   D. 84

12. (2 × 3) × 4 = _?_

  A. 6   B. 10
  C. 12   D. 24

13. 2 × (1 × 8) = _?_

  A. 10   B. 16
  C. 17   D. 24

14. 4 × (3 × 3) = _?_

  A. 9   B. 12
  C. 36   D. 49

15. (5 × 6) × 1 = _?_

  A. 30   B. 40
  C. 56   D. 60

16. (3 × 2) × 2 = _?_

  A. 8   B. 12   C. 18   D. 24

17. 2 × (4 × 2) = _?_

  A. 8   B. 10   C. 16   D. 32

For questions 18–22, choose the number sentence that can be used to solve the problem.

18. Kip has 2 shelves in his room. There are 2 rows of 4 model airplanes on each shelf. How many airplanes are there?

  A. (2 × 1) × 4 = _?_
  B. (2 × 4) + 2 = _?_
  C. (2 × 2) + 4 = _?_
  D. 2 × (2 × 4) = _?_

19. Rosa has a pumpkin patch. There are 6 rows with 3 pumpkins in each row. How many pumpkins are there in all?

  A. 6 + 3 = _?_
  B. 6 × 3 = _?_
  C. 9 × 3 = _?_
  D. 6 − 3 = _?_

20. Derek collected 6 stones on a class trip. Amy collected 4 stones. How many more stones did Derek collect?

  A. 6 × 4 = _?_
  B. 4 + 6 = _?_
  C. 6 − 4 = _?_
  D. 4 + _?_ = 6

21. A class took a walk. There were 5 groups of students. There were 5 students in each group. How many students were there in all?

  A. 5 × 5 = _?_
  B. 5 + 5 = _?_
  C. 5 − 1 = _?_
  D. 5 − 5 = _?_

22. In the morning, Myra walked 4 mi. In the afternoon, she walked 2 mi. How many miles did she walk in all?

  A. 4 + 2 = _?_
  B. 4 − 2 = _?_
  C. 4 × 2 = _?_
  D. 2 + _?_ = 4

Form A • Multiple-Choice   A10   ▶ Stop!

Choose the letter of the correct answer.

1. A softball team has 12 softballs. The team keeps the same number of balls in each of 4 boxes. How many softballs are in each box?

  A. 3 softballs   B. 6 softballs
  C. 8 softballs   D. 16 softballs

2. There are 25 students in a spelling bee. How many students are on each of 5 teams?

  A. 3 students   B. 5 students
  C. 10 students   D. 20 students

3. What operation is the inverse of division?

  A. addition   B. subtraction
  C. multiplication   D. not here

4. Which number sentence is in the same fact family as 4 × 5 = 20?

  A. 5 − 4 = 1   B. 4 + 5 = 9
  C. 20 ÷ 5 = 4   D. 20 + 4 = 24

For questions 5–6, use the multiplication fact to help you find the quotient.

5. 30 ÷ 5 = _?_

  5 × 6 = 30

  A. 5   B. 6
  C. 25   D. 35

6. 21 ÷ 7 = _?_

  3 × 7 = 21

  A. 3   B. 7
  C. 14   D. 28

For questions 7–8, use the model to find the quotient.

7. 18 ÷ 4 = _?_

  A. 4   B. 4 r1
  C. 4 r2   D. 4 r3

8. 19 ÷ 3 = _?_

  A. 5 r4   B. 6
  C. 6 r1   D. 6 r2

9. There are 28 students in Miss Lo's class. She wants the students to work in small groups to make maps. How many students will be in each group if Miss Lo has 7 groups?

  A. 3 students   B. 4 students
  C. 5 students   D. 6 students

10. Vivian made 36 cookies to give away. She gave 6 cookies to each of her friends. How many friends got cookies?

  A. 4 friends   B. 6 friends
  C. 8 friends   D. 9 friends

Form A • Multiple-Choice   A11   Go on. ▶

For questions 11–14, use the multiplication table to find the quotient.

x	0	1	2	3	4	5
0	0	0	0	0	0	0
1	0	1	2	3	4	5
2	0	2	4	6	8	10
3	0	3	6	9	12	15
4	0	4	8	12	16	20
5	0	5	10	15	20	25

11. 20 ÷ 4 = _?_

  A. 2   B. 3
  C. 5   D. 6

12. 16 ÷ 4 = _?_

  A. 4   B. 5
  C. 8   D. 9

13. 3 ÷ 3 = _?_

  A. 1   B. 3
  C. 4   D. 6

14. 15 ÷ 5 = _?_

  A. 2   B. 3
  C. 5   D. 7

15. 6)̄42

  A. 5   B. 6
  C. 7   D. 8

16. 9)̄72

  A. 3   B. 4
  C. 6   D. 8

For questions 17–18, use the table.

Bake Sale Item	Cookies Sold
Chocolate-chip cookies	64
Oatmeal cookies	36
Peanut-butter cookies	24
Chocolate cookies	43

17. The oatmeal cookies were sold 4 cookies to a bag. How many bags were sold?

  A. 5 bags   B. 6 bags
  C. 7 bags   D. 9 bags

18. Four students each brought in the same number of peanut-butter cookies. How many cookies did each bring in?

  A. 4 cookies   B. 5 cookies
  C. 6 cookies   D. 9 cookies

For questions 19–20, solve each problem.

19. Gary earned $20 for walking his neighbor's dogs. He earned $5 each day. How many days did he walk the dogs?

  A. 2 days   B. 3 days
  C. 4 days   D. 5 days

20. Wanda was packing 32 glasses in boxes. She put 8 glasses in each box. How many boxes did Wanda pack?

  A. 4 boxes   B. 6 boxes
  C. 8 boxes   D. 12 boxes

Form A • Multiple-Choice   A12   ▶ Stop!

Multiple Choice • Test Answers

Harcourt Brace School Publishers

Choose the letter of the correct answer.

1. $6 - 3 = 8 - \underline{?}$
   A. 2   B. 4   (C.) 5   D. 6
1-A.1

2.
$$\begin{array}{r} 58 \\ 16 \\ +45 \\ \hline \end{array}$$
A. 109
(B.) 119
C. 124
D. not here
1-A.2

3. A rectangular table has a perimeter of 90 inches. The table is 20 inches wide. How long is it?
(A.) 25 in.   B. 30 in.
C. 50 in.   D. 70 in.
1-A.2

4. Which is the best estimate of this sum?
$$\begin{array}{r} 489 \\ 102 \\ +276 \\ \hline \end{array}$$
A. 600
B. 700
C. 800
(D.) 900
1-A.3

5.
$$\begin{array}{r} \$15.82 \\ -8.41 \\ \hline \end{array}$$
A. $6.41
B. $7.23
(C.) $7.41
D. not here
1-A.4

6. Dan bought a burger for $4.29, salad for $1.29, and lemonade for $1.36. How much did he spend in all?
A. $6.84   B. $6.85
C. $6.88   (D.) $6.94
1-A.4

7. The perimeter of this figure is 96 yards. What is the missing length?

(A.) 18 yd   B. 20 yd
C. 24 yd   D. 26 yd
2-A.1

8.
$$\begin{array}{r} 700 \\ -519 \\ \hline \end{array}$$
(A.) 181
B. 191
C. 201
D. 291
2-A.2

9. There are 3,200 students at a high school and 1,450 students at a middle school. How many more students are at the high school?
A. 1,650 more students
(B.) 1,750 more students
C. 1,850 more students
D. not here
2-A.2

10. What is 565 rounded to the nearest hundred?
A. 500 B. 560 C. 570 (D.) 600
2-A.3

For questions 11–12, use the table.

SALES AT JOE'S BICYCLE SHOP	
Year	Sales
1994	1,414
1995	1,978
1996	2,036
1997	3,159

11. How many bicycles were sold in 1994 and 1995?
A. 2,382 bicycles
B. 2,392 bicycles
(C.) 3,392 bicycles
D. 3,402 bicycles
2-A.4

12. How many more bicycles were sold in 1997 than in 1996?
A. 123 more bicycles
B. 223 more bicycles
C. 564 more bicycles
(D.) 1,123 more bicycles
2-A.4

---

13. Which number sentence tells how many legs there are in all?

A. $4 + 3 = 7$ (B.) $3 \times 4 = 12$
C. $3 \times 3 = 9$ D. $4 - 3 = 1$
3-A.1

14. Which number sentence shows the Zero Property for Multiplication?
A. $6 \times 5 = 30$ B. $6 \times 1 = 1 \times 6$
(C.) $6 \times 0 = 0$ D. $6 \times 6 = 36$
3-A.2

15. $7 \times 4 = 28$, so $4 \times 7 = \underline{?}$
A. 21   B. 24   C. 27   (D.) 28
3-A.2

16. $(5 \times 3) \times 4 = \underline{?}$
A. 12   B. 32
(C.) 60   D. not here
3-A.3

17. Greg's school has 8 rows with 9 lockers in each row. How many lockers are there in all?
A. 17 lockers   B. 27 lockers
C. 63 lockers   (D.) 72 lockers
3-A.3

18. Choose the number sentence that can be used to solve the problem.

On Monday Cal read 4 pages. On Tuesday he read 8 pages. How many pages did he read in all?
(A.) $4 + 8 = \underline{?}$
B. $4 \times 8 = \underline{?}$
C. $8 \div 4 = \underline{?}$
D. $4 + \underline{?} = 8$
3-A.4

19. The tennis team has 18 tennis balls. The balls are kept in 6 cans. How many tennis balls are in each can?
A. 2 tennis balls
(B.) 3 tennis balls
C. 6 tennis balls
D. not here
4-A.1

20. Which number sentence is in the same fact family as $32 \div 8 = 4$?
(A.) $4 \times 8 = 32$
B. $32 - 18 = 14$
C. $8 + 4 = 12$
D. not here
4-A.2

21. Use the model to find the quotient.
$$13 \div 2 = ?$$

A. 2   B. 2 r3   C. 3 r2   (D.) 5 r3
4-A.3

22. A bookstore sold a total of 35 books to 5 customers. Each customer bought the same number of books. How many books did each customer buy?
A. 5 books   B. 6 books
(C.) 7 books   D. 30 books
4-A.3

23. $7\overline{)56}$
A. 6   B. 7   (C.) 8   D. 9
4-A.5

24. The P.E. class has 36 students. They are grouped in teams of 9 for baseball. How many teams are there?
A. 3 teams   (B.) 4 teams
C. 6 teams   D. 18 teams
4-A.6

Choose the letter of the correct answer.

1. $2 + 5 = \underline{?} + 3$
A. 1   B. 3
(C.) 4   D. 7
1-A.1

2. $9 - 4 = 6 - \underline{?}$
(A.) 1   B. 2
C. 4   D. not here
1-A.1

3.
$$\begin{array}{r} 15 \\ 26 \\ +14 \\ \hline \end{array}$$
A. 45
(B.) 55
C. 60
D. not here
1-A.2

4.
$$\begin{array}{r} 37 \\ 74 \\ +56 \\ \hline \end{array}$$
A. 147
B. 151
C. 157
(D.) 167
1-A.2

5. What is 412 rounded to the nearest hundred?
A. 300   (B.) 400
C. 410   D. 500
1-A.3

6. Use the price list.

Movie	$4.25
Popcorn	$2.15
Soda	$1.65

Pete uses a $10 bill to pay for a movie, popcorn, and a soda. About how much change will he receive?
A. about $1   (B.) about $2
C. about $3   D. about $5
1-A.3

7.
$$\begin{array}{r} \$8.19 \\ -3.57 \\ \hline \end{array}$$
A. $3.62
B. $4.52
(C.) $4.62
D. not here
1-A.4

8.
$$\begin{array}{r} \$3.89 \\ 1.12 \\ +4.37 \\ \hline \end{array}$$
(A.) $9.38
B. $9.48
C. $10.28
D. $10.68
1-A.4

9. At a baseball game, Tony bought a scorebook for $2.95, baseball cards for $4.75, and a bag of peanuts for $1.50. How much change should he get back from a $10 bill?
A. $0.60   B. $0.70
(C.) $0.80   D. not here
1-A.4

10. The perimeter of the figure is 1,168 feet. What is the missing length?

A. 99 ft   B. 109 ft
C. 117 ft   (D.) 119 ft
2-A.1

11. Mrs. Green put the flags of different countries on the classroom walls. Out of 212 flags, 41 were on the front wall, and the side walls had 57 on each. How many flags were on the back wall?
(A.) 57 flags   B. 62 flags
C. 67 flags   D. 77 flags
2-A.1

12.
$$\begin{array}{r} 900 \\ -387 \\ \hline \end{array}$$
A. 503
(B.) 513
C. 523
D. 613
2-A.2

13.
$$\begin{array}{r} 6,000 \\ -3,254 \\ \hline \end{array}$$
A. 2,536
B. 2,646
C. 2,736
(D.) 2,746
2-A.2

14. What is 383 rounded to the nearest hundred?
(A.) 400   B. 500
C. 800   D. 900
2-A.3

15. What is the best estimate of the sum?
$$\begin{array}{r} 9,789 \\ +3,975 \\ \hline \end{array}$$
A. 10,000
B. 12,000
C. 13,000
(D.) 14,000
2-A.3

For questions 16–18, use the table.

PINTS OF MILK USED BY CAFETERIA	
August	1,881
September	1,957
October	2,112
November	1,925
December	1,949

16. How many pints were used in September and October?
A. 3,069 pints   (B.) 4,069 pints
C. 4,169 pints   D. 4,179 pints
2-A.4

17. How many fewer pints were used in August than in September?
A. 56 pints   B. 58 pints
C. 66 pints   (D.) 76 pints
2-A.4

18. How many fewer pints were used in November than in October?
A. 87 pints   B. 167 pints
(C.) 187 pints   D. 197 pints
2-A.4

19. Which number sentence tells how many rolls are on the plates?

A. $4 + 7$ B. $7 - 4$
(C.) 4×7 D. $7 \div 4$
3-A.1

20. Which number sentence shows the Property of One for Multiplication?
A. $6 \times 0 = 0$
B. $6 \times 3 = 3 \times 6$
(C.) $6 \times 1 = 6$
D. $6 \times 6 = 36$
3-A.2

21. $7 \times 6 = 42$ so $6 \times 7 = \underline{?}$

(A.) 42   B. 48
C. 49   D. not here

3-A.2

22. $(9 \times 1) \times 3 = \underline{?}$

A. 0   B. 3
C. 9   (D.) 27

3-A.3

23. $5 \times (4 \times 4) = \underline{?}$

A. 16   B. 40
(C.) 80   D. not here

3-A.3

24. Danny bought 3 packs of sports cards. Each pack had 6 cards. How many cards in all did Danny buy?

A. 8 cards   B. 12 cards
C. 15 cards   (D.) 18 cards

3-A.4

For questions 25–27, choose the number sentence that can be used to solve the problem.

25. In June, Ray read 7 books. In July, he read 9 books. How many books did he read in all?

A. $9 - 7 = \underline{?}$
B. $9 \times 7 = \underline{?}$
C. $7 + \underline{?} = 9$
(D.) $9 + 7 = \underline{?}$

3-A.4

26. There were 3 classes that took part in a school project. Each class was divided into 4 groups. How many groups were there in all?

(A.) $3 \times 4 = \underline{?}$
B. $4 + 3 = \underline{?}$
C. $3 + 4 = \underline{?}$
D. $4 - 3 = \underline{?}$

3-A.4

27. On a bird-watching trip, Mariah saw 5 kinds of birds. Jack saw 8 kinds of birds. How many more kinds of birds did Jack see?

A. $8 + 5 = \underline{?}$
B. $8 \times 5 = \underline{?}$
C. $5 \times 8 = \underline{?}$
(D.) $8 - 5 = \underline{?}$

3-A.4

28. A school band has 27 students. The band has 3 sections with an equal number of students in each section. How many students are in each section?

A. 6 students   B. 7 students
(C.) 9 students   D. 20 students

4-A.1

29. A zoo has 3 monkey pens. There are 6 monkeys in each pen. How many monkeys are there in all?

A. 6 monkeys   B. 12 monkeys
(C.) 18 monkeys   D. 24 monkeys

4-A.1

30. Which number sentence is in the same fact family as $3 \times 7 = 21$?

A. $7 - 3 = 4$ B. $3 + 7 = 10$
C. $21 - 7 = 14$ (D.) $21 \div 3 = 7$

4-A.2

---

31. Use the multiplication fact $5 \times 7 = 35$ to help you find the quotient.

$35 \div 7 = \underline{?}$

(A.) 5   B. 7   C. 25   D. 42

4-A.2

32. Use the model to find the quotient.

$19 \div 5 = \underline{?}$

A. 3 r3   (B.) 3 r4
C. 4   D. 4 r4

4-A.3

33. Ms. Martin's art class was divided into 5 groups. The groups got 58 markers to share equally. How many markers did each group get? How many markers were left over?

A. 10 markers; 3 left over
B. 10 markers; 4 left over
(C.) 11 markers; 3 left over
D. 12 markers; 3 left over

4-A.3

For questions 34–35, use the multiplication table to find the quotient.

×	2	3	4	5
2	4	6	8	10
3	6	9	12	15
4	8	12	16	20
5	10	15	20	25

34. $12 \div 3 = \underline{?}$

A. 3   (B.) 4   C. 5   D. 6

4-A.4

35. $10 \div 2 = \underline{?}$

A. 2   B. 4   (C.) 5   D. 8

4-A.4

36. $8\overline{)64}$

A. 4   B. 5   C. 6   (D.) 8

4-A.5

37. $7\overline{)56}$

(A.) 8   B. 9   C. 10   D. 11

4-A.5

For questions 38–40, use the table.

CLASS TRIP	NUMBER OF STUDENTS
Museum	36
Library	24
Nature Trail	29
Zoo	32

38. On a trip to the library, 3 vans each carried the same number of students. How many students rode in each van?

A. 6 students   B. 7 students
(C.) 8 students   D. 9 students

4-A.6

39. On a trip to the museum, students rode in parents' cars that held 4 students each. How many cars were needed?

A. 6 cars   B. 7 cars
(C.) 9 cars   D. 12 cars

4-A.6

40. Of the students who went to the nature trail, 17 were girls. How many boys went to the nature trail?

A. 3 boys   (B.) 12 boys
C. 15 boys   D. 18 boys

4-A.6

Choose the letter of the correct answer.

1. Which is a *cardinal* number?

A. 134 High Street
(B.) 2 students
C. Fifth in line
D. Radio station 103.7

2. Which is an *ordinal* number?

For questions 3–6, use the grid.

3. Which ordered pair shows the location of the lake?

(A.) (5,7)   B. (7,5)
C. (4,8)   D. not here

4. What is located at (2,2)?

A. Lake   (B.) Cabin
C. Barn   D. Windmill

5. Which ordered pair shows the location of the windmill?

A. (4,8)   B. (5,4)
(C.) (4,5)   D. (8,4)

6. What is located at (8,4)?

A. Lake   B. Cabin
(C.) Barn   D. Windmill

For questions 7–8, use the base-ten blocks.

7. What does the large cube stand for?

(A.) 1 thousand   B. 1 hundred
C. 1 ten   D. 1 one

8. Which number is shown by all these base-ten blocks?

A. 1,043   (B.) 1,314
C. 1,433   D. 2,204

9. How many thousands are in 6,235?

A. 2 thousands
B. 3 thousands
C. 5 thousands
(D.) 6 thousands

10. How many tens are in 4,801?

(A.) 0 tens   B. 1 ten
C. 4 tens   D. 8 tens

11. Which number has a 5 in the hundreds place?

A. 1,357   B. 3,715
C. 5,731   (D.) not here

12. Which number has the comma in the correct place?

A. 426,8   B. 42,68
(C.) 4,268   D. not here

---

13. The engine is the first car of the train. The dining car is after the engine. The cattle car comes next. The freight car is next in line, and the caboose is the last car. Which car is fourth on this train?

(A.) freight car   B. dining car
C. cattle car   D. caboose

14. Cara has twice as many mystery books as her brother. Her brother has 9 books. How many mystery books does Cara have?

A. 11 books   B. 16 books
(C.) 18 books   D. 27 books

15. Which benchmark number can you use to estimate the number of crackers in Box B?

A. 3 crackers   B. 5 crackers
(C.) 10 crackers   D. 15 crackers

16. Which benchmark number can you use to estimate the number of squares on Quilt B?

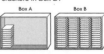

A. 10 squares   B. 15 squares
C. 20 squares   (D.) 25 squares

17. About how many marbles are in Jar B?

A. about 5 marbles
B. about 10 marbles
C. about 15 marbles
(D.) about 20 marbles

18. About how many tiles are on Floor B?

(A.) about 50 tiles
B. about 100 tiles
C. about 150 tiles
D. not here

19. A 6-inch sub costs $1.95. About how much should a 12-inch sub cost?

A. about $2.00   B. about $3.00
(C.) about $4.00   D. about $5.00

20. There are 100 jelly beans in the jar now. About how many could the jar hold?

A. about 120 jelly beans
B. about 150 jelly beans
(C.) about 200 jelly beans
D. not here

Multiple Choice • Test Answers

Name _____

Choose the letter of the correct answer.

1. What is the value of the digit 4 in the number 345?

   A. $4 \times 0 = 0$
   B. $4 \times 1 = 4$
   C. $4 \times 10 = 40$
   D. $4 \times 100 = 400$

2. In which number does the digit 5 have a value of 500?

   A. 155
   B. 3,851
   C. 5,048
   D. 7,521

3. Which number is written in expanded form?

   A. 5,364
   B. $5,000 + 300 + 60 + 4$
   C. fifty-three hundred, sixty-four
   D. five thousand, three hundred sixty-four

4. What is the standard form for the number shown in this place-value chart?

Thousands	Hundreds	Tens	Ones
2	1	3	6
$2 \times 1,000 = 2,000$	$1 \times 100 = 100$	$3 \times 10 = 30$	$6 \times 1 = 6$

   A. 2,136
   B. 21,036
   C. 21,306
   D. 21,360

5. What is *one hundred eighty-one* written in standard form?

   A. 180
   B. 181
   C. 800
   D. 80

6. What is *six thousand, two hundred two* written in standard form?

   A. 622
   B. 6,022
   C. 6,202
   D. 6,220

7. What is $3,000 + 70 + 4$ in written form?

   A. three thousand, seven
   B. three thousand, seventy-four
   C. three thousand, seven hundred four
   D. three thousand, seven hundred forty

8. What is 8,015 written in expanded form?

   A. $800 + 10 + 5$
   B. $8,000 + 10 + 5$
   C. $8,000 + 100 + 5$
   D. $8,000 + 100 + 50$

9. What is another name for 1,500?

   A. 15 hundreds
   B. 150 ones
   C. 150 hundreds
   D. 1,500 tens

10. Henri did the following addition problem. How should he write the sum in standard form?

    9 hundreds
    +8 hundreds
    17 hundreds

    A. 117
    B. 170
    C. 1,700
    D. 17,100

Form A • Multiple-Choice   A21   **Go on.** ▶

Name _____

For questions 11–12, use mental math.

11. 600
    +500

    A. 1,100
    B. 1,110
    C. 11,000
    D. not here

12. 8,000
    +7,000

    A. 1,500
    B. 15,000
    C. 150,000
    D. not here

13. In which number are the commas correctly used to separate the periods?

    A. 42,40,7216
    B. 4,240,7216
    C. 424,07,216
    D. 42,407,216

14. Millions could be used to count the people in a __?__.

    A. school
    B. neighborhood
    C. state
    D. movie theater

15. What is *one million, two hundred twenty thousand, three hundred fifteen* written in standard form?

    A. 1,220,315
    B. 1,313,220
    C. 1,220,000,315
    D. 1,220,315,000

16. What is *three hundred eight million, four hundred thousand, seven hundred nine* written in standard form?

    A. 384,709
    B. 3,084,709
    C. 38,479,000
    D. not here

17. Which shows how to write 11,345,867 with period names?

    A. 11 thousand, 345 hundred, 867
    B. 11 hundred thousand, 345 thousand, 867 hundred
    C. 11 million, 345 thousand, 867
    D. not here

18. Which shows how to write 107,006,200 with period names?

    A. 1 million, 76 thousand
    B. 107 million, 6 thousand, 200
    C. 107 million, 60 thousand, 200
    D. not here

For questions 19–20, use the table.

LEWIS COUNTY FAIR ATTENDANCE		
Year	Number of People	Increase from Previous Year
1994	14,370	–
1995	16,492	2,122
1996	19,058	2,566
1997	23,135	4,077

19. Between which two years did fair attendance increase the most?

    A. 1994–1995   B. 1995–1996
    C. 1996–1997   D. 1997–1998

20. How many more people attended the fair in 1996 than in 1994?

    A. 2,122 more people
    B. 2,566 more people
    C. 4,077 more people
    D. 4,688 more people

Form A • Multiple-Choice   A22   ▶ **Stop!**

Name _____

Choose the letter of the correct answer.

1. Use the number line to compare.

   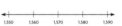
   0 10 20 30 40 50 60 70 80 90 100

   $50 > \underline{\ ?\ }$

   A. 40   B. 50   C. 60   D. 100

2. Use the number line to compare.

   0 100 200 300 400 500 600 700 800 900 1,000

   $700 < \underline{\ ?\ }$

   A. 400   B. 500   C. 700   D. 900

3. Choose the statement that is correct.

   A. $814 > 841$ B. $340 < 304$
   C. $125 = 251$ D. $520 > 502$

4. Choose the statement that is correct.

   A. $7,117 > 7,217$
   B. $9,348 = 3,984$
   C. $8,361 > 8,316$
   D. $4,957 > 4,975$

5. Choose the statement that is correct.

   A. $1,245 > 2,145$
   B. $5,306 < 5,063$
   C. $2,215 > 2,451$
   D. $8,846 = 8,846$

6. In which pair of numbers do the digits differ in the ones position?

   A. 243; 245   B. 132; 232
   C. 303; 313   D. 141; 151

7. In which pair of numbers do the digits differ in the hundreds position?

   A. 3,710; 1,710   B. 2,453; 2,455
   C. 2,235; 2,435   D. 3,846; 3,866

For questions 8–9, compare the numbers and choose the correct statement.

8. 483 ● 438

   A. $483 > 438$ B. $483 = 438$
   C. $483 < 438$ D. not here

9. 6,912 ● 6,972

   A. $6,912 = 6,972$
   B. $6,912 > 6,972$
   C. $6,912 < 6,972$
   D. not here

10. There are 27 children in Mrs. Enrique's class. There are 3 more girls than boys. How many boys are there?

    A. 12 boys   B. 13 boys
    C. 14 boys   D. 15 boys

11. Malcolm has 8 coins that total $1.02. He has at least 1 penny, 1 nickel, 1 dime, and 1 quarter. How many dimes does he have?

    A. 1 dime   B. 2 dimes
    C. 3 dimes   D. not here

12. Which numbers are written in order from the least to the greatest?

    600 610 620 630 640 650 660 670 680 690 700

    A. 680, 608, 688
    B. 608, 688, 680
    C. 680, 688, 608
    D. 608, 680, 688

Form A • Multiple-Choice   A23   **Go on.** ▶

Name _____

13. Which numbers are written in order from the least to the greatest?

    1,550 1,560 1,570 1,580 1,590

    A. 1,557; 1,575; 1,570
    B. 1,575; 1,557; 1,570
    C. 1,570; 1,557; 1,575
    D. 1,557; 1,570; 1,575

14. Which numbers are written in order from the least to the greatest?

    A. 702, 678, 617
    B. 617, 678, 702
    C. 702, 617, 678
    D. not here

15. Which numbers are written in order from the greatest to the least?

    A. 2,742; 1,983; 2,344
    B. 2,344; 1,983; 2,742
    C. 2,742; 2,344; 1,983
    D. 1,983; 2,344; 2,742

For questions 16–17, use the table.

LIBRARY BOOKS BORROWED	
Day of Week	Number of Books Borrowed
Monday	1,037
Tuesday	1,861
Wednesday	1,495
Thursday	1,019
Friday	1,798

16. On which day was the greatest number of books borrowed?

    A. Monday   B. Tuesday
    C. Thursday   D. Friday

17. On which day was the least number of books borrowed?

    A. Monday   B. Tuesday
    C. Thursday   D. Friday

For questions 18–20, use the Venn diagram.

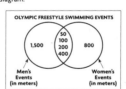

OLYMPIC FREESTYLE SWIMMING EVENTS

1,500 | 50 100 200 400 | 800

Men's Events (in meters)   Women's Events (in meters)

18. In which event do only women compete?

    A. 50-meter freestyle
    B. 400-meter freestyle
    C. 800-meter freestyle
    D. 1,500-meter freestyle

19. In which event do only men compete?

    A. 50-meter freestyle
    B. 400-meter freestyle
    C. 800-meter freestyle
    D. 1,500-meter freestyle

20. In which event do both men and women compete?

    A. 100-meter freestyle
    B. 800-meter freestyle
    C. 1,000-meter freestyle
    D. 1,500-meter freestyle

Form A • Multiple-Choice   A24   ▶ **Stop!**

Name _____

Choose the letter of the correct answer.

1. Which unit of time would you use to measure the time it takes to turn on a radio?
   Ⓐ seconds   B. minutes
   C. hours   D. days

2. Which unit of time would you use to measure how long you sleep at night?
   A. seconds   B. minutes
   Ⓒ hours   D. days

3. Which clock shows 4 minutes past five?
   A. 4:05   B. 4:50
   Ⓒ 5:04   D. 5:40

4. What time is shown on the clock?
   A. 1:05 and 9 seconds
   Ⓑ 1:15 and 45 seconds
   C. 1:45 and 15 seconds
   D. 3:05 and 9 seconds

5. Mr. Wong leaves for work at 8:05 every day. Which clock shows below the time Mr. Wong leaves?
   A.   Ⓑ
   C.   D.

6. Corinna gets on the school bus at 7:35 each morning. Which clock shows the time she gets on the bus?
   A.   B.
   C.   Ⓓ

7. Which time is closest to the time that the sun sets?
   A. 6:00 A.M.   B. 1:00 P.M.
   Ⓒ 6:00 P.M.   D. 1:00 A.M.

8. Which time is closest to the time that many people eat lunch?
   Ⓐ 12:30 P.M.   B. 7:30 P.M.
   C. 7:30 A.M.   D. 12:30 A.M.

9. Samuel walks his dog from 12:15 P.M. to 12:40 P.M. How many minutes pass from the beginning to the end of his walk?
   A. 15 minutes   Ⓑ 25 minutes
   C. 30 minutes   D. 35 minutes

10. Hannah's dance lesson begins at 4:30 P.M. and ends at 5:20 P.M. How many minutes pass from the beginning to the end of her dance lesson?
    A. 40 minutes   B. 45 minutes
    Ⓒ 50 minutes   D. 60 minutes

Form A • Multiple-Choice   A25   Go on. ▶

Name _____

For questions 11–16, use the schedule.

BUS	LEAVES CHICAGO	ARRIVES MILWAUKEE
A	8:15 A.M.	9:45 A.M.
B	10:45 A.M.	?
C	12:15 P.M.	?
D	2:45 P.M.	?

Trip lasts 1 hour and 30 minutes.

11. What time does Bus B arrive in Milwaukee?
    A. 11:15 A.M.   B. 11:45 A.M.
    C. 12:30 A.M.   Ⓓ 12:15 P.M.

12. What time does Bus C arrive in Milwaukee?
    A. 1:00 P.M.   Ⓑ 1:45 P.M.
    C. 2:15 P.M.   D. 2:45 P.M.

13. It takes Ms. Street 30 minutes to get to the bus station. She wants to take Bus A. What is the latest time she can leave her house?
    A. 7:15 A.M.   Ⓑ 7:45 A.M.
    C. 8:00 A.M.   D. 8:05 A.M.

14. Mr. Blum has a meeting in Milwaukee at 3:30 P.M. Which is the latest bus he could take to arrive at the meeting on time?
    A. Bus A   B. Bus B
    Ⓒ Bus C   D. Bus D

15. Janine plans to take Bus A to a band concert in Milwaukee. The concert begins at 12:05 P.M. Is there another bus on the schedule she can also take?
    Ⓐ No, there is not.
    B. Yes, she can take Bus B.
    C. Yes, she can take Bus C.
    D. Yes, she can take Bus D.

16. Kirk plans to leave Chicago on Bus D. It takes him 15 minutes to walk home after the bus arrives. At what time will he get home?
    A. 3:30 P.M.   Ⓑ 4:30 P.M.
    C. 5:00 P.M.   D. 5:15 P.M.

For questions 17–20, use the calendars.

June / July calendars

17. How many days is it from June 29 to July 3?
    A. 3 days   Ⓑ 4 days
    C. 6 days   D. 8 days

18. How many weeks is it from June 9 to July 28?
    Ⓐ 7 weeks   B. 8 weeks
    C. 9 weeks   D. 10 weeks

19. Ramon's family is going on a trip for 2 weeks. The trip will end on July 17. On what date will it begin?
    A. June 30   Ⓑ July 3
    C. July 24   D. July 31

20. Marion is going on a trip from June 27 until July 9. How many days will her trip last?
    A. 9 days   B. 11 days
    Ⓒ 12 days   D. 15 days

Form A • Multiple-Choice   A26   ▶ Stop!

Name _____

Choose the letter of the correct answer.

For questions 1–2, use the grid.

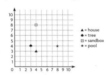

▲ = house   ◆ = tree   ☐ = sandbox   ✳ = pool

1. Which ordered pair shows the location of the tree?
   Ⓐ (3,4)   B. (4,3)
   C. (4,6)   D. (4,8)
   5-A.1

2. What is located at (8,4)?
   A. house   B. tree
   C. sandbox   Ⓓ pool
   5-A.1

3. How many thousands are in 3,975?
   Ⓐ 3 thousands   B. 5 thousands
   C. 7 thousands   D. 9 thousands
   5-A.2

4. Mark is 3 times as old as Kate. Kate is 3 years old. How old is Mark?
   A. 3 years old   B. 6 years old
   Ⓒ 9 years old   D. not here
   5-A.2

5. Which benchmark number can you use to estimate the number of cookies on Tray A and Tray B?

   Tray A   Tray B
   A. 3 cookies   Ⓑ 5 cookies
   C. 10 cookies   D. 20 cookies
   5-A.3

6. A 6-pack of juice costs $2.89. About how much should a 12-pack cost?
   A. about $3.00   B. about $4.00
   C. about $8.00   Ⓓ not here
   5-A.3

7. What is four hundred thirty in standard form?
   A. 340   B. 400   C. 403   Ⓓ 430
   6-A.1

8. What is 2,035 in expanded form?
   A. 200 + 30 + 5
   Ⓑ 2,000 + 30 + 5
   C. 2,000 + 300 + 5
   D. 2,000 + 30 + 50
   6-A.1

9. What is another name for 2,400?
   A. 240 ones   B. 24 tens
   Ⓒ 24 hundreds   D. 240 hundreds
   6-A.1

For questions 10–11, use the table.

POPULATION OF OAK CITY	
Year	Population
1994	22,096
1995	22,608
1996	24,910
1997	25,999

10. Between which two years did the population increase the most?
    A. 1994 and 1995
    Ⓑ 1995 and 1996
    C. 1996 and 1997
    6-A.2

11. How many more people lived in Oak City in 1997 than in 1994?
    A. 2,903 more people
    B. 3,003 more people
    Ⓒ 3,903 more people
    D. not here
    6-A.2

Form A • Multiple-Choice   A27   Go on. ▶

Name _____

12. Choose the statement that is correct.
    A. 724 > 742   B. 819 > 825
    Ⓒ 259 < 261   D. 102 = 120
    7-A.2

13. What is the greatest place-value position in which the digits differ in these numbers?
    6,405
    6,505
    A. ones   B. tens
    Ⓒ hundreds   D. thousands
    7-A.2

14. Which numbers are in order from least to greatest?

    2,850   2,860   2,870   2,880   2,890

    A. 2,884; 2,876; 2,887
    B. 2,876; 2,887; 2,884
    Ⓒ 2,876; 2,884; 2,887
    D. not here
    7-A.3

For questions 15–16, use the Venn diagram.

Ages of Ann's Cousins

15. Which is the age of a boy cousin only?
    A. 7 years old   Ⓑ 9 years old
    C. 14 years old   Ⓓ 15 years old
    7-A.4

16. Which is the age of both a boy cousin and a girl cousin?
    Ⓐ 3 years old   B. 4 years old
    C. 5 years old   D. 12 years old
    7-A.4

17. Which clock shows ten minutes past three?
    A. 3:01   Ⓑ 3:10
    C. 10:03   D. 10:30
    8-A.1

18. A class lasts from 1:10 P.M. to 1:55 P.M. How many minutes pass from the beginning to the end of the class?
    A. 25 minutes   B. 35 minutes
    Ⓒ 45 minutes   D. not here
    8-A.1

For questions 19–20, use the schedule.

Train	Leave Newark	Arrive New York
A	8:05 A.M.	8:55 A.M.
B	9:55 A.M.	?
C	11:05 A.M.	?
D	1:55 P.M.	?

The trip lasts 50 minutes.

19. What time does Train B arrive in New York?
    Ⓐ 10:45 A.M.   B. 11:05 P.M.
    C. 11:55 A.M.   D. not here
    8-A.3

20. Mrs. Eng has to be in New York at 11:30 A.M. Which is the latest train she could take to arrive on time?
    A. Train A   Ⓑ Train B
    C. Train C   D. Train D
    8-A.3

Form A • Multiple-Choice   A28   ▶ Stop!

Multiple Choice • Test Answers   **117**

CUMULATIVE TEST
PAGE 1

Choose the letter of the correct answer.

1.
```
   34
   17
 + 29
```
A. 70
B. 71
C. 80
D. 90
1-A.2

2. What is the best estimate of the difference?
```
 $68.79
 − 19.57
```
A. $40.00
B. $50.00
C. $60.00
D. $70.00
1-A.3

3.
```
 $3.27
  4.09
 + 1.25
```
A. $8.21
B. $8.41
C. $8.51
D. $8.61
1-A.4

4.
```
  600
 −312
```
A. 268
B. 278
C. 288
D. not here
2-A.2

5. What is the best estimate of the difference?
```
  717
 −513
```
A. 100
B. 200
C. 300
D. 400
2-A.3

6. Ann has 3 fish tanks. There are 2 fish in each tank.

Which number sentence shows how many fish there are in all?

A. 2 + 3 = 5
B. 3 − 2 = 1
C. 3 × 3 = 9
D. 2 × 3 = 6
3-A.1

7. Which number sentence shows the Order Property of Multiplication?
A. 4 × 7 = 7 × 4
B. 4 × 1 = 4
C. 7 × 0 = 0
D. 4 × 7 = 28
3-A.2

8. 9 × (2 × 3) = ?
A. 45   B. 54   C. 57   D. 64
3-A.3

9. Choose the number sentence that can be used to solve the problem.

Kyle read 3 chapters every day for 5 days. How many chapters did he read in all?
A. 5 − 3 = 2
B. 3 × 5 = 15
C. 3 + 2 = 5
D. 3 + 5 = 8
3-A.4

10. A P.E. class has 4 volleyball teams. There are 6 players on each team. How many players are there in all?
A. 20 players
B. 22 players
C. 24 players
D. 28 players
4-A.1

11. Which number sentence is in the same fact family as 18 ÷ 3 = 6?
A. 3 × 6 = 18
B. 3 + 6 = 9
C. 18 − 6 = 12
D. 18 − 3 = 15
4-A.2

Form A • Multiple-Choice   A29   Chapters 1–8   **Go on. ▶**

CUMULATIVE TEST
PAGE 2

12. Use the model to find the quotient.
16 ÷ 5 = ?

A. 2 r1   B. 3
C. 3 r1   D. not here
4-A.3

For questions 13–14, use the multiplication table to find the quotient.

×	3	4	5
3	9	12	15
4	12	16	20
5	15	20	25

13. 12 ÷ 4 = ?
A. 1   B. 2   C. 3   D. 4
4-A.4

14. 16 ÷ 4 = ?
A. 2   B. 3   C. 4   D. 5
4-A.4

15. 8)48
A. 3   B. 4
C. 5   D. not here
4-A.5

16. Laura sold 42 boxes of cookies. She sold 7 boxes each day. For how many days did she sell cookies?
A. 4 days   B. 5 days
C. 6 days   D. 7 days
4-A.6

17. Which shows a *cardinal* number?
A. 8 books
B. Channel 12
C. 3rd place
D. the number 6 on a shirt
5-A.1

18. What number is in the hundreds place in the number 1,876?
A. 1   B. 6   C. 7   D. 8
5-A.2

19. There are 25 golf balls in a container. About how many could the container hold?

A. about 50 golf balls
B. about 75 golf balls
C. about 100 golf balls
D. about 150 golf balls
5-A.3

20. What is the value of the digit 2 in the number 214?
A. 2 × 100 = 200
B. 2 × 10 = 20
C. 2 × 1 = 2
D. 2 × 0 = 0
6-A.1

Form A • Multiple-Choice   A30   Chapters 1–8   **Go on. ▶**

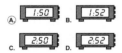
CUMULATIVE TEST
PAGE 3

21. What is *four hundred twenty-six* written in standard form?
A. 46   B. 426
C. 462   D. 4,260
6-A.1

22. What is *four million, three hundred twenty-seven thousand, four hundred twenty-four* written in standard form?
A. 4,027,424   B. 4,273,424
C. 4,307,424   D. 4,327,424
6-A.1

23. Which shows how to write 9,727,409 with period names?
A. 9 thousand, 727 hundred, 409
B. 9 million, 727 thousand, 409
C. 9 hundred thousand, 727 hundred, 409
D. not here
6-A.2

For questions 24–25, use mental math.

24.
```
  500
 +700
```
A. 200
B. 1,100
C. 1,200
D. 3,500
6-A.2

25.
```
 7,000
 +4,000
```
A. 10,000
B. 11,000
C. 12,000
D. not here
6-A.2

26. Use the number line to compare.

```
+--+--+--+--+--+--+--+--+--+--+
0 10 20 30 40 50 60 70 80 90 100
```

60 > ?
A. 30   B. 60   C. 70   D. 90
7-A.1

27. Which statement is correct?
A. 336 < 329
B. 412 > 421
C. 625 = 652
D. 356 > 327
7-A.2

28. Compare the numbers. Which statement is correct?
536 ● 563
A. 536 > 563
B. 536 < 563
C. 536 = 563
D. not here
7-A.2

For questions 29–30, use the table.

VISITORS TO THE ZOO	
Day of Week	**Number of Visitors**
Tuesday	1,282
Wednesday	1,104
Thursday	1,676
Friday	1,881
Saturday	1,890

29. On which day did the most visitors go to the zoo?
A. Tuesday   B. Wednesday
C. Friday   D. Saturday
7-A.3

30. On which day did the fewest visitors go to the zoo?
A. Wednesday   B. Thursday
C. Friday   D. Saturday
7-A.3

Form A • Multiple-Choice   A31   Chapters 1–8   **Go on. ▶**

CUMULATIVE TEST
PAGE 4

For questions 31–32, use the Venn diagram.

Scores On Math Test

```
    72      83      78
    85      86      84
    92      93      91
 Mrs. Turner's Class  Mr. Nelson's Class
```

31. Which score was made only in Mr. Nelson's class?
A. 83   B. 84   C. 85   D. 86
7-A.4

32. Which score was made in both Mr. Nelson's class and Ms. Turner's class?
A. 84   B. 85   C. 86   D. 92
7-A.4

33. Which clock shows ten minutes before two?

A. 1:50   B. 1:52
C. 2:50   D. 2:52
8-A.1

34. Which time is closest to the time that you arrive home from school?
A. 11 A.M.   B. 11 P.M.
C. 4 A.M.   D. 4 P.M.
8-A.2

For questions 35–36, use the schedule.

MOVIE SCHEDULE		
Movie	**Start Time**	**Finish Time**
A	4:30 P.M.	6:15 P.M.
B	5:00 P.M.	?
C	5:45 P.M.	?
All movies last 1 hour 45 minutes.		

35. At what time does Movie B end?
A. 5:00 P.M.   B. 6:15 P.M.
C. 6:30 P.M.   D. 6:45 P.M.
8-A.3

36. At what time does Movie C end?
A. 7:15 P.M.   B. 7:30 P.M.
C. 7:45 P.M.   D. 8:00 P.M.
8-A.3

For questions 37–38, use the calendars.

February						
Su	M	T	W	Th	F	Sa
						1
2	3	4	5	6	7	8
9	10	11	12	13	14	15
16	17	18	19	20	21	22
23	24	25	26	27	28	

March						
Su	M	T	W	Th	F	Sa
						1
2	3	4	5	6	7	8
9	10	11	12	13	14	15
16	17	18	19	20	21	22
23	24	25	26	27	28	29
30	31					

37. How many days is it from February 26 to March 4?
A. 6 days   B. 8 days
C. 9 days   D. 10 days
8-A.4

38. How many weeks is it from February 7 to March 14?
A. 3 weeks   B. 4 weeks
C. 5 weeks   D. 6 weeks
8-A.4

Form A • Multiple-Choice   A32   Chapters 1–8   **▶ Stop!**

Multiple Choice • Test Answers

Choose the letter of the correct answer.

For questions 1–3, use the frequency table.

MAGAZINE SUBSCRIPTION DRIVE

Week	Number Sold (Frequency)	Cumulative Frequency
1	111	111
2	97	208
3	74	?
4	105	?

1. During which week were the most subscriptions sold?
   - (A.) Week 1
   - B. Week 2
   - C. Week 3
   - D. Week 4

2. How many more subscriptions were sold in Week 2 than in Week 3?
   - A. 14 more subscriptions
   - (B.) 23 more subscriptions
   - C. 74 more subscriptions
   - D. 208 more subscriptions

3. What is the cumulative frequency for the magazine subscriptions sold in all 4 weeks?
   - A. 111 magazines
   - B. 209 magazines
   - C. 248 magazines
   - (D.) 387 magazines

4. For dessert, there are strawberries, blueberries, or raspberries. The berries can be served with ice cream, frozen yogurt, or whipped cream. How many dessert choices are there?
   - A. 6 choices
   - (B.) 9 choices
   - C. 10 choices
   - D. 12 choices

5. The copy center can make posters in small, regular, and large sizes. The paper for the posters can be blue, green, yellow, pink, or white. How many poster choices are there?
   - A. 7 choices
   - B. 12 choices
   - C. 14 choices
   - (D.) 15 choices

6. The school librarian will make a survey to find out what types of books students like to read. Which question would be the most useful?
   - A. Do you like mysteries more than adventure stories?
   - (B.) What is your favorite kind of book?
   - C. Where do you look for books to read?
   - D. What was the last book you read?

For questions 7–8, use the table.

FAVORITE SEASON

Choice	Votes
Summer	卌 卌 |||
Fall	卌	
Winter	卌 |||
Spring	卌 卌 ||

7. Which season was chosen as the favorite by the greatest number of people?
   - (A.) Summer
   - B. Fall
   - C. Winter
   - D. Spring

8. Which season was the favorite choice of the fewest people?
   - A. Summer
   - (B.) Fall
   - C. Winter
   - D. Spring

For questions 9–12, use the graph.

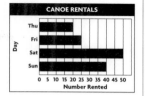

9. How many canoes were rented on Friday?
   - A. 15 canoes
   - (B.) 25 canoes
   - C. 40 canoes
   - D. 50 canoes

10. What interval is used in the scale of the graph?
    - A. 1
    - (B.) 5
    - C. 10
    - D. 25

11. How many more canoes were rented on Saturday than were rented on Friday?
    - A. 5 more canoes
    - B. 10 more canoes
    - (C.) 25 more canoes
    - D. 50 more canoes

12. How many canoes were rented on Friday, Saturday, and Sunday?
    - (A.) 115 canoes
    - B. 150 canoes
    - C. 175 canoes
    - D. 200 canoes

For questions 13–16, use the graph.

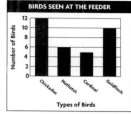

13. What interval is used in the scale of the graph?
    - A. 1
    - (B.) 2
    - C. 3
    - D. 4

14. How would the bars change if an interval of 3 were used in the graph?
    - A. The bars would be longer.
    - B. The bars would be exactly the same.
    - C. The bars would be wider.
    - (D.) The bars would be shorter.

15. How many more chickadees than cardinals were seen at the feeder?
    - A. 3 more
    - B. 5 more
    - (C.) 7 more
    - D. 9 more

16. How many birds were seen at the feeder altogether?
    - A. 5 birds
    - B. 15 birds
    - C. 25 birds
    - (D.) 33 birds

Choose the letter of the correct answer.

For questions 1–6, use the line graph.

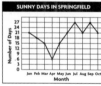

1. Why is a line graph a good choice for showing this information?
   - A. It is easy to compare groups.
   - B. It helps keep a count of the data as they are collected.
   - C. It has a key.
   - (D.) It shows how something changes over time.

2. What interval is used on the scale of this graph?
   - (A.) 3
   - B. 5
   - C. 10
   - D. 24

3. How many sunny days were there in January?
   - A. 18 days
   - (B.) 21 days
   - C. 22 days
   - D. 24 days

4. Which month had the fewest sunny days?
   - A. March
   - (B.) April
   - C. May
   - D. June

5. How many months had exactly 21 sunny days?
   - A. 1 month
   - B. 2 months
   - C. 3 months
   - (D.) 4 months

6. How many more sunny days were there in September than in February?
   - (A.) 9 more days
   - B. 15 more days
   - C. 18 more days
   - D. 21 more days

For questions 7–11, use the line plot. There is one X for each student.

```
                    X
                    X       X
        X   X       X   X   X   X
    X   X   X   X   X   X   X   X
   ─┼───┼───┼───┼───┼───┼───┼───┼─
    0   1   2   3   4   5   6   7   8
              Magazines Sold
```

7. What do the numbers on the line plot represent?
   - (A.) number of magazines sold
   - B. number of students
   - C. price of the magazines
   - D. cost of the field trip

8. What is the range of data used in this line plot?
   - A. 7
   - (B.) 8
   - C. 10
   - D. 12

9. How many students sold 8 magazines?
   - A. 1 student
   - (B.) 2 students
   - C. 3 students
   - D. 4 students

10. What was the greatest number of magazines sold by any student?
    - A. 3 magazines
    - B. 7 magazines
    - (C.) 8 magazines
    - D. 10 magazines

11. How many magazines were sold in all by students who sold 3?
    - A. 4 magazines
    - B. 6 magazines
    - (C.) 12 magazines
    - D. 15 magazines

For questions 12–16, use the stem-and-leaf plot.

HEIGHT OF MR. VICKER'S STUDENTS IN INCHES

Stem	Leaves
4	8 9 9
5	0 1 3 4 4 4 5 7 8
6	0 0 1 2 3 3 4

12. How would you find the height of the shortest person?
    - (A.) By looking at the first number in the plot
    - B. By looking at the last number in the plot
    - C. By finding the number that happens most
    - D. By finding the middle number

13. What is the number that happens most often in this set of data called?
    - A. stem
    - B. leaf
    - (C.) mode
    - D. median

14. What is the mode for the data?
    - A. 4 in.
    - B. 40 in.
    - (C.) 54 in.
    - D. 55 in.

15. What is the median for the data?
    - A. 48 in.
    - B. 50 in.
    - C. 54 in.
    - (D.) 55 in.

16. What is the difference in height between the shortest member and the tallest member of the class?
    - A. 12 in.
    - (B.) 16 in.
    - C. 24 in.
    - D. 30 in.

For questions 17–20, choose the type of graph that would be best to display the data described.

17. What kind of graph or plot would be best to list the spelling test scores for 30 students?
    - A. Bar graph
    - (B.) Stem-and-leaf plot
    - C. Line graph
    - D. Double-bar graph

18. What kind of graph or plot would be best to show the favorite TV programs of 30 fourth-grade students?
    - (A.) Bar graph
    - B. Stem-and-leaf plot
    - C. Line graph
    - D. Line plot

19. What kind of graph or plot would be best to show how a bean plant has grown over time?
    - A. Double-bar graph
    - B. Stem-and-leaf plot
    - (C.) Line graph
    - D. Line plot

20. What kind of graph or plot would be best to display these data?

FAVORITE BOOKS OF FOURTH GRADERS

Type	Mr. Bell's Class	Ms. Smith's Class
Mystery	15	14
Biography	3	8
Sports	6	2

   - (A.) Double-bar graph
   - B. Line plot
   - C. Stem-and-leaf plot
   - D. Line graph

Choose the letter of the correct answer.

1. An event is certain if it __?__ happens.
   A. always
   B. sometimes
   C. usually
   D. never

2. A bag contains quarters, dimes, and pennies. It is impossible to pull out a __?__.
   A. quarter
   B. dime
   C. nickel
   D. penny

For questions 3–4, use the spinner.

3. Using this spinner, you are certain to spin a number less than __?__.
   A. 2   B. 3   C. 4   D. 5

4. Using this spinner, it is impossible to spin a number greater than __?__.
   A. 1   B. 2   C. 3   D. 4

For questions 5–6, use the tally table.

NUMBER OF BLOCKS IN A BAG	
White	ⅢⅢ ⅢⅢ ⅢⅢ Ⅱ
Black	Ⅲ
Red	ⅢⅢ Ⅱ
Green	ⅢⅢ ⅢⅢ ⅢⅢ ⅢⅢ Ⅲ

5. Which outcome is most likely if a block is pulled from the bag?
   A. white
   B. black
   C. red
   D. green

6. Which block are you unlikely to pull?
   A. white
   B. black
   C. red
   D. green

For questions 7–8, use the spinner.

7. Which number are you most likely to spin on this spinner?
   A. 1
   B. 2
   C. 3
   D. All the numbers are equally likely.

8. Which number are you unlikely to spin?
   A. 1
   B. 2
   C. 3
   D. not here

For questions 9–10, use the bag.

9. If you pull a counter from the bag ten times, which color counter are you most likely to pull?
   A. blue
   B. green
   C. red
   D. Blue, green, and red are equally likely.

10. If you pull a counter from the bag ten times, which color counter are you unlikely to pull?
   A. blue
   B. green
   C. red
   D. Blue, green, and red are equally likely.

Form A • Multiple-Choice   A37   **Go on. ▶**

For questions 11–12, use a number cube that has 6 sides, labeled 1, 2, 3, 4, 5, and 6.

11. What is the probability of rolling a 4?
   A. $\frac{1}{6}$
   B. $\frac{1}{4}$
   C. $\frac{1}{2}$
   D. not here

12. What is the probability of rolling an odd number?
   A. $\frac{1}{6}$
   B. $\frac{1}{5}$
   C. $\frac{1}{3}$
   D. $\frac{1}{2}$

For questions 13–14, use the spinner.

13. What is the probability of spinning a 1 or a 2?
   A. $\frac{1}{3}$
   B. $\frac{1}{2}$
   C. $\frac{2}{3}$
   D. not here

14. What is the probability of spinning a 4?
   A. $\frac{0}{3}$
   B. $\frac{1}{4}$
   C. $\frac{1}{3}$
   D. $\frac{3}{3}$

15. A game is fair if each player has __?__.
   A. a good time playing
   B. an equal chance of winning
   C. the same number of turns
   D. the same final score

For questions 16–17, use the spinners.

In this game, the "odd" player gets points for odd numbers and the "even" player gets points for even numbers.

16. Which spinner gives both players an equal chance to win?
   A. spinner A
   B. spinner B
   C. spinner C
   D. all of them

17. If you were the "odd" player, which spinner would give you the greatest probability of winning?
   A. spinner A
   B. spinner B
   C. spinner C
   D. none of them

18. Lane's spinner is divided into 6 equal sections. There are 2 red sections, 2 white sections, and 2 blue sections. Which is the best explanation of whether the spinner is fair or not fair?
   A. It is fair because there is an equal chance of spinning each color.
   B. It is not fair because there are two sections of each color.
   C. It is not fair because there is a greater chance of spinning red.
   D. It is not fair because there is no chance of spinning green.

Form A • Multiple-Choice   A38   **▶ Stop!**

Choose the letter of the correct answer.

For questions 1–2, use the frequency table.

SCHOOL LUNCHES SOLD		
Day	Number Sold (Frequency)	Cumulative Frequency
Monday	136	136
Tuesday	101	237
Wednesday	98	335
Thursday	115	?
Friday	90	?

9-A.1
1. On which day were the most lunches sold?
   A. Monday
   B. Tuesday
   C. Wednesday
   D. Thursday

9-A.1
2. What is the cumulative frequency for the lunches sold on all 5 days?
   A. 335 lunches
   B. 450 lunches
   C. 550 lunches
   D. not here

9-A.1
For questions 3–4, use the table.

FAVORITE SPORT	
Choice	Votes
Baseball	ⅢⅢ Ⅲ
Football	ⅢⅢ Ⅱ
Basketball	ⅢⅢ ⅢⅢ Ⅰ
Soccer	ⅢⅢ ⅢⅢ Ⅱ

3. Which sport was chosen as their favorite by the most people?
   A. baseball
   B. football
   C. basketball
   D. soccer

9-A.2
4. Which sport was the favorite of the fewest people?
   A. baseball
   B. football
   C. basketball
   D. soccer

9-A.2

For questions 5–6, use the bar graph.

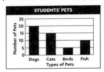

5. What interval is used on the scale?
   A. 1   B. 3   C. 5   D. 10

9-A.3
6. How would the bars change if an interval of 2 is used on the graph?
   A. The bars would be longer.
   B. The bars would be the same.
   C. The bars would be wider.
   D. The bars would be shorter.

9-A.3
For questions 7–8, use the line graph.

7. What interval is used on the scale of the graph?
   A. 5   B. 10   C. 20   D. 50

10-A.1
8. How many months had a high temperature of 65°F?
   A. 0 months   B. 1 month
   C. 2 months   D. 3 months

10-A.1

Form A • Multiple-Choice   A39   **Go on. ▶**

For questions 9–10, use the line plot. There is one X for each student.

9. What is the range of data used in the line plot?
   A. 2   B. 5   C. 7   D. 9

10-A.2
10. What number of states was visited by the most students?
   A. 3 states   B. 4 states
   C. 6 states   D. 9 states

10-A.2
For questions 11–12, use the stem-and-leaf plot.

Stem	Leaves
6	8 8 9 9
7	1 2 2 5 7 7 7 9
8	2 5 5 6 8 9
9	1 1 2 2

Prices of Cameras

11. What number is the mode for the data?
   A. 69
   B. 77
   C. 85
   D. 91

10-A.3
12. What is the difference between the highest price and the lowest price?
   A. $21.00
   B. $24.00
   C. $30.00
   D. not here

10-A.3

For questions 13–14, use the box.

13. Which shape is it impossible for you to pull?
   A. circle
   B. rectangle
   C. trapezoid
   D. triangle

11-A.1
14. If you pull a shape from the box ten times, which of these are you unlikely to pull?
   A. circle
   B. rectangle
   C. triangle
   D. square

11-A.1
For questions 15–16, use the spinners.

In this game, the "odd" player gets points for odd numbers and the "even" player gets points for even numbers.

15. Which spinner gives both players an equal chance to win?
   A. Spinner A
   B. Spinner B
   C. Spinner C
   D. all of them

11-A.3
16. If you were the "even" player, which spinner would give you the greatest probability of winning?
   A. Spinner A
   B. Spinner B
   C. Spinner C
   D. none of them

11-A.3

Form A • Multiple-Choice   A40   **▶ Stop!**

Multiple Choice • Test Answers

Name _____

Choose the letter of the correct answer.

1. Which is the best estimate of the sum?
318
289
+207
A. 600
B. 700
C. 800
D. 1,000
1-A.3

2. 9,000
−4,878
A. 4,022
B. 4,122
C. 4,222
D. 5,122
2-A.2

3. Diane has 3 music lessons each week. She has taken lessons for 4 weeks. How many music lessons has she taken in all?
A. 7 lessons   B. 8 lessons
C. 12 lessons   D. not here
3-A.1

4. $(5 \times 2) \times 6 = $?
A. 10   B. 16
C. 60   D. 106
3-A.3

5. There are 64 players in a soccer league. How many players are on each of 4 teams?
A. 16 players   B. 18 players
C. 20 players   D. not here
4-A.1

6. Which number sentence is in the same fact family as $3 \times 7 = 21$?
A. $7 - 3 = 4$ B. $7 + 3 = 10$
C. $7 + 3 = 10$ D. $21 \div 7 = 3$
4-A.2

7. $18 \div 4 = $?

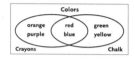

A. 3 r3   B. 4 r1
C. 4 r2   D. not here
4-A.3

For questions 8–9, use the multiplication table to find the quotient.

×	3	4	5
3	9	12	15
4	12	16	20
5	15	20	25

8. $25 \div 5 = $?
A. 2   B. 3   C. 4   D. 5
4-A.4

9. $12 \div 4 = $?
A. 3   B. 4
C. 6   D. not here
4-A.4

10. Mary earned a total of 10 extra credit points for her grade. She earned 2 extra credit points on each test. How many tests did she take?
A. 2 tests   B. 4 tests
C. 5 tests   D. not here
4-A.6

Form A • Multiple-Choice   A41   Chapters 1–11   Go on. ▶

Name _____

11. Which is a *nominal* number?
A. 110 pounds   B. 2 dollars
C. Third row   D. Channel 6
5-A.1

12. How many tens are in 3,658?
A. 3 tens   B. 5 tens
C. 6 tens   D. 8 tens
5-A.2

13. In the number 800, what is the value of 8?
A. 8 ones   B. 8 tens
C. 8 hundreds   D. not here
6-A.1

14. Which numbers are written in order from the least to the greatest?
A. 757, 765, 772
B. 765, 757, 772
C. 772, 765, 757
D. not here
7-A.3

For questions 15–16, use the Venn diagram.

15. Which color is used only for chalk?
a. red   b. yellow
c. blue   d. purple
7-A.4

16. Which color is used for both crayons and chalk?
A. orange   B. blue
C. green   D. purple
7-A.4

17. Which unit of time would you use to measure how long most people take to get dressed in the morning?
A. seconds   B. minutes
C. hours   D. days
8-A.1

18. Which time is closest to the time that a public library closes?
A. 8:00 A.M.   B. 1:00 P.M.
C. 8:00 P.M.   D. 1:00 P.M.
8-A.2

For questions 19–20, use the schedule.

TRAIN	LEAVE BALTIMORE	ARRIVE RICHMOND
A	9:00 A.M.	11:20 A.M.
B	9:40 A.M.	?
C	12:20 P.M.	?
D	3:50 P.M.	?
Trip lasts 2 hours and 20 minutes.		

19. At what time does Train B arrive in Richmond?
A. 11:20 A.M.   B. 11:40 A.M.
C. 12:00 noon   D. not here
8-B.1

20. If Mr. Ryan has a meeting in Richmond at 6:30 P.M., which is the latest train he can take?
A. Train A   B. Train B
C. Train C   D. Train D
8-B.1

Form A • Multiple-Choice   A42   Chapters 1–11   Go on. ▶

Name _____

For questions 21–22, use the table.

RAFFLE TICKETS SOLD		
Week	Number Sold (Frequency)	Cumulative Frequency
1	103	103
2	126	229
3	96	?
4	117	?

21. During which week were the most tickets sold?
A. Week 1   B. Week 2
C. Week 3   D. Week 4
9-A.1

22. By the end of Week 3, how many tickets had been sold?
A. 96 tickets   B. 229 tickets
C. 325 tickets   D. not here
9-A.1

23. Joey is making a survey to find out which season students like best. Which question would be the most useful for him to ask?
A. What did you do last winter?
B. Do you like spring best?
C. Did you go on a trip last fall?
D. What is your favorite time of year?
9-A.2

For questions 24–25, use the graph.

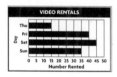

VIDEO RENTALS

24. What interval is used in the scale of the graph?
A. 1   B. 5   C. 10   D. 25
9-A.3

25. How many more videos were rented on Sunday than on Thursday?
A. 5 more videos
B. 15 more videos
C. 20 more videos
D. not here
9-A.3

For questions 26–27, use the line graph.

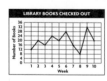

LIBRARY BOOKS CHECKED OUT

26. How many library books were checked out in Week 4?
A. 24 books   B. 26 books
C. 28 books   D. not here
10-A.1

27. During which week were the fewest books checked out?
A. Week 1   B. Week 3
C. Week 7   D. Week 8
10-A.1

Form A • Multiple-Choice   A43   Chapters 1–11   Go on. ▶

Name _____

For questions 28–29, use the line plot. There is one X for each student.

```
              X
        X X X X   X
  X   X X X X X X X
  0 1 2 3 4 5 6 7 8
```
Shots Made During Basketball Game

28. How many students made 5 shots?
A. 1 student   B. 3 students
C. 4 students   D. 6 students
10-A.2

29. What was the greatest number of shots made by any student?
A. 3 shots   B. 5 shots
C. 7 shots   D. 8 shots
10-A.2

For questions 30–31, use the stem-and-leaf plot.

Points Scored by Basketball Team in 18 Games

Stem	Leaves
7	4 7 8 8
8	3 4 4 6 6 6 7
9	2 2 2 2 5 8 8

30. What number is the mode for the data?
A. 86   B. 92   C. 95   D. 98
10-A.3

31. What number is the median for the data?
A. 86   B. 87   C. 92   D. 98
10-A.3

32. What kind of graph would best show the changes in the time of sunrise for one month?
A. double bar graph
B. line graph
C. stem-and-leaf plot
D. line plot
10-A.4

For questions 33–36, use the spinner.

33. Using this spinner, you are certain to spin a number less than ? .
A. 2   B. 3   C. 5   D. 6
11-A.1

34. Using this spinner, it is impossible to spin a number greater than ? .
A. 2   B. 3   C. 4   D. 5
11-A.1

35. What is the probability of spinning a 1 or a 2?
A. $\frac{2}{8}$ B. $\frac{3}{8}$
C. $\frac{4}{8}$ D. not here
11-A.2

36. What is the probability of spinning a 3?
A. $\frac{2}{8}$ B. $\frac{3}{8}$
C. $\frac{4}{8}$ D. $\frac{3}{3}$
11-A.2

Form A • Multiple-Choice   A44   Chapters 1–11   ▶ Stop!

Multiple Choice • Test Answers

Harcourt Brace School Publishers

Choose the letter of the correct answer.

1. Which figure is two-dimensional?

   A. ◁— Ⓑ△ C. ▽ D. ∿

2. Which of the following is a three-dimensional figure?

   A. square   B. rectangle
   C. circle   Ⓓ cylinder

3. Which unit could be used to measure the area of a basketball court?

   A. yards   B. feet
   Ⓒ square feet   D. cubic feet

4. Which unit could be used to measure the volume of a packing box?

   A. yards   B. feet
   C. square feet   Ⓓ cubic feet

For questions 5–6, use the figure.

5. How many faces are on this figure?

   A. 3 faces   Ⓑ 5 faces
   C. 6 faces   D. 8 faces

6. What two plane figures are the faces of this figure?

   A. rectangles and squares
   B. rectangles and pentagons
   Ⓒ triangles and rectangles
   D. triangles and squares

For questions 7–8, use the figure.

7. How many faces does this figure have?

   Ⓐ 4 faces   B. 5 faces
   C. 6 faces   D. 8 faces

8. Each face on this figure is a __?__.

   A. circle   Ⓑ triangle
   C. square   D. rectangle

For questions 9–11, use the figure.

9. How many faces does this figure have?

   A. 4 faces   Ⓑ 6 faces
   C. 8 faces   D. 12 faces

10. How many edges does this figure have?

   A. 4 edges   B. 6 edges
   C. 8 edges   Ⓓ 12 edges

11. How many vertices does this figure have?

   A. 4 vertices   B. 6 vertices
   Ⓒ 8 vertices   D. 12 vertices

For questions 12–15, use the grid.

12. What is the ordered pair of point X?

    Ⓐ (2,3)   B. (3,2)
    C. (3,3)   D. not here

13. Which set of ordered pairs identifies the vertices of the square marked on the grid?

    A. (2,3), (2,7), (7,2), (7,7)
    Ⓑ (3,3), (3,7), (7,3), (7,7)
    C. (4,4), (4,8), (8,4), (8,8)
    D. not here

14. Which set of ordered pairs identifies the vertices of the triangle marked on the grid?

    A. (6,3), (7,3), (8,3)
    B. (3,6), (3,7), (3,8)
    C. (6,1), (6,7), (6,8)
    Ⓓ not here

15. Which ordered pair identifies the point that is a vertex of the square *and* the triangle?

    A. (3,7)   Ⓑ (7,3)
    C. (7,4)   D. not here

16. Mary placed a book, a cereal box, a shoe box, and a crayon box on the same shelf. Which term best describes these figures?

    A. triangular prism
    Ⓑ rectangular prism
    C. square pyramid
    D. sphere

17. Which list of items suggests the same shape?

    A. basketball, straw, drinking cup, football
    B. golf ball, party hat, box of candies, ice-cream cone
    Ⓒ balloon, baseball, globe, marbles
    D. book, feathered hat, tennis ball, building block

18. Which figure belongs in the overlapped section of this Venn diagram?

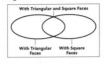

    A. ◁◁   B. ▭
    Ⓒ △   D. △

For questions 19–20, use the organized list.

Cylinders	Cubes	?
drinking glass	ice cubes	baseball
telescope	toy blocks	marble
?	dice	orange

19. Which heading is missing?

    A. Squares   B. Triangles
    Ⓒ Spheres   D. Pyramids

20. Which object should be listed under **Cylinders**?

    Ⓐ paint can   B. football
    C. textbook   D. poster paper

Choose the letter of the correct answer.

1. Which term names this figure?

   A. points   B. line
   C. line segment   Ⓓ plane

2. Which figure is a line segment?

   A.   Ⓑ A———B
   C. C   D. G———H

3. Which line segments are parallel?

   A. ⌐   Ⓑ ———
   C.   D. ∥

4. Which term names these figures?

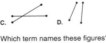

   Ⓐ points   B. line
   C. line segment   D. plane

5. Which of the following is an obtuse angle?

   A. ⌐   B. ∠
   C. ∠   Ⓓ ∠

6. What is the name of this figure?

   Ⓐ ray ST   B. line ST
   C. ray T   D. line segment T

7. What kind of angles are formed when two lines are perpendicular?

   A. acute angles   B. obtuse angles
   Ⓒ right angles   D. not here

8. Which pair of lines are perpendicular?

   A. ✕   Ⓑ ✛
   C. ⋌   D. ⟷

For questions 9–10, use the map.

9. Which street is *not* perpendicular to Street 2?

   A. Street A   B. Street B
   Ⓒ Street C   D. Street D

10. Which street is parallel to Street B?

    A. Street 2   B. Street 3
    C. Street C   Ⓓ Street D

---

11. Which figure is a polygon?

    Ⓐ ⬡   B. ⬭
    C. ◺   D. ⬚

12. What is this figure called?

    A. triangle   B. quadrilateral
    C. hexagon   Ⓓ octagon

13. A hexagon has 6 sides. How many angles does it have?

    A. 3 angles   B. 4 angles
    C. 5 angles   Ⓓ 6 angles

14. Which figure is a quadrilateral?

    A. ◿   Ⓑ ◇
    C. ⬠   D. ⌐

15. All quadrilaterals have __?__.

    Ⓐ 4 angles
    B. parallel sides
    C. acute angles
    D. no parallel sides

16. Only 2 of my sides are parallel. What am I?

    A. parallelogram
    Ⓑ trapezoid
    C. rectangle
    D. rhombus

17. What is the name of this figure?

    A. square
    B. trapezoid
    C. rectangle
    Ⓓ rhombus

18. Which of these figures is *not* a parallelogram?

    Ⓐ ◺   B. ▭
    C. ▱   D. ▭

19. Ken brought a box of cookies and 5 extra cookies to share equally among 3 of his friends and himself. After sharing, he has 15 cookies. No cookies were left. How many cookies were in the box?

    A. 15 cookies
    B. 30 cookies
    C. 40 cookies
    Ⓓ 55 cookies

20. Five students are in a line. Al is third. Nan is next to Al. Bea is first. Ed is between Bea and Al. Where is Jim?

    A. second
    B. in the middle
    C. fourth
    Ⓓ last in line

Choose the letter of the correct answer.

1. Which tells how to find the perimeter of this figure?

- (A.) Add. 1 + 1 + 2 + 2 + 3 + 3
- B. Add. 2 + 1 + 3
- C. Multiply. 3 × 2
- D. Multiply. 6 × 3

2. Which tells how to find the perimeter of this figure?

- A. Multiply. 4 × 9
- B. Multiply. 9 × 3
- C. Add. 9 + 3
- (D.) Add. (2 × 9) + (2 × 3)

For questions 3–4, find the perimeter.

3.

3 m
5 m

- A. 8 m
- B. 12 m
- (C.) 16 m
- D. 64 m

4.

4 cm 4 cm
4 cm 4 cm
4 cm

- A. 16 cm
- (B.) 20 cm
- C. 24 cm
- D. 44 cm

5. A field is 84 yards long and 50 yards wide. How many yards of fencing are needed to go around the field?
- A. 134 yd
- (B.) 268 yd
- C. 420 yd
- D. 4,200 yd

6. Carlita is buying a wallpaper border for her room. Each wall is 12 feet long. How long does the border need to be?
- A. 24 ft
- B. 36 ft
- (C.) 48 ft
- D. 144 ft

For questions 7–8, find the area.

7.

- A. 6 sq units
- (B.) 9 sq units
- C. 10 sq units
- D. 12 sq units

8.

- A. 8 sq units
- (B.) 10 sq units
- C. 12 sq units
- D. 15 sq units

9. Estimate the area.

- A. about 2 sq units
- B. about 6 sq units
- (C.) about 10 sq units
- D. about 25 sq units

---

10. Estimate the area.

- A. 5 sq units
- B. 8 sq units
- C. 12 sq units
- (D.) 20 sq units

11. Find the area.

3 m
3 m

- A. 6 sq m
- (B.) 9 sq m
- C. 12 sq m
- D. 18 sq m

12. Find the area.

6 ft
9 ft

- A. 15 sq ft
- B. 30 sq ft
- C. 42 sq ft
- (D.) 54 sq ft

13. How many square yards of carpet do you need to cover a floor that is 5 yards long and 4 yards wide?
- A. 9 sq yd
- B. 18 sq yd
- (C.) 20 sq yd
- D. 81 sq yd

14. Lee's garden is 6 feet by 6 feet. To buy fertilizer for it, Lee needs to know its area. What is the area?
- A. 24 sq ft
- (B.) 36 sq ft
- C. 48 sq ft
- D. 66 sq ft

For questions 15–18, use the shaded figures below.

A   B   C   D

15. What is the perimeter of figure D?
- A. 9 units
- (B.) 12 units
- C. 14 units
- D. 18 units

16. What is the area of figure A?
- A. 1 sq unit
- B. 3 sq units
- (C.) 4 sq units
- D. 9 sq units

17. Which two figures have the same areas but different perimeters?
- (A.) A and B
- B. A and C
- C. A and D
- D. B and D

18. Which two figures have the same perimeters but different areas?
- A. A and B
- (B.) A and C
- C. B and D
- D. C and D

19. Tile costs $2.00 per square foot. The floor is 5 feet by 6 feet. How much does the tile cost?
- A. $20.00
- B. $30.00
- C. $40.00
- (D.) $60.00

20. A man has 32 feet of fencing for a dog pen. Which shape has the greatest area?
- (A.) 8 ft by 8 ft
- B. 9 ft by 7 ft
- C. 10 ft by 6 ft
- D. 12 ft by 4 ft

Choose the letter of the correct answer.

1. A figure that has been flipped over a line is called a __?__.

- A. translation
- (B.) reflection
- C. rotation
- D. slide

For questions 2–3, use the figures.

A   B   C

2. Which is a translation?
- (A.) A
- B. B
- C. C
- D. not here

3. Which is a rotation?
- A. A
- B. B
- (C.) C
- D. not here

4. Two figures are congruent if they have the same __?__.
- (A.) size and shape
- B. number of sides
- C. number of angles
- D. position on a page

5. Which figure is congruent with this figure?

- A.
- B.
- C.
- (D.)

6. Which pair of figures is congruent?
- A.
- B.
- C.
- (D.)

7. Which figure has point symmetry?
- A.
- B.
- C.
- (D.)

8. Which figure shows a line symmetry?
- (A.)
- B.
- C.
- D.

9. Which figure has line symmetry?
- A.
- B.
- (C.)
- D.

---

10. A pattern of repeated polygons is a tessellation if it has no __?__.
- A. squares
- B. triangles
- (C.) gaps or overlaps
- D. lines of symmetry

11. What figure tessellates in this design?

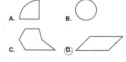

- A. circle
- B. square
- C. rectangle
- (D.) triangle

12. Which figure will tessellate?

- A.
- B.
- C.
- (D.)

13. This tessellation includes squares and __?__.

- A. circles
- B. rectangles
- (C.) octagons
- D. hexagons

14. A figure is drawn on 1-cm grid paper. If you copy the figure on 0.5-cm paper, it will be __?__.
- A. similar but larger
- (B.) similar but smaller
- C. symmetrical
- D. congruent

For questions 15–17, use the pairs of figures.

A   B
C   D

15. Which pair of figures is similar and congruent?
- A. A
- B. B
- C. C
- (D.) D

16. Which pair of figures is similar but not congruent?
- (A.) A
- B. B
- C. C
- D. D

17. Which best describes the pair of figures in B?
- A. similar and congruent
- B. similar but not congruent
- C. congruent but not similar
- (D.) neither similar nor congruent

18. You have a design on grid paper. How can you enlarge the design and be sure it is similar to the original design?
- A. Trace it.
- B. Copy a mirror image of it.
- C. Copy it onto smaller grid paper.
- (D.) Copy it onto larger grid paper.

Multiple Choice • Test Answers

Name _____

Choose the letter of the correct answer.

1. Which of these is a two-dimensional figure?
   A. pyramid   (B) triangle
   C. cube   D. prism
   12-A.1

For questions 2–3, use the figure.

2. How many faces are on the figure?
   A. 4 faces   (B) 6 faces
   C. 8 faces   D. 10 faces
   12-A.1

3. What plane figures are the faces of the figure?
   (A) rectangles   B. squares
   C. triangles   D. pentagons
   12-A.1

For questions 4–6, use the grid.

4. What is the ordered pair of point x?
   A. (2,7) B. (7,2) C. (5,8) (D) (8,5)
   12-A.2

5. Which set of ordered pairs identifies the vertices of the square marked on the grid?
   (A) (2,2), (2,7), (7,7), (7,2)
   B. (2,3), (2,8), (8,2), (8,8)
   C. (3,3), (3,7), (7,3), (7,7)
   D. not here
   12-A.2

6. Which ordered pair identifies the point that is a vertex of the triangle but *not* a vertex of the square?
   A. (2,7)   B. (7,7)
   (C) (5,9)   D. (9,5)
   12-A.2

7. The figure shows a _?_.
   A. point   (B) line
   C. plane   D. line segment
   13-A.1

For questions 8–9, use the map.

8. Which street is perpendicular to Oak Street?
   A. Street 1   B. Street 2
   C. Street 3   (D) not here
   13-A.1

9. Which street intersects Street 1 but is *not* perpendicular to it?
   (A) Oak Street   B. Main Street
   C. Elm Street   D. Street 2
   13-A.1

10. What is the figure called?
   A. hexagon   B. quadrilateral
   (C) octagon   D. triangle
   13-A.1

Form A • Multiple-Choice   A53   Go on. ▶

Name _____

11. A square has a side 8 meters long. What is the perimeter of the square?
    A. 8 m   B. 16 m
    (C) 32 m   D. 64 m
    14-A.1

12. A frame is 28 inches long and 18 inches wide. How many inches of ribbon are needed to go around the frame?
    A. 46 in.   B. 64 in.
    C. 74 in.   (D) 92 in.
    14-A.1

13. What is the area of the shaded figure?
    A. 5 sq units
    B. 6 sq units
    (C) 7 sq units
    D. not here
    14-A.2

14. How many square meters are in a field that is 50 meters long and 25 meters wide?
    A. 1,000 sq m   (B) 1,250 sq m
    C. 1,400 sq m   D. 1,500 sq m
    14-A.2

For questions 15–16, use the shaded figures.

A   B
C   D

15. What is the perimeter of Figure B?
    A. 5 units   B. 10 units
    (C) 12 units D. 14 units
    14-A.1

16. Which two figures have the same area but different perimeters?
    A. Figures A and B
    B. Figures A and C
    C. Figures B and C
    (D) Figures C and D
    14-A.3

17. To turn a figure around a point is called a _?_.
    A. flip
    B. slide
    C. translation
    (D) rotation
    15-A.1

18. Which figure is congruent to the figure shown?
    A.   B.
    (C)   D. not here
    15-A.2

19. Which figure has line symmetry?
    (A)   B.
    C.   D. not here
    15-A.3

Form A • Multiple-Choice   A54   ▶ Stop!

Name _____

Choose the letter of the correct answer.

1. $9 - 6 = 5 - ?$
   A. 1   (B) 2   C. 3   D. 4
   1-A.1

2. The four sides of a store have 114 parking spaces. There are 27 spaces on one side. There are 32 on another side and 29 on the third side. How many spaces are on the fourth side?
   A. 21 spaces   B. 24 spaces
   (C) 26 spaces D. not here
   2-A.1

3. Hal got 11 words right in the spelling bee. Michael got 9 words right. Which number sentence can you use to find how many more words Hal got right?
   A. $11 \times 9 = ?$
   B. $11 + 9 = ?$
   (C) $11 - 9 = ?$
   D. $9 + 11 = ?$
   3-A.4

4. $3\overline{)27}$
   A. 7   B. 8
   (C) 9   D. not here
   4-A.5

5. Which is a *cardinal* number?
   (A) 4 tennis players   B. 6th floor
   C. 1510 Main Street   D. Channel 5
   5-A.1

6. An ice-cream cone with 1 dip costs $0.89. About how much should a cone with 2 dips cost?
   A. about $1.00   (B) about $2.00
   C. about $3.00   D. about $4.00
   5-A.3

7. In which number does the digit 2 have a value of 200?
   A. 327   B. 2,592
   (C) 7,217   D. not here
   6-A.1

8. 700
   +600
   (A) 1,300
   B. 1,310
   C. 12,000
   D. 13,000
   6-A.1

9. Compare the numbers. Which statement is correct?
   A. $5,217 > 5,712$
   (B) $8,642 > 8,624$
   C. $4,327 = 4,372$
   D. $3,974 > 3,987$
   7-A.2

10. Compare the numbers. Which statement is correct?
    389 ● 398
    (A) $389 < 398$
    B. $389 = 398$
    C. $389 > 398$
    D. not here
    7-A.2

11. A diner serves hot dogs, steak, fish, and chicken. With this, you can have french fries, baked potato, or cole slaw. How many choices are there?
    A. 7 choices   B. 9 choices
    (C) 12 choices D. 14 choices
    9-A.1

Form A • Multiple-Choice   A55   Chapters 1–15   Go on. ▶

Name _____

12. Omar wanted to find out what type of movie his friends would prefer. Which question should he ask his friends?
    A. Do you like action movies?
    B. Where do you like to watch movies?
    C. What was the last movie you saw?
    (D) What kind of movie do you like best?
    9-A.2

For questions 13–14, use the graph.

ANIMALS AT THE CIRCUS

13. What interval is used in the scale of the graph?
    A. 3   (B) 4   C. 5   D. 6
    9-A.3

14. How many more tigers than elephants were there?
    A. 4   B. 6   (C) 8   D. 20
    9-A.3

For questions 15–16, use the line plot. There is one X for each student.

Minutes Spent Studying for Test

15. What is the range of data used in the line plot?
    (A) 60   B. 70
    C. 80   D. not here
    10-A.2

16. How many students studied for 40 minutes?
    A. 1 student   B. 2 students
    C. 3 students   (D) 4 students
    10-A.2

17. Which graph would be best to show the kinds of pets owned by a class of fourth-grade students?
    A. line graph
    B. line plot
    (C) bar graph
    D. stem-and-leaf plot
    10-A.4

18. Which graph would be best to show how many boys and how many girls are in 3 classes?
    A. line plot
    (B) double-bar graph
    C. stem-and-leaf plot
    D. line graph
    10-A.4

19. A bag contains jelly beans, gum drops, and lollipops. It is impossible to pull out a _?_.
    A. gum drop   B. lollipop
    C. jelly bean (D) mint
    11-A.1

20. Which unit would be used to measure the area of a page in a book?
    (A) square inches
    B. cubic inches
    C. inches
    D. feet
    12-A.1

Form A • Multiple-Choice   A56   Chapters 1–15   Go on. ▶

Multiple Choice • Test Answers

Harcourt Brace School Publishers

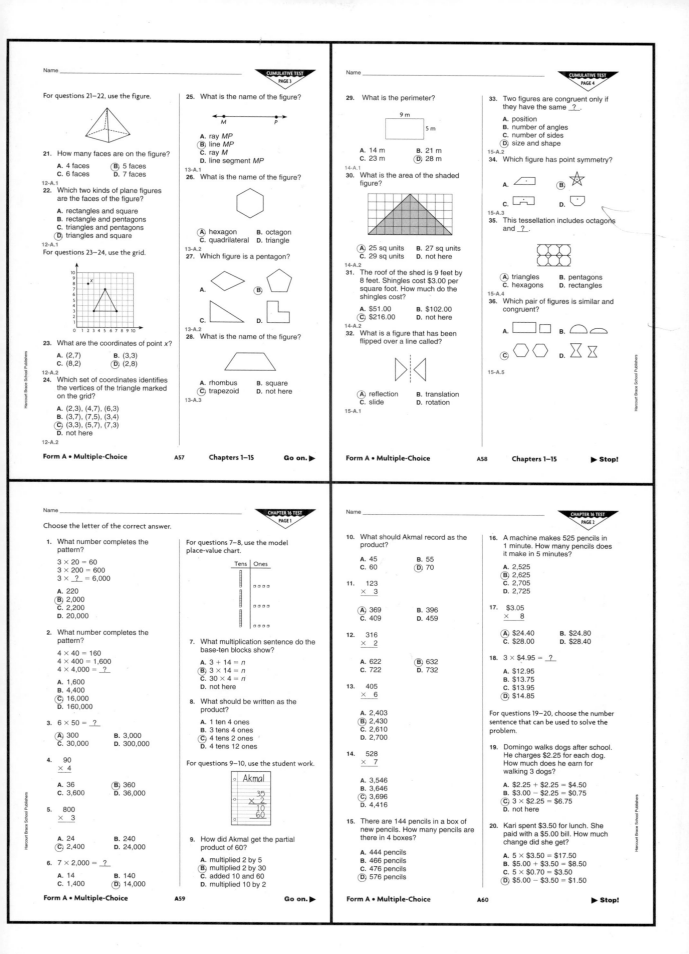

For questions 21–22, use the figure.

21. How many faces are on the figure?
    A. 4 faces   (B) 5 faces
    C. 6 faces   D. 7 faces
12-A.1

22. Which two kinds of plane figures are the faces of the figure?
    A. rectangles and square
    B. rectangle and pentagons
    C. triangles and pentagons
    (D) triangles and square
12-A.1

For questions 23–24, use the grid.

23. What are the coordinates of point x?
    A. (2,7)   B. (3,3)
    C. (8,2)   (D) (2,8)
12-A.2

24. Which set of coordinates identifies the vertices of the triangle marked on the grid?
    A. (2,3), (4,7), (6,3)
    B. (3,7), (7,5), (3,4)
    (C) (3,3), (5,7), (7,3)
    D. not here
12-A.2

25. What is the name of the figure?
    A. ray MP
    (B) line MP
    C. ray M
    D. line segment MP
13-A.1

26. What is the name of the figure?
    (A) hexagon   B. octagon
    C. quadrilateral D. triangle
13-A.2

27. Which figure is a pentagon?
    A.   (B)
    C.   D.
13-A.2

28. What is the name of the figure?
    A. rhombus   B. square
    (C) trapezoid   D. not here
13-A.3

29. What is the perimeter?
    9 m
    5 m
    A. 14 m   B. 21 m
    C. 23 m   (D) 28 m
14-A.1

30. What is the area of the shaded figure?
    (A) 25 sq units   B. 27 sq units
    C. 29 sq units   D. not here
14-A.2

31. The roof of the shed is 9 feet by 8 feet. Shingles cost $3.00 per square foot. How much do the shingles cost?
    A. $51.00   B. $102.00
    (C) $216.00   D. not here
14-A.2

32. What is a figure that has been flipped over a line called?
    (A) reflection   B. translation
    C. slide   D. rotation
15-A.1

33. Two figures are congruent only if they have the same _?_ .
    A. position
    B. number of angles
    C. number of sides
    (D) size and shape
15-A.2

34. Which figure has point symmetry?
    A.   (B)
    C.   D.
15-A.3

35. This tessellation includes octagons and _?_ .
    (A) triangles   B. pentagons
    C. hexagons   D. rectangles
15-A.4

36. Which pair of figures is similar and congruent?
    A.   B.
    (C)   D.
15-A.5

Choose the letter of the correct answer.

1. What number completes the pattern?
    $3 \times 20 = 60$
    $3 \times 200 = 600$
    $3 \times \_?\_ = 6,000$
    A. 220
    (B) 2,000
    C. 2,200
    D. 20,000

2. What number completes the pattern?
    $4 \times 40 = 160$
    $4 \times 400 = 1,600$
    $4 \times 4,000 = \_?\_$
    A. 1,600
    B. 4,400
    (C) 16,000
    D. 160,000

3. $6 \times 50 = \_?\_$
    (A) 300   B. 3,000
    C. 30,000   D. 300,000

4. 90
   $\times 4$
    A. 36   (B) 360
    C. 3,600   D. 36,000

5. 800
   $\times 3$
    A. 24   B. 240
    (C) 2,400   D. 24,000

6. $7 \times 2,000 = \_?\_$
    A. 14   B. 140
    C. 1,400   (D) 14,000

For questions 7–8, use the model place-value chart.

Tens	Ones

7. What multiplication sentence do the base-ten blocks show?
    A. $3 + 14 = n$
    (B) $3 \times 14 = n$
    C. $30 \times 4 = n$
    D. not here

8. What should be written as the product?
    A. 1 ten 4 ones
    B. 3 tens 4 ones
    (C) 4 tens 2 ones
    D. 4 tens 12 ones

For questions 9–10, use the student work.

Akmal
    35
  $\times 2$
    10
    60

9. How did Akmal get the partial product of 60?
    A. multiplied 2 by 5
    (B) multiplied 2 by 30
    C. added 10 and 60
    D. multiplied 10 by 2

10. What should Akmal record as the product?
    A. 45   B. 55
    C. 60   (D) 70

11. 123
   $\times 3$
    (A) 369   B. 396
    C. 409   D. 459

12. 316
   $\times 2$
    A. 622   (B) 632
    C. 722   D. 732

13. 405
   $\times 6$
    A. 2,403
    (B) 2,430
    C. 2,610
    D. 2,700

14. 528
   $\times 7$
    A. 3,546
    B. 3,646
    (C) 3,696
    D. 4,416

15. There are 144 pencils in a box of new pencils. How many pencils are there in 4 boxes?
    A. 444 pencils
    B. 466 pencils
    C. 476 pencils
    (D) 576 pencils

16. A machine makes 525 pencils in 1 minute. How many pencils does it make in 5 minutes?
    A. 2,525
    (B) 2,625
    C. 2,705
    D. 2,725

17. $\$3.05$
   $\times 8$
    (A) $24.40   B. $24.80
    C. $28.00   D. $28.40

18. $3 \times \$4.95 = \_?\_$
    A. $12.95
    B. $13.75
    C. $13.95
    (D) $14.85

For questions 19–20, choose the number sentence that can be used to solve the problem.

19. Domingo walks dogs after school. He charges $2.25 for each dog. How much does he earn for walking 3 dogs?
    A. $2.25 + $2.25 = $4.50
    B. $3.00 − $2.25 = $0.75
    (C) $3 \times \$2.25 = \$6.75$
    D. not here

20. Kari spent $3.50 for lunch. She paid with a $5.00 bill. How much change did she get?
    A. $5 \times \$3.50 = \$17.50$
    B. $5.00 + $3.50 = $8.50
    C. $5 \times \$0.70 = \$3.50$
    (D) $5.00 − $3.50 = $1.50

Multiple Choice • Test Answers

Choose the letter of the correct answer.

For questions 1–3, find the product by using a basic fact and a pattern of zeros.

1. $5 \times 6 = 30$
    $5 \times 60 = 300$
    $50 \times 60 = 3,000$
    $50 \times 600 = n$

    A. 300
    B. 3,000
    C. 3,300
    (D.) 30,000

2. $90 \times 30 = n$

    A. 270
    (B.) 2,700
    C. 27,000
    D. 270,000

3. $70 \times 600 = n$

    (A.) 42,000   B. 420,000
    C. 4,200,000   D. 42,000,000

4. One box of paper contains 500 sheets. How many sheets are in 80 boxes?

    A. 400 sheets
    B. 4,000 sheets
    (C.) 40,000 sheets
    D. 400,000 sheets

5. Duane has a puzzle. When he says 10, the answer is 200. When he says 20, the answer is 400. When he says 50, the answer is 1,000. What is the pattern?

    A. Add 5.
    B. Add 10.
    C. Subtract 10.
    (D.) Multiply by 20.

6. To estimate the product of 29×42, which number sentence should you use?

    A. 20×40
    B. 25×40
    (C.) 30×40
    D. 30×50

For questions 7–8, choose the best estimate for each product.

7. $67 \times 52 = n$

    A. 3,000   (B.) 3,500
    C. 3,600   D. 4,200

8. 79
    $\times 19$

    A. 700   B. 800
    C. 1,400   (D.) 1,600

9. There are 29 students in each class. There are 21 classes in the school. Which is the best estimate of the number of students?

    A. 200 students
    B. 400 students
    (C.) 600 students
    D. 900 students

10. The school spends about $617 each month on paper. Which is the best estimate of how much the school spends on paper in 10 months?

    (A.) $6,000
    B. $8,000
    C. $12,000
    D. $14,000

11. Suzanne is using the partial-products method to multiply 37 and 25. What should she do next?

    A. add 35 and 150
    (B.) multiply 7 by 20
    C. multiply 30 by 20
    D. multiply 7 by 5

12. Benton is using a shorter way to multiply 37 and 25. What should he do next?

    A. multiply 3 by 5
    B. multiply 7 by 5
    C. multiply 37 by 5
    (D.) multiply 37 by 20

13. 94
    $\times 45$

    A. 846
    B. 3,760
    C. 4,130
    (D.) not here

14. $73
    $\times 56$

    (A.) $4,088
    B. $4,808
    C. $4,888
    D. not here

15. $87 \times 73 = n$

    A. 5,861   (B.) 6,351
    C. 6,391   D. not here

16. Lena is multiplying 102 by 13. What should she do next?

    A. estimate the product
    B. multiply by the ones
    C. multiply by the tens
    (D.) add the products

17. 367
    $\times 24$

    (A.) 8,808   B. 8,888
    C. 9,024   D. not here

18. $4.31
    $\times 72$

    A. $31.32   B. $309.32
    (C.) $310.32   D. $400.32

19. Maureen has 12 rolls of film. She can take 36 pictures with each roll. How many pictures can she take in all?

    (A.) 432 pictures   B. 512 pictures
    C. 720 pictures   D. 756 pictures

20. A carton of film holds 48 rolls. How many rolls are in 150 cartons?

    A. 720 rolls   B. 2,400 rolls
    C. 5,200 rolls   (D.) 7,200 rolls

Choose the letter of the correct answer.

1. To check the quotient for this division problem, first multiply 4 and 9, and then ___?___ .

    9 r2
    4)38

    A. multiply by 2
    B. divide by 2
    C. subtract 2
    (D.) add 2

2. A number can always be divided by 5 with no remainder if the number ___?___ .

    A. is even
    B. is odd
    (C.) ends with 0 or 5
    D. is greater than 5

3. 8)30

    (A.) 3 r6
    B. 3 r7
    C. 4
    D. not here

4. 5)27

    A. 4 r7
    B. 5
    (C.) 5 r2
    D. not here

5. When you divide by 9, what is the largest possible remainder?

    A. 3
    (B.) 8
    C. 9
    D. 10

6. Angela is solving the following problem. What should she do next?

    Angela
    2
    2)53
    -4
    1

    A. divide the 5 tens
    (B.) bring down the 3 ones
    C. multiply 2 by 2
    D. write the remainder

7. 3)72

    A. 20 r2   B. 23 r1
    C. 23 r3   (D.) not here

8. 6)86

    A. 11   (B.) 14 r2
    C. 16   D. not here

9. In which place should the first digit in the quotient be placed?

    4)27

    (A.) ones place
    B. tens place
    C. hundreds place
    D. divisor

10. 7)58

    A. 6   B. 7 r1
    (C.) 8 r2   D. not here

11. The art teacher is dividing 96 sheets of colored paper among 8 groups of students. How many sheets will each group get?

    A. 11 sheets
    (B.) 12 sheets
    C. 16 sheets
    D. 17 sheets

12. There are 255 beads in a box. They will be divided equally to make 5 necklaces. How many beads will be on each necklace?

    (A.) 51 beads
    B. 53 beads
    C. 55 beads
    D. 56 beads

13. On a field trip, 100 students saw a play. They were in equal groups, and 4 students were left over. How many groups were formed?

    A. 10 groups
    B. 11 groups
    (C.) 12 groups
    D. 13 groups

14. Which problem shows where the first digit of the quotient should be placed?

    (A.) 3)577   B. 3)577
    C. 3)577   D. not here

15. 5)467

    (A.) 93 r2   B. 94 r2
    C. 95 r2   D. not here

16. $428 \div 7 = n$

    A. 60
    B. 60 r1
    C. 61
    (D.) not here

17. $305 \div 2 = n$

    A. 102 r1
    B. 150 r1
    (C.) 152 r1
    D. not here

18. A full bag holds 3 popcorn balls. There are 89 popcorn balls. How many bags are full?

    (A.) 29 full bags
    B. 30 full bags
    C. 31 full bags
    D. 33 full bags

19. Cans of juice come in six-packs. One store has 246 cans. How many six-packs are there?

    A. 40 six-packs
    (B.) 41 six-packs
    C. 42 six-packs
    D. 44 six-packs

20. Elize has 640 stamps from around the world. There is an equal number of stamps in each of 8 books. How many stamps are in each book?

    A. 60 stamps
    B. 70 stamps
    (C.) 80 stamps
    D. 90 stamps

Multiple Choice • Test Answers

Choose the letter of the correct answer.

For questions 1–2, use a basic fact and a pattern of zeros to find the quotient.

1. $16 \div 8 = 2$
   $16,000 \div 8 = n$
   A. 200   B. 220
   C. 2,000   D. 2,200

2. $35 \div 5 = 7$
   $3,500 \div 5 = n$
   A. 70   B. 700
   C. 770   D. 7,700

For questions 3–4, estimate. Use a basic fact and a pattern of zeros to estimate the quotient.

3. $49,159 \div 7 = n$
   A. 600   B. 700
   C. 6,000   D. 7,000

4. $3,020 \div 6 = n$
   A. 5   B. 50   C. 55   D. 500

5. What number belongs in the tens place of the quotient?

   A. 0   B. 1   C. 4   D. 7

6. $9\overline{)453}$
   A. 5 r3   B. 50
   C. 50 r3   D. 53

7. $3\overline{)609}$
   A. 23   B. 203   C. 230   D. 233

8. A baker makes 735 cakes in 7 days. How many cakes does he make each day?
   A. 15 cakes   B. 105 cakes
   C. 147 cakes   D. 150 cakes

9. There are 104 students on a field trip. The students are in groups of 8. How many groups are there?
   A. 10 groups   B. 12 groups
   C. 13 groups   D. 15 groups

10. Which shows the correct quotient?
    A. $4\overline{)\$5.00}$ = $\$1.25$ B. $4\overline{)\$5.00}$ = $\$12.5$
    C. $4\overline{)\$5.00}$ = $\$.125$ D. $4\overline{)\$5.00}$ = $\$125.00$

11. $2\overline{)\$12.08}$
    A. $\$0.64$ B. $\$6.04$
    C. $\$6.40$ D. $\$64.00$

12. $8\overline{)\$6.48}$
    A. $\$0.81$ B. $\$0.88$
    C. $\$8.10$ D. $\$8.80$

13. Movie tickets cost $22.50 for 5. What is the cost for each ticket?
    A. $\$0.45$ B. $\$4.05$
    C. $\$4.10$ D. $\$4.50$

14. Mrs. Ho buys 6 pounds of apples for $5.70. What is the cost for each pound of apples?
    A. $\$0.95$ B. $\$0.99$
    C. $\$9.05$ D. $\$9.50$

Form A • Multiple-Choice   A65   Go on. ▶

For questions 15–16, tell how you interpret the remainder.

15. Mr. Sal needs 129 sheets of poster paper. There are 8 sheets in a package. How many packages does he need to buy?
    A. Round the quotient to the next greater whole number.
    B. Drop the remainder.
    C. Use the remainder as part of your answer.
    D. Not enough information is given.

16. Mrs. Haley has 304 pennies and 6 grandchildren. She wants to give each child an equal share of the pennies. How many pennies can each child get?
    A. Round the quotient to the next greater whole number.
    B. Drop the remainder.
    C. Use the remainder in the answer.
    D. Not enough information is given.

17. Lea has 157 inches of ribbon. How many bows can she make if she uses 9 inches of ribbon in each bow?
    A. 13 bows   B. 15 bows
    C. 17 bows   D. 18 bows

18. Jack has to read 126 pages. How many pages should he plan to read each day to be sure he finishes in 5 days?
    A. 18 pages   B. 20 pages
    C. 24 pages   D. 26 pages

19. Mia can paint 1 T-shirt in 8 minutes. How many T-shirts can she paint in 140 minutes?
    A. 14 T-shirts   B. 17 T-shirts
    C. 18 T-shirts   D. 22 T-shirts

20. Al plays the piano. He plays each song for 10 minutes. How many songs can he play in 115 minutes?
    A. 11 songs   B. 12 songs
    C. 15 songs   D. 16 songs

For questions 21–24, solve. Name the operation you used.

21. Ed's family drove 157 miles on Monday, 223 miles on Tuesday, and 118 miles on Wednesday. How many miles did they drive in all?
    A. 498 miles, addition
    B. 105 miles, subtraction
    C. 18,526 miles, multiplication
    D. 166 miles, division

22. The school play lasts 90 minutes. Each of the 3 acts takes the same amount of time. How long is each act?
    A. 93 minutes; addition
    B. 87 minutes; subtraction
    C. 270 minutes; multiplication
    D. 30 minutes; division

23. Vin is reading a book with 221 pages. He has read 118 pages. How many more pages does he have to read?
    A. 339 pages; addition
    B. 103 pages; subtraction
    C. 3,000 pages; multiplication
    D. 2 pages; division

24. Jessica travels 13 miles round trip to school. How many miles does she travel to school and back in 21 days?
    A. 34 miles; addition
    B. 8 miles; subtraction
    C. 273 miles; multiplication
    D. 2 miles; division

Form A • Multiple-Choice   A66   ▶ Stop!

Choose the letter of the correct answer.

1. What number completes the pattern?
   $4 \times 80 = 320$
   $4 \times 800 = 3,200$
   $4 \times \underline{?} = 32,000$
   A. 800   B. 880
   C. 888   D. 8,000
   16-A.1

2. 600
   $\times\ 7$
   A. 420   B. 4,200   C. 42,000   D. 420,000
   16-A.2

3. 306
   $\times\ 5$
   A. 153   B. 1,503   C. 1,530   D. 15,030
   16-A.2

4. There are 126 crayons in a box of new crayons. How many crayons are in 6 boxes?
   A. 626 crayons   B. 656 crayons
   C. 726 crayons   D. 756 crayons
   16-A.2

5. $5 \times \$5.35 = \underline{?}$
   A. $\$25.55$ B. $\$25.75$
   C. $\$26.65$ D. not here
   16-A.3

6. Choose the number sentence that can be used to solve the problem.

   Earlene sells her drawings. She charges $3.25 for each drawing. How much does she earn for 4 drawings?
   A. $\$3.25 \times 4 = n$
   B. $\$3.25 + \$4.00 = n$
   C. $\$4.00 - \$3.25 = n$
   D. $\$3.25 \div 4 = n$
   16-A.3

7. $50 \times 700 = n$
   A. 3,500   B. 35,000
   C. 350,000   D. 3,500,000
   17-A.1

8. On Earth Day 10 groups of volunteers planted new trees. Each group planted 50 trees. What was the total number of trees planted?
   A. 50 trees   B. 500 trees
   C. 550 trees   D. 5,000 trees
   17-A.1

9. James sleeps about 8 hours per night. Which of these is the best estimate of the number of hours he sleeps in 12 nights?
   A. about 50 hours
   B. about 60 hours
   C. about 100 hours
   D. about 160 hours
   17-A.2

10. 92
    $\times 53$
    A. 955   B. 4,776   C. 4,876   D. not here
    17-A.3

11. $\$5.12$
    $\times\ 17$
    A. $\$40.96$ B. $\$86.94$ C. $\$97.04$ D. not here
    17-A.3

12. There are 70 chocolate chip cookies in a bag. Each cookie has 18 chocolate chips. How many chocolate chips are in the bag?
    A. 700 chocolate chips
    B. 1,180 chocolate chips
    C. 1,260 chocolate chips
    D. 1,560 chocolate chips
    17-A.4

Form A • Multiple-Choice   A67   Go on. ▶

---

13. $7\overline{)46}$
    A. 6 r4   B. 6 r6
    C. 7 r4   D. 8 r2
    18-A.1

14. When you divide by 7, what is the largest possible remainder?
    A. 3   B. 4   C. 6   D. 8
    18-A.1

15. $5\overline{)63}$
    A. 10 r3   B. 11 r2
    C. 12 r2   D. 12 r3
    18-A.1

16. Larry set up 70 chairs. They were in equal rows with 6 chairs left over. How many rows were formed?
    A. 8 rows   B. 9 rows
    C. 11 rows   D. 12 rows
    18-A.4

17. $538 \div 7 = n$
    A. 76 r5   B. 76 r6
    C. 78 r2   D. not here
    18-A.3

18. A carton contains 336 small toys. Inside the carton, there are 2 toys in each box. How many boxes are in the carton?
    A. 118 boxes   B. 158 boxes
    C. 168 boxes   D. 169 boxes
    18-A.4

19. Use a basic fact and a pattern of zeros to find the quotient.
    $28 \div 7 = 4$
    $280 \div 7 = 40$
    $2,800 \div 7 = 400$
    $28,000 \div 7 = n$
    A. 40   B. 400
    C. 440   D. 4,000
    19-A.1

20. $6\overline{)364}$
    A. 6 r4   B. 60
    C. 60 r4   D. not here
    19-A.2

21. $4\overline{)850}$
    A. 212 r2   B. 213 r3
    C. 214 r2   D. 215 r2
    19-A.2

22. $9\overline{)\$7.38}$
    A. $\$0.80$ B. $\$0.82$
    C. $\$8.00$ D. not here
    19-A.3

23. Val has 242 baseball cards. It takes 16 cards to fill a page. How many album pages can he fill? How many baseball cards will be left over?
    A. 14 pages; 2 baseball cards
    B. 15 pages; 2 baseball cards
    C. 15 pages; 3 baseball cards
    D. 16 pages; 2 baseball cards
    19-A.4

24. Solve, and name the operation you used.

    A game lasts 36 minutes. Each of the 4 periods takes the same amount of time. How long is each period?
    A. 9 minutes; division
    B. 32 minutes; subtraction
    C. 40 minutes; addition
    D. 144 minutes; multiplication
    19-A.5

Form A • Multiple-Choice   A68   ▶ Stop!

Multiple Choice • Test Answers   **127**

Choose the letter of the correct answer.

1. The perimeter of the figure is 642 feet. What is the missing length?

130 ft   167 ft
210 ft

A. 100 ft   B. 125 ft
C. 135 ft   D. 507 ft
2-A.1

2. Use the multiplication fact to help you find the quotient.

$5 \times 8 = 40$
$40 \div 8 = \underline{\ ?\ }$

A. 5   B. 8   C. 16   D. 40
4-A.2

3. How many tens are in 5,263?

A. 2 tens   B. 3 tens
C. 5 tens   D. 6 tens
6-A.1

4. Which numbers are written in order from the greatest to the least?

A. 3,745; 3,459; 2,973
B. 2,973; 3,459; 3,745
C. 2,973; 3,745; 3,459
D. 3,459; 2,973; 3,745
7-A.3

For questions 5–7, use the graph.

BOOKS READ BY ONE CLASS

Number of Books
Mystery Adventure Sports Humor
Type of Book

5. What interval is used in the scale of the graph?

A. 1   B. 2   C. 3   D. 4
9-A.3

6. How many more mystery books than sports books did the class read?

A. 2   B. 4   C. 6   D. 8
9-A.3

7. How many books did the class read in all?

A. 10 books   B. 22 books
C. 24 books   D. 28 books
9-A.3

For questions 8–9, use the stem-and-leaf-plot.

Scores on a Science Test

Stem	Leaves
7	5 7 9
8	0 1 2 3 3 3 4 8 9
9	0 1 2 2 3 3 4

8. What number is the mode for the data?

A. 79   B. 83   C. 92   D. 93
10-A.3

9. What is the difference between the lowest score and the highest score on the test?

A. 19   B. 20   C. 22   D. 24
10-A.3

For questions 10–11, use the tally table.

NUMBER OF BLOCKS IN A BAG	
White	JHT JHT JHT
Black	JHT JHT
Red	JHT II
Green	JHT JHT JHT III

10. Which outcome is most likely if a block is pulled from the bag?

A. pulling a white block
B. pulling a black block
C. pulling a red block
D. pulling a green block
11-A.1

11. Which color block are you least likely to pull?

A. white   B. black
C. red   D. green
11-A.1

12. Which unit would be used to measure the area of a floor?

A. feet   B. square feet
C. yards   D. cubic yards
12-A.1

For questions 13–14, use the organized list.

Cylinders	?	Spheres
can	boxes	ball
flashlight	dice	globe
pencil holder	blocks	?

13. Which heading is missing?

A. Cubes   B. Triangles
C. Squares   D. Pyramids
12-A.1

14. Which object should be listed under Spheres?

A. toy block   B. pencil
C. marble   D. telescope
12-A.1

15. What is a flat surface with no end called?

A. line   B. line segment
C. angle   D. plane
13-A.1

16. I am a 4-sided polygon. None of my sides are parallel. What am I?

A. parallelogram
B. trapezoid
C. rectangle
D. general quadrilateral
13-A.3

17. What is the area of the shaded figure?

A. 4 sq units   B. 6 sq units
C. 8 sq units   D. 12 sq units
14-A.2

18. Ross has 24 feet of rope to make a border around his garden. Which shape has the greatest area?

A. 6 ft by 6 ft   B. 8 ft by 4 ft
C. 10 ft by 2 ft   D. 5 ft by 7 ft
14-A.3

---

19. Which pair of figures is congruent?

A.   B.
C.   D.
15-A.2

20. Which figure will not tessellate?

A.   B.
C.   D.
15-A.4

21. $5 \times 80 = \underline{\ ?\ }$

A. 400   B. 4,000
C. 40,000   D. 400,000
16-A.2

22. $4 \times 6,000 = \underline{\ ?\ }$

A. 24   B. 240
C. 2,400   D. 24,000
16-A.2

For questions 23–24, use the model place-value chart.

Tens	Ones
	◦◦
	◦◦
	◦◦
	◦◦

23. Which multiplication sentence do the base-ten blocks show?

A. $3 \times 2 = n$ B. $3 \times 6 = n$
C. $3 \times 10 = n$ D. $3 \times 12 = n$
16-A.2

24. What should Anna record as the product?

A. 1 ten 2 ones
B. 3 tens 2 ones
C. 3 tens 6 ones
D. 4 tens 6 ones
16-A.2

25. $4 \times \$2.95 = \underline{\ ?\ }$

A. $5.90   B. $11.80
C. $18.80   D. $38.80
16-A.3

26. $20 \times 70 = n$

A. 140   B. 14,000
C. 140,000   D. not here
17-A.1

27. What is the best estimate of the product?

58
×21

A. about 210   B. about 1,160
C. about 1,200   D. about 12,000
17-A.2

28. 72
×48

A. 1,200   B. 3,456
C. 7,248   D. 8,496
17-A.3

29. $5.49
× 23

A. $26.27   B. $124.07
C. $126.27   D. $226.27
17-A.3

---

30. Philip has 11 boxes of cookie mix. He can make 24 cookies with each box. How many cookies can he make in all?

A. 264 cookies   B. 360 cookies
C. 480 cookies   D. 512 cookies
17-A.4

31. $7\overline{)60}$

A. 8   B. 8 r2
C. 8 r6   D. not here
18-A.1

32. $5\overline{)64}$

A. 12 r1   B. 12 r4
C. 12 r6   D. not here
18-A.1

33. A total of 83 students went to a park. They were in equal groups with 2 students left over. How many equal groups were there?

A. 9 groups   B. 10 groups
C. 11 groups   D. 12 groups
18-A.4

34. $364 \div 6 = n$

A. 60   B. 60 r1
C. 60 r4   D. not here
18-A.4

For questions 35–36, use a basic fact and a pattern of zeros to find the quotient.

35. $20 \div 4 = 5$
$20,000 \div 4 = n$

A. 50   B. 500
C. 5,000   D. 50,000
19-A.1

36. $63 \div 9 = 7$
$6,300 \div 9 = n$

A. 70   B. 700
C. 770   D. 7,700
19-A.1

37. $3\overline{)217}$

A. 72 r1   B. 72 r2
C. 72 r7   D. 80
19-A.2

38. $8\overline{)\$16.08}$

A. $0.20   B. $2.01
C. $2.10   D. $20.10
19-A.3

39. How would you interpret the remainder?

Mrs. Jenks has 38 cookies. She wants to give an equal number of cookies to each of 9 children. How many cookies should she give each child?

A. Drop the remainder.
B. Use the remainder as part of your answer.
C. Round the quotient to the next greater whole number.
D. not here
19-A.4

40. Solve and name the operation you used.

Lynn jogs 14 miles each week. How many miles does she jog in 52 weeks?

A. 3 miles; division
B. 38 miles; subtraction
C. 66 miles; addition
D. 728 miles; multiplication
19-A.5

Harcourt Brace School Publishers

Choose the letter of the correct answer.

1. What fraction of the bar is shaded?

   A. $\frac{1}{5}$　B. $\frac{1}{4}$　C. $\frac{1}{3}$　D. $\frac{1}{2}$

2. What fraction of the circle is shaded?

   A. $\frac{2}{5}$　B. $\frac{2}{3}$　C. $\frac{3}{4}$　D. $\frac{7}{8}$

3. Which figure is one-sixth shaded?

   A.　B.　C　D.

4. Which fraction means the same as four out of five?

   A. $\frac{4}{5}$　B. $\frac{5}{4}$　C. $\frac{5}{9}$　D. $\frac{9}{10}$

For questions 5–6, use this figure.

5. What fraction of the figure is striped?

   A. $\frac{1}{8}$　B. $\frac{3}{8}$　C. $\frac{5}{8}$　D. $\frac{7}{8}$

6. What fraction of the figure is NOT striped or shaded?

   A. $\frac{1}{8}$　B. $\frac{3}{8}$
   C. $\frac{5}{8}$　D. $\frac{7}{8}$

For questions 7–10, choose the fraction that represents the group that is shaded.

7.

   A. $\frac{1}{5}$　B. $\frac{1}{4}$
   C. $\frac{1}{3}$　D. $\frac{1}{6}$

8.

   A. $\frac{1}{10}$　B. $\frac{1}{5}$
   C. $\frac{1}{3}$　D. $\frac{1}{2}$

9.

   A. $\frac{2}{5}$　B. $\frac{3}{5}$
   C. $\frac{2}{3}$　D. $\frac{3}{4}$

Form A • Multiple-Choice　　A73　　　　**Go on. ▶**

10.

   A. $\frac{1}{8}$　B. $\frac{5}{10}$
   C. $\frac{7}{7}$　D. $\frac{7}{24}$

11. Small cans of juice come in four-packs. The Hennessey twins share a four-pack equally. What fraction of a four-pack does each twin drink?

   A. $\frac{1}{4}$　B. $\frac{2}{4}$
   C. $\frac{3}{4}$　D. $\frac{4}{2}$

12. Terry takes 5 books out of the library. Of the books, 2 are mystery stories. What fraction of the books are mystery stories?

   A. $\frac{2}{5}$　B. $\frac{3}{5}$
   C. $\frac{2}{7}$　D. $\frac{5}{2}$

For questions 13–14, use the fraction bars to compare the fractions. Choose < , > , or = for each ●.

13.

   $\frac{6}{8}$ ● $\frac{3}{4}$
   A. <
   B. >
   C. =

14.

   $\frac{4}{5}$ ● $\frac{2}{3}$
   A. <　B. >　C. =

15. Which group of fractions is in order from least to greatest?

   A. $\frac{2}{3}, \frac{1}{6}, \frac{5}{6}$　B. $\frac{1}{6}, \frac{5}{6}, \frac{2}{3}$
   C. $\frac{5}{6}, \frac{2}{3}, \frac{1}{6}$　D. $\frac{1}{6}, \frac{2}{3}, \frac{5}{6}$

16. Which group of fractions is in order from greatest to least?

   A. $\frac{1}{4}, \frac{3}{8}, \frac{3}{4}$　B. $\frac{1}{4}, \frac{3}{4}, \frac{3}{8}$
   C. $\frac{3}{4}, \frac{3}{8}, \frac{1}{4}$　D. $\frac{3}{8}, \frac{3}{4}, \frac{1}{4}$

17. A muffin recipe calls for $\frac{3}{4}$ cup coconut, $\frac{1}{4}$ cup nuts, and $\frac{1}{2}$ cup dates. Which shows the ingredients listed in order from least to greatest?

   A. coconut, nuts, dates
   B. nuts, dates, coconut
   C. nuts, coconut, dates
   D. dates, nuts, coconut

18. A spinner has 10 equal sections. Of the sections, 2 are blue, 3 are yellow, 1 is white, and 4 sections are red. Which two colors together cover more than $\frac{1}{2}$ the spinner?

   A. blue and yellow
   B. yellow and white
   C. red and white
   D. blue and red

Form A • Multiple-Choice　　A74　　　　**Go on. ▶**

For questions 19–20, choose the mixed number that matches the picture.

19.

   A. $1\frac{1}{4}$　B. $1\frac{3}{4}$
   C. $3\frac{1}{4}$　D. $4\frac{1}{3}$

20.

   A. $1\frac{2}{3}$　B. $2\frac{1}{3}$
   C. $2\frac{2}{3}$　D. $3\frac{1}{3}$

For questions 21–24, rename each fraction as a mixed number.

21. $\frac{13}{8} = \underline{?}$

   A. $\frac{8}{13}$　B. $1\frac{1}{8}$
   C. $1\frac{3}{8}$　D. $1\frac{5}{8}$

22. $\frac{11}{4} = \underline{?}$

   A. $2\frac{3}{4}$　B. $3\frac{1}{4}$
   C. $3\frac{1}{2}$　D. $3\frac{3}{4}$

23. $\frac{7}{3} = \underline{?}$

   A. $\frac{3}{7}$　B. $1\frac{2}{3}$
   C. $2\frac{1}{3}$　D. $3\frac{1}{2}$

24. $\frac{9}{5} = \underline{?}$

   A. $\frac{5}{9}$　B. $1\frac{4}{5}$
   C. $2\frac{1}{5}$　D. $2\frac{1}{4}$

Form A • Multiple-Choice　　A75　　　　**▶ Stop!**

Choose the letter of the correct answer.

1. Which number sentence matches the model?

   A. $\frac{1}{4} + \frac{3}{4} = 1$　B. $\frac{1}{5} + \frac{4}{5} = 1$
   C. $\frac{1}{2} + \frac{1}{2} = 1$　D. $\frac{4}{8} + \frac{4}{8} = 1$

2. Use the fraction bars to help you find the sum.

   $\frac{2}{3} + \frac{2}{3} = \underline{?}$
   A. $\frac{4}{6}$　B. 1
   C. $1\frac{1}{3}$　D. $1\frac{2}{3}$

3. Which is the number sentence for this problem?

   four tenths plus five tenths

   A. $\frac{4}{10} + \frac{5}{10} = \underline{?}$
   B. $\frac{10}{4} + \frac{10}{5} = \underline{?}$
   C. $4 + \frac{5}{10} = \underline{?}$
   D. $410 + 510 = \underline{?}$

4. Which sum is greater than 1?

   A. $\frac{1}{5} + \frac{2}{5} = \underline{?}$　B. $\frac{5}{7} + \frac{4}{7} = \underline{?}$
   C. $\frac{3}{8} + \frac{3}{8} = \underline{?}$　D. $\frac{7}{10} + \frac{1}{10} = \underline{?}$

5. $\frac{1}{6} + \frac{4}{6} = \underline{?}$

   A. $\frac{5}{12}$　B. $\frac{1}{2}$
   C. $\frac{5}{6}$　D. $1\frac{1}{6}$

6. $\frac{3}{8} + \frac{4}{8} = \underline{?}$

   A. $\frac{7}{16}$　B. $\frac{7}{8}$
   C. $\frac{11}{12}$　D. $\frac{15}{8}$

7. Jerome ate $\frac{1}{4}$ cup of cereal before school. He ate $\frac{2}{4}$ cup of cereal after school. How much cereal did Jerome eat?

   A. $\frac{3}{4}$ cup　B. $\frac{7}{8}$ cup
   C. 1 cup　D. $1\frac{1}{4}$ cup

8. Using a ruler, Dottie draws a line that is $\frac{5}{8}$-inch long. Then she makes the line $\frac{3}{8}$-inch longer. How long is the line now?

   A. $\frac{8}{16}$ in.　B. $\frac{7}{8}$ in.
   C. $\frac{15}{16}$ in.　D. $\frac{8}{8}$, or 1 in.

9. Which number sentence matches the model?

   A. $\frac{3}{6} - \frac{1}{6} = \underline{?}$
   B. $\frac{6}{6} - \frac{3}{6} = \underline{?}$
   C. $\frac{5}{6} - \frac{3}{6} = \underline{?}$
   D. $\frac{5}{6} - \frac{2}{6} = \underline{?}$

Form A • Multiple-Choice　　A76　　　　**Go on. ▶**

Multiple Choice • Test Answers

Name _____

10. Use the model to help you find the difference.

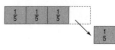

$\frac{4}{5} - \frac{1}{5} =$?

A. $\frac{1}{5}$ B. $\frac{2}{5}$
C.(✓) $\frac{3}{5}$ D. $\frac{5}{5}$

11. Kyle ate $\frac{1}{4}$ of a blueberry pie. How much of the pie is left?
A. $\frac{1}{4}$ of the pie
B. $\frac{2}{4}$ of the pie
C. $\frac{5}{8}$ of the pie
D.(✓) $\frac{3}{4}$ of the pie

12. Frederico and Danielle each ate $\frac{3}{8}$ of a large pizza. What fraction of the pizza is left?
A. $\frac{1}{8}$ of the pizza
B.(✓) $\frac{2}{8}$ of the pizza
C. $\frac{3}{8}$ of the pizza
D. $\frac{5}{8}$ of the pizza

13. Use the model to help you find the sum.
$2\frac{1}{3}$
$+1\frac{1}{3}$

A. $2\frac{2}{3}$ B. $3\frac{1}{3}$
C.(✓) $3\frac{2}{3}$ D. $4\frac{1}{3}$

14. $3\frac{1}{5}$
$+2\frac{3}{5}$
A. $4\frac{4}{5}$ B.(✓) $5\frac{4}{5}$
C. $6\frac{1}{5}$ D. $6\frac{3}{5}$

15. $4\frac{3}{8}$
$+2\frac{5}{8}$
A. 6   B. $6\frac{5}{8}$
C. $6\frac{7}{8}$ D.(✓) $6\frac{8}{8}$, or 7

16. $6\frac{7}{10} + 2\frac{4}{10} =$?
A.(✓) $8\frac{7}{10}$ B. $8\frac{9}{10}$
C. 9   D. $9\frac{1}{10}$

17. A bread recipe calls for $1\frac{1}{4}$ cups whole wheat flour and $2\frac{3}{4}$ cups white flour. How many cups of flour are used in the recipe?
A. 3 cups flour
B. $3\frac{4}{8}$ cups flour
C.(✓) $3\frac{4}{4}$, or 4 cups flour
D. $4\frac{1}{4}$ cups flour

18. Moira and Kelly made cookies for a bake sale. Moira made $2\frac{2}{6}$ dozen cookies. Kelly made $3\frac{3}{6}$ dozen cookies. How many dozen cookies did they make in all?
A.(✓) $5\frac{5}{6}$ dozen
B. 6 dozen
C. $6\frac{1}{6}$ dozen
D. $6\frac{5}{6}$ dozen

Form A • Multiple-Choice   A77   **Go on. ▶**

Name _____

19. $3\frac{2}{3}$
$-1\frac{1}{3}$

A. $1\frac{1}{3}$ B. $1\frac{2}{3}$
C. 2   D.(✓) $2\frac{1}{3}$

20. $6\frac{2}{4}$
$-2\frac{1}{4}$
A.(✓) $4\frac{1}{4}$ B. $4\frac{2}{4}$, or $4\frac{1}{2}$
C. $4\frac{3}{4}$ D. $4\frac{7}{8}$

21. $8\frac{7}{8}$
$-6\frac{5}{8}$
A. $2\frac{1}{8}$ B.(✓) $2\frac{2}{8}$, or $2\frac{1}{4}$
C. $2\frac{3}{8}$ D. $2\frac{3}{4}$

22. $7\frac{3}{5} - 4\frac{1}{5} =$?
A. $2\frac{4}{5}$ B. $3\frac{1}{5}$
C.(✓) $3\frac{2}{5}$ D. $3\frac{3}{5}$

23. The bow for a large holiday wreath uses $4\frac{5}{8}$ feet of ribbon. The bow for a small wreath uses $2\frac{4}{8}$ feet of ribbon. How much more ribbon is needed for the large bow than for the small bow?
A. 2 feet
B.(✓) $2\frac{1}{8}$ feet
C. $2\frac{3}{8}$ feet
D. $3\frac{1}{8}$ feet

24. The Scouts hiked $5\frac{6}{10}$ miles. They stopped for lunch. Then they hiked $2\frac{3}{10}$ miles. How many miles did they hike in all?
A. $3\frac{3}{10}$ miles
B. $3\frac{9}{10}$ miles
C. $7\frac{3}{10}$ miles
D.(✓) $7\frac{9}{10}$ miles

Form A • Multiple-Choice   A78   **▶ Stop!**

Name _____

Choose the letter of the correct answer.

1. The model shows 0.8. How is this written as a fraction?
A.(✓) $\frac{8}{10}$ B. $\frac{8}{100}$
C. $\frac{18}{100}$ D. $\frac{88}{100}$

2. The model shows $\frac{25}{100}$. How is this written as a decimal?
A.(✓) 0.25   B. 0.3   C. 0.4   D. 0.52

3. What is $\frac{3}{10}$ written as a decimal?
A. 0.03   B.(✓) 0.3   C. 0.33   D. 3.10

4. What is 0.15 written as a fraction?
A.(✓) $\frac{15}{100}$ B. $\frac{1}{15}$ C. $\frac{1}{5}$ D. $\frac{10}{15}$

5. What is the decimal name for the shaded part of the model?
A. seven tenths
B. seventy-two hundredths
C. seventy tenths
D.(✓) seven hundredths

6. What is the decimal for the shaded part of the model?
A. 0.02   B.(✓) 0.2   C. 2.0   D. 2.2

7. What is 9 dimes written as a money amount?
A. $0.09   B.(✓) $0.90
C. $0.99   D. $9.00

8. What is 5 pennies written as a money amount?
A.(✓) $0.05   B. $0.50
C. $0.55   D. $5.00

9. Sandi has 76 pennies in a jar. What part of a dollar is that?
A. 1.60   B. 1.76
C.(✓) 0.76   D. 76

10. Marco has $\frac{50}{100}$ of a dollar. How many pennies is that?
A. 5 pennies   B. 15 pennies
C.(✓) 50 pennies   D. 150 pennies

For questions 11–12, use the number line.

[number line: 0.5 0.6 0.7 0.8 0.9 1.0]

11. The number line has small ticks and large ticks. What do the small ticks show?
A.(✓) hundredths   B. tenths
C. ones   D. tens

Form A • Multiple-Choice   A79   **Go on. ▶**

Name _____

12. Which pair of decimal numbers would be at the same place on the number line?
A. 0.8 and 0.88   B. 0.7 and 0.8
C. 0.79 and 0.80   D.(✓) 0.8 and 0.80

For questions 13–14, compare the decimals.

13. Which number is less than 0.4?
A.(✓) 0.24   B. 0.42
C. 0.8   D. not here

14. Which number is less than 0.05?
A. 0.06   B. 0.14
C.(✓) 0.04   D. not here

15. Which group of decimals is written in order from least to greatest?
A. 0.5, 0.45, 0.6
B. 0.5, 0.6, 0.45
C.(✓) 0.45, 0.5, 0.6
D. 0.6, 0.5, 0.45

16. Which group of decimals is written in order from greatest to least?
A. 0.14, 0.8, 0.09
B. 0.14, 0.09, 0.8
C. 0.09, 0.8, 0.14
D.(✓) 0.8, 0.14, 0.09

17. What mixed decimal is shown by the model?
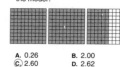
A. 0.26   B. 2.00
C.(✓) 2.60   D. 2.62

18. Which mixed decimal is equivalent to 2.60?
A. 2.0   B.(✓) 2.6
C. 6.0   D. 6.2

19. What is an equivalent mixed decimal for 5.90?
A. 0.59   B.(✓) 5.9
C. 5.09   D. 9.50

20. What is $10\frac{1}{10}$ written as a decimal?
A. 1.01   B. 1.10
C. 10.01   D.(✓) 10.1

21. What is $3\frac{5}{100}$ written as a decimal?
A. 0.35   B.(✓) 3.05
C. 3.50   D. not here

22. What is 6.33 written as a mixed number?
A. $6\frac{3}{100}$ B. $6\frac{3}{3}$
C.(✓) $6\frac{33}{100}$ D. $6\frac{33}{3}$

23. At a gymnastics meet, Dee scored 9.43, Meg scored 8.95, Val scored 9.50, and Wendy scored 9.38. Who had the highest score?
A. Dee   B. Meg
C.(✓) Val   D. Wendy

24. Dan has $4.94. Ed has $4.49. Ben has $4.69. Tom has $4.96. Which boy has the least amount of money?
A. Dan   B.(✓) Ed
C. Ben   D. Tom

Form A • Multiple-Choice   A80   **▶ Stop!**

Multiple Choice • Test Answers

Name _____

CHAPTER 23 TEST
PAGE 1

Choose the letter of the correct answer.

For questions 1–2, use the decimal-square model.

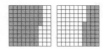

1. Which number sentence matches the model?
   A. $0.7 + 0.3 = n$
   B. $0.75 + 0.36 = n$
   C. $0.76 + 0.35 = n$
   D. $7.5 + 3.6 = n$

2. What is the sum of the shaded parts of the model?
   A. 0.95   B. 1.00
   C. 1.05   D. 1.11

3. $\begin{array}{r}0.9\\+0.6\end{array}$
   A. 0.15
   B. 0.96
   C. 1.15
   D. 1.5

4. $\begin{array}{r}0.85\\+0.34\end{array}$
   A. 1.19
   B. 0.119
   C. 1.91
   D. 11.9

5. $\begin{array}{r}1.42\\+0.71\end{array}$
   A. 0.113
   B. 1.03
   C. 2.13
   D. 21.3

6. Lil has 1.3 pounds of grapes and 2.2 pounds of oranges. How many pounds of fruit does she have?
   A. 3.3 lb   B. 3.32 lb
   C. 3.4 lb   D. 3.5 lb

7. Ricky swims the first half of a race in 1.53 minutes and the second half in 1.51 minutes. What is his total time?
   A. 2.04 minutes
   B. 2.4 minutes
   C. 3.04 minutes
   D. 3.4 minutes

8. Use the model to find the difference.

   $0.8 - 0.2 = n$

   A. 0.06   B. 0.6
   C. 0.66   D. 6.0

9. Use the model to find the difference.

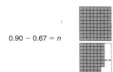

   $0.90 - 0.67 = n$

   A. 0.15   B. 0.23
   C. 1.05   D. 1.57

10. $\begin{array}{r}1.3\\-0.6\end{array}$
    A. 0.7
    B. 1.7
    C. 1.9
    D. not here

Form A • Multiple-Choice   A81   Go on. ▶

Name _____

CHAPTER 23 TEST
PAGE 2

11. $\begin{array}{r}0.73\\-0.32\end{array}$
    A. 1.05
    B. 0.41
    C. 0.49
    D. not here

12. $\begin{array}{r}1.05\\-0.29\end{array}$
    A. 0.86
    B. 1.24
    C. 1.34
    D. not here

13. Myra is 1.56 meters tall. Phil is 1.34 meters tall. What is the difference in their heights?
    A. 0.22 m   B. 0.90 m
    C. 1.22 m   D. 2.90 m

14. Dewey walks 2.4 miles. Xavier walks 0.9 miles. How many miles farther does Dewey walk?
    A. 0.5 mi   B. 1.5 mi
    C. 2.3 mi   D. 3.3 mi

15. $\begin{array}{r}0.89\\+0.39\end{array}$
    A. 0.50
    B. 1.18
    C. 1.28
    D. not here

16. $\begin{array}{r}0.70\\-0.25\end{array}$
    A. 0.45
    B. 0.50
    C. 0.95
    D. not here

17. $\begin{array}{r}1.60\\-0.04\end{array}$
    A. 1.20
    B. 1.24
    C. 1.56
    D. not here

18. $0.23 + 0.3 = n$
    A. 0.233   B. 0.26
    C. 0.5   D. not here

For questions 19–20, choose the number sentence that shows how to solve the problem.

19. Cal ran 2.6 miles. Ben ran 1.3 miles. How much farther did Cal run?
    A. $2.6 + 1.3 = 3.9$
    B. $2.6 - 1.3 = 1.3$
    C. $2.6 \times 1.3 = 3.38$
    D. $2.6 \div 1.3 = 2$

20. Eva played soccer for 1.2 hours on Saturday and 4.5 hours on Sunday. How many hours did she play in all?
    A. $1.2 + 4.5 = 5.7$
    B. $4.5 - 1.2 = 3.3$
    C. $1.2 \times 4.5 = 5.40$
    D. $4.5 \div 1.2 = 3.75$

21. What is 6.7 rounded to the nearest whole number?
    A. 2   B. 5   C. 7   D. 8

For questions 22–24, estimate the sum or difference by rounding to the nearest whole number.

22. $\begin{array}{r}3.9\\+1.7\end{array}$
    A. 4
    B. 5
    C. 6
    D. 7

23. $\begin{array}{r}8.8\\-1.2\end{array}$
    A. 6
    B. 7
    C. 8
    D. 9

24. Mel ran 2.8 miles on Monday, 2.9 miles on Tuesday, and 3.1 miles on Wednesday. About how many miles did he run those 3 days?
    A. about 6 mi   B. about 7 mi
    C. about 8 mi   D. about 9 mi

Form A • Multiple-Choice   A82   ▶ Stop!

Name _____

TEST • CHAPTERS 20–23
PAGE 1

Choose the letter of the correct answer.

1. Which fraction of the rectangle is shaded?

   A. $\frac{1}{4}$ B. $\frac{3}{8}$
   C. $\frac{5}{8}$ D. $\frac{3}{4}$
   20-A.1

2. Which fraction represents the group that is shaded?

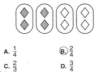

   A. $\frac{1}{4}$ B. $\frac{2}{9}$
   C. $\frac{2}{3}$ D. $\frac{3}{4}$
   20-A.1

3. Lisa went out for 7 hours. She spent 3 hours at the park. What fraction of her time was spent at the park?
   A. $\frac{3}{7}$ of her time   B. $\frac{4}{7}$ of her time
   C. $\frac{7}{3}$ of her time   D. not here
   20-A.1

4. Which group of fractions is in order from greatest to least?
   A. $\frac{1}{4}, \frac{3}{8}, \frac{3}{4}$ B. $\frac{1}{4}, \frac{3}{4}, \frac{3}{8}$
   C. $\frac{3}{8}, \frac{3}{4}, \frac{1}{4}$ D. $\frac{3}{4}, \frac{3}{8}, \frac{1}{4}$
   20-A.2

5. Which mixed number matches the picture?

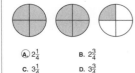

   A. $2\frac{1}{4}$ B. $2\frac{3}{4}$
   C. $3\frac{1}{4}$ D. $3\frac{3}{4}$
   20-A.3

6. $\frac{4}{6} + \frac{3}{6} = \underline{?}$
   A. $\frac{1}{12}$ B. $1\frac{1}{6}$
   C. $1\frac{1}{3}$ D. $1\frac{5}{12}$
   21-A.1

7. $2\frac{2}{9} + 6\frac{4}{9} = \underline{?}$
   A. $8\frac{6}{9}$ B. 9
   C. $9\frac{2}{9}$ D. $12\frac{2}{3}$
   21-A.1

8. A recipe for hot sauce uses $3\frac{2}{5}$ ounces of red pepper and $4\frac{2}{5}$ ounces of black pepper. How many ounces of pepper are needed in all?
   A. $1\frac{4}{5}$ oz   B. $7\frac{4}{10}$ oz
   C. $7\frac{4}{5}$ oz   D. $8\frac{1}{5}$ oz
   21-A.1

9. Mike rode his bike $3\frac{2}{8}$ miles. Then he rode $2\frac{5}{8}$ miles. How many miles did he ride in all?
   A. $1\frac{3}{8}$ mi   B. $5\frac{5}{16}$ mi
   C. $5\frac{3}{8}$ mi   D. $5\frac{7}{8}$ mi
   21-A.1

Form A • Multiple-Choice   A83   Go on. ▶

Name _____

TEST • CHAPTERS 20–23
PAGE 2

10. $8\frac{6}{7} - 5\frac{2}{7} = \underline{?}$
    A. $3\frac{3}{7}$ B. $3\frac{4}{7}$
    C. $3\frac{5}{7}$ D. $4\frac{4}{7}$
    21-A.2

11. Steve fed his dog $\frac{2}{5}$ of a can of dog food. How much of the can is left?
    A. $\frac{2}{3}$ of the can   B. $\frac{4}{5}$ of the can
    C. $\frac{5}{3}$ of the can   D. not here
    21-A.2

12. What is $\frac{56}{100}$ written as a decimal?
    A. 0.44   B. 0.56
    C. 0.6   D. 5.60
    22-A.1

13. What is 34 pennies written as a money amount?
    A. $0.03   B. $0.33
    C. $0.34   D. not here
    22-A.1

14. What is 4.24 written as a mixed number?
    A. $4\frac{14}{100}$ B. $4\frac{2}{10}$
    C. $4\frac{24}{100}$ D. not here
    22-A.3

15. Which group of decimals is in order from greatest to least?
    A. 0.4, 0.55, 0.6
    B. 0.6, 0.55, 0.4
    C. 0.6, 0.4, 0.55
    D. 0.55, 0.6, 0.4
    22-A.4

16. Which mixed decimal is equivalent to 4.70?
    A. 4.7   B. 4.77
    C. 7.0   D. 7.4
    22-A.4

17. Mickey's spelling average is 0.95, Ted's is 0.90, Jon's is 0.89, and Robby's is 0.96. Who has the highest average?
    A. Mickey   B. Jon
    C. Robby   D. Ted
    22-A.4

18. Which number sentence matches the model?

    A. $0.67 + 0.32 = n$
    B. $0.68 + 0.31 = n$
    C. $0.77 + 0.33 = n$
    D. $6.6 + 3.4 = n$
    23-A.1

19. $\begin{array}{r}1.59\\+0.87\end{array}$
    A. 2.46
    B. 2.56
    C. 2.66
    D. not here
    23-A.1

20. $\begin{array}{r}2.5\\-0.6\end{array}$
    A. 1.4
    B. 1.8
    C. 1.9
    D. not here
    23-A.2

21. What is 4.3 rounded to the nearest whole number?
    A. 2   B. 3   C. 4   D. 7
    23-A.2

22. Linda read her book for 2.8 hours at home, 5.7 hours at the library, and 3.1 hours at Abby's house. About how many hours did she read?
    A. about 8 hr   B. about 10 hr
    C. about 12 hr   D. about 14 hr
    23-A.2

Form A • Multiple-Choice   A84   ▶ Stop!

Multiple Choice • Test Answers

131

Harcourt Brace School Publishers

Choose the letter of the correct answer.

1. Which number sentence shows the Zero Property for Multiplication?

A. $8 \times 5 = 40$ **B.** $8 \times 0 = 0$
C. $8 \times 7 = 7 \times 8$ D. $8 \times 1 = 8$

3-A.2

2. Which is a *cardinal* number?

A. third quarter   B. 477-4146
C. 104.5 FM   **D.** 15 minutes

5-A.1

3. A 5-lb bag of potatoes costs $1.45. About how much should a 10-lb bag of potatoes cost?

A. about $2.00   **B.** about $3.00
C. about $4.00   D. about $5.00

5-A.3

4. What is *two hundred eleven million, four hundred thirty–two thousand, one hundred sixty–five* written in standard form?

A. 2,132,165   B. 21,432,165
C. 211,032,165   **D.** 211,432,165

6-A.2

5. A bicycle can be red, blue, or white. It can have 3, 10, or 15 speeds. How many bicycle choices are there?

A. 9 choices   B. 11 choices
C. 12 choices   D. 18 choices

9-A.1

For questions 6–7, use the line plot. There is one X for each student.

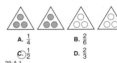

Days Absent from School

6. What is the range of data used in the line plot?

A. 7   B. 8   **C.** 9   D. 10

10-A.2

7. How many students were absent on 5 days?

A. 1 student   B. 2 students
C. 3 students   D. 4 students

10-A.2

8. A cookie jar contains oatmeal, lemon, and chocolate chip cookies. It is impossible to pull out ___?___ .

A. a chocolate chip cookie
B. a lemon cookie
C. an oatmeal cookie
D. an almond cookie

11-A.1

For questions 9–10, use the spinners.

In this game, the "odd" player gets points for odd numbers and the "even" player gets points for even numbers.

9. Which spinner gives the "even" player the greatest probability of winning?

A. Spinner A   B. Spinner B
C. Spinner C   D. all of them

11-A.3

10. Which spinner gives the "odd" player the greatest probability of winning?

A. Spinner A   **B.** Spinner B
C. Spinner C   D. none of them

11-A.3

11. Use the figure.

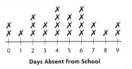

How many faces are on the figure?

A. 3 faces   B. 5 faces
C. 6 faces   D. 8 faces

12-A.1

12. What angle is formed when two intersecting lines that are not perpendicular cross?

A. acute angle   B. obtuse angle
C. right angle   **D.** both A and B

13-A.1

13. What is the perimeter?

9 ft   4 ft

A. 22 ft   **B.** 26 ft
C. 32 ft   D. 36 ft

14-A.1

14. A figure that has been moved to a new location as shown is called a ___?___ .

A. translation   B. reflection
C. rotation   D. flip

15-A.1

15. Which figure has point symmetry?

A.   B.   C.   D.

15-A.3

16. $\begin{array}{r} 70 \\ \times\ 6 \\ \hline \end{array}$

A. 4.2   B. 42
C. 420   D. 4,200

16-A.1

17. Use the model place-value chart.

Tens	Ones
	□
	□
	□

Which multiplication sentence do the base-ten blocks show?

A. $3 \times 10 = n$ **B.** $3 \times 11 = n$
C. $30 \times 1 = n$ D. not here

16-A.2

18. $\begin{array}{r} \$4.19 \\ \times\ 7 \\ \hline \end{array}$

A. $22.33   B. $27.33
C. $28.03   **D.** $29.33

6-A.3

19. Choose the best estimate for the product.

$88 \times 31 = n$

A. about 2,200   B. about 2,400
C. about 2,700   D. about 2,800

17-A.2

20. $\begin{array}{r} 229 \\ \times\ 38 \\ \hline \end{array}$

A. 8,502   **B.** 8,702
C. 8,802   D. not here

17-A.4

21. $4\overline{)71}$

A. 17 r3   B. 18
C. 18 r3   D. not here

18-A.3

22. $255 \div 3 = n$

A. $n = 85$ B. $n = 85$ r2
C. $n = 86$ D. not here

18-A.4

23. Use a basic fact and a pattern of zeros to estimate the quotient.

$2,816 \div 7 = n$

A. about 4   B. about 40
C. about 44   **D.** about 400

19-A.1

24. $7\overline{)\$5.25}$

A. $0.71   **B.** $0.75
C. $7.50   D. $7.70

19-A.3

25. Which fraction means the same as *one out of nine*?

A. $\frac{1}{9}$ B. $\frac{2}{7}$
C. $\frac{7}{9}$ D. $\frac{9}{7}$

20-A.1

26. Which fraction represents the group that is shaded?

A. $\frac{1}{4}$ B. $\frac{2}{6}$
C. $\frac{1}{3}$ D. $\frac{2}{3}$

20-A.1

27. What is the fraction renamed as a mixed number?

$\frac{12}{7} = $ ___?___

A. $\frac{7}{12}$ B. $1\frac{2}{7}$
C. $1\frac{4}{7}$ **D.** $1\frac{5}{7}$

20-A.3

28. Use the fraction bars to help you find the sum.

1

| $\frac{1}{6}$ | $\frac{1}{6}$ | $\frac{1}{6}$ | $\frac{1}{6}$ | $\frac{1}{6}$ | $\frac{1}{6}$ |

$\frac{2}{6} + \frac{5}{6} = $ ___?___

A. $\frac{4}{6}$ B. $\frac{5}{6}$
C. $1\frac{1}{6}$ D. $\frac{17}{18}$

21-A.1

29. $\frac{2}{9} + \frac{5}{9} = $ ___?___

A. $\frac{7}{18}$ B. $\frac{3}{9}$
C. $\frac{7}{9}$ D. $\frac{17}{18}$

21-A.1

30. Clara spent $\frac{1}{8}$ of her allowance on a notebook. What fraction of her allowance is left?

A. $\frac{1}{4}$ B. $\frac{4}{8}$
C. $\frac{5}{8}$ **D.** $\frac{7}{8}$

21-A.2

31. $\begin{array}{r} 2\frac{5}{7} \\ +6\frac{1}{7} \\ \hline \end{array}$

A. $8\frac{6}{7}$ B. $8\frac{7}{7}$
C. $9\frac{4}{7}$ D. $9\frac{6}{7}$

21-A.1

32. $\begin{array}{r} 9\frac{5}{7} \\ -7\frac{2}{7} \\ \hline \end{array}$

A. $2\frac{2}{7}$ **B.** $2\frac{3}{7}$
C. $2\frac{5}{7}$ D. $2\frac{6}{7}$

21-A.2

33. What is 0.37 written as a fraction?

A. $\frac{37}{1,000}$ B. $\frac{3}{10}$
C. $\frac{37}{100}$ D. $\frac{7}{10}$

22-A.1

34. What is 8 nickels written as a money amount?

A. $0.08   **B.** $0.40
C. $0.44   D. $0.80

22-A.2

35. Which number is less than 0.09?

A. 0.07   B. 0.11
C. 0.44   D. not here

22-A.4

36. What is 5.79 written as a mixed number?

A. $5\frac{7}{100}$ B. $5\frac{7}{7}$
C. $5\frac{79}{100}$ D. $5\frac{79}{10}$

22-A.1

37. Jake worked on his science project for 1.8 hours on Tuesday, 2.2 hours on Thursday, and 4.7 hours on Saturday. On which day did he work on his project the longest?

A. Tuesday
B. Thursday
C. Saturday
D. He worked about the same amount of time each day.

22-A.4

38. $\begin{array}{r} 0.79 \\ +0.22 \\ \hline \end{array}$

A. 0.67   B. 0.91
C. 0.97   **D.** 1.01

23-A.1

39. $\begin{array}{r} 0.86 \\ -0.39 \\ \hline \end{array}$

A. 0.45   **B.** 0.47
C. 1.25   D. not here

23-A.1

40. What is 8.9 rounded to the nearest whole number?

A. 1   B. 7   C. 8   **D.** 9

23-A.2

Harcourt Brace School Publishers

CUMULATIVE TEST PAGE 1
CUMULATIVE TEST PAGE 2
CUMULATIVE TEST PAGE 3
CUMULATIVE TEST PAGE 4

Name _____

Choose the letter of the correct answer.
For some items, an inch ruler may be needed.

1. Which of the following is a linear unit?
   A. mile
   B. gallon
   C. ton
   D. ounce

2. Use a ruler to measure the length of this string.

   A. 1 in. B. 2 in. C. 3 in. D. 4 in.

For questions 3–4, choose the reasonable unit of measure.

3. Bess is in fourth grade. She is 4 _?_ tall.
   A. inches
   B. feet
   C. yards
   D. miles

4. The width of a doorway is about 1 _?_.
   A. inch B. foot C. yard D. mile

5. A Scout troop hiked all day. Which unit is best for describing the distance they hiked?
   A. inches
   B. feet
   C. yards
   D. miles

6. Mrs. Weston is sewing a dress. Which unit is best for describing the amount of material she needs?
   A. yards
   B. miles
   C. cups
   D. pounds

For questions 7–9, find the equivalent measurement.

7. 4 ft = _?_ in.
   A. 12 B. 36 C. 48 D. not here

8. 12 ft = _?_ yd
   A. 1
   B. 2
   C. 3
   D. not here

9. 5 ft = _?_ in.
   A. 50
   B. 60
   C. 70
   D. not here

For questions 10–11, use the diagram.

Mr. Rodgers's Garden

1 square = 1 yard

10. How many fence posts are in Mr. Rodgers's garden?
    A. 10 fence posts
    B. 20 fence posts
    C. 30 fence posts
    D. 40 fence posts

11. How far is it from the fence post at A to the fence post at B?
    A. 8 in. B. 8 ft C. 8 yd D. 8 mi

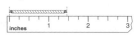

inches 1 2 3

12. How long is the crayon to the nearest ¼ in.?
    A. 2 in.
    B. 2¼ in.
    C. 2½ in.
    D. 2¾ in.

Form A • Multiple-Choice   A89   Go on. ▶

Name _____

13. How long is the string to the nearest ½ in.?

    inches 1 2 3

    A. 1 in.
    B. 1½ in.
    C. 2 in.
    D. 2½ in.

For questions 14–16, use an inch ruler to measure length.

14. How long is this nail to the nearest ½ in.?

    A. 2½ in.
    B. 2¾ in.
    C. 3 in.
    D. not here

15. How long is this pencil to the nearest ¼ in.?

    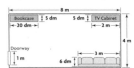

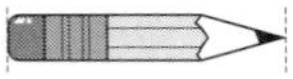

    A. 1¼ in.
    B. 1½ in.
    C. 1¾ in.
    D. not here

16. How long is this line to the nearest ¼ in.?

    A. 2¾ in.
    B. 2¼ in.
    C. 3½ in.
    D. not here

17. To change pounds to ounces, ___.
    A. multiply by 16
    B. divide by 16
    C. multiply by 2,000
    D. divide by 2,000

18. Which is the best estimate of the weight of a pair of jeans?
    A. about 1 ounce
    B. about 1 pound
    C. about 10 pounds
    D. about 1 ton

19. Which is the best estimate of the weight of a large dog?
    A. about 80 ounces
    B. about 8 pounds
    C. about 80 pounds
    D. about 8 tons

20. Find the equivalent measure.

    3 tons = _?_ lb
    A. 48
    B. 60
    C. 600
    D. 6,000

21. Mr. Kim hauls boxes that weigh 50 lb each. His truck can carry 200 boxes. How many pounds can he haul at a time?
    A. 10,000 lb B. 20,000 lb
    C. 30,000 lb D. 40,000 lb

22. Jan is making fish stew for 8 people. The recipe calls for 6 oz of fish per person. How many ounces of fish should Jan use?
    A. 16 oz B. 24 oz
    C. 36 oz D. 48 oz

Form A • Multiple-Choice   A90   ▶ Stop!

Name _____

Choose the letter of the correct answer.

1. Which shows metric units in order from smallest to largest?
   A. dm, cm, cm
   B. m, dm, cm
   C. cm, m, dm
   D. cm, dm, m

2. 1 dm = _?_ m
   A. 0.01
   B. 0.1
   C. 10
   D. 100

3. 1 cm = _?_ m
   A. 0.01
   B. 0.1
   C. 10
   D. 100

4. 1 dm = _?_ cm
   A. 0.01
   B. 0.1
   C. 10
   D. not here

5. 2 m = _?_ dm
   A. 0.02
   B. 0.2
   C. 20
   D. not here

6. 3 m = _?_ cm
   A. 0.03
   B. 0.3
   C. 30
   D. not here

7. Doreen has 1 m of blue ribbon and 10 cm of red ribbon. Doreen's blue ribbon is _?_ as the red ribbon.
   A. the same length
   B. 0.1 times as long
   C. 10 times as long
   D. 100 times as long

8. Sam needs 1 m of string. He has 50 cm of string. How much more string does he need?
   A. 25 cm
   B. 50 cm
   C. 60 cm
   D. 75 cm

9. Which number sentence shows how to change 5 m to dm?
   A. 5 × 10 = 50
   B. 5 × 100 = 500
   C. 5 ÷ 10 = 0.5
   D. 5 ÷ 100 = 0.05

10. How do you change 4 m to cm?
    A. multiply 4 by 0.1
    B. multiply 4 by 10
    C. multiply 4 by 100
    D. not here

For questions 11–14, find the equivalent measurement.

11. 6 dm = _?_ cm
    A. 6
    B. 60
    C. 600
    D. 6,000

12. 7 m = _?_ dm
    A. 70
    B. 700
    C. 770
    D. 7,000

13. 12 m = _?_ cm
    A. 12
    B. 120
    C. 1,200
    D. not here

14. 18 m = _?_ dm
    A. 180
    B. 1,800
    C. 18,000
    D. not here

Form A • Multiple-Choice   A91   Go on. ▶

Name _____

For questions 15–16, use the diagram.

Floor Plan of Amy's Family Room

15. About how far is it from the doorway to the edge of the sofa?
    A. 3 m
    B. 5 m
    C. 8 m
    D. 9 m

16. Which of these are the same size in length?
    A. doorway and sofa
    B. sofa and TV cabinet
    C. TV cabinet and bookcase
    D. bookcase and doorway

17. Which is a unit of measure of capacity?
    A. meter
    B. liter
    C. millimeter
    D. gram

18. Which is the most reasonable measurement of the amount of water in the glass?

    A. 2 mL
    B. 20 mL
    C. 200 mL
    D. 2 L

19. Which is the most reasonable measurement of the amount of soup in the large spoon?

    A. 1 mL
    B. 10 mL
    C. 500 mL
    D. 1 L

For questions 20–21, find the equivalent measure.

20. 2 liters = _?_ milliliters
    A. 20
    B. 200
    C. 2,000
    D. 4,000

21. 4 metric cups = _?_ L
    A. 1
    B. 2
    C. 4
    D. 8

22. If 8 cups of water are needed each day, what is a reasonable estimate of the number of liters of water a person should drink in a day?
    A. 0.2 L
    B. 2 L
    C. 20 L
    D. 200 L

23. A 3-L bottle of soda costs $1.59. How much would 12 L of soda cost?
    A. $3.82
    B. $5.25
    C. $5.41
    D. $6.36

24. A hiker's canteen holds 750 mL. How many liters are needed to fill the canteens of 8 hikers?
    A. 6 L
    B. 60 L
    C. 12 L
    D. 125 L

Form A • Multiple-Choice   A92   ▶ Stop!

Multiple Choice • Test Answers

Harcourt Brace School Publishers

Top-left — Chapter 26 Test, Page 1

Name _____

CHAPTER 26 TEST
PAGE 1

Choose the letter of the correct answer.

For questions 1–2, choose the correct clock.

A.   B.

C.   D.

1. Which clock shows a quarter to eight?

   A. A   **B.** B   C. C   D. D

2. Which clock shows half past eight?

   A. A   B. B   C. C   **D.** D

3. What is another way to write *a quarter past ten*?

   A. 9:45   **B.** 10:15
   C. 10:30   D. 10:45

4. What is another way to write *half past three*?

   A. 2:30   B. 2:45   C. 3:15   **D.** 3:30

5. What is another way to write 6:45?

   A. half past six
   B. a quarter to six
   C. a quarter past six
   D. a quarter to seven

6. What is another way to write 9:15?

   A. a quarter to nine
   B. a quarter past nine
   C. a quarter to ten
   D. half past nine

7. The perimeter of a square is 20 in. If the same square is measured in cm, the number of units would be __?__.

   A. less than 20   B. exactly 20
   C. greater than 20   D. 0

8. Which is the most reasonable estimate for the length of this line?

   A. 5 cm   B. 10 in.
   C. 50 cm   D. 50 in.

9. Which is the most reasonable estimate for the length of the insect?

   A. 1.2 cm   **B.** 2 in.
   C. 12 cm   D. 12 in.

10. Which is the most reasonable estimate of the length of the ribbon?

   A. 2 cm   **B.** 8 cm
   C. 15 cm   D. 60 cm

11. Use the ruler to find the perimeter of the square in inches.

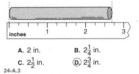

   A. 1 in.   B. 2.5 in.   **C.** 4 in.   D. 10 in.

Form A • Multiple-Choice   A93   Go on. ▶

Top-right — Chapter 26 Test, Page 2

Name _____

CHAPTER 26 TEST
PAGE 2

12. Al's pen is 5 in. long. His pencil is 5 cm long. Which is longer?

   A. the pen
   B. the pencil
   C. They are the same length.
   D. More information is needed.

13. Carrie's thumb is 2 cm shorter than her ring finger. Her ring finger is 7 cm long. How long is Carrie's thumb?

   A. 2 cm   **B.** 5 cm
   C. 7 cm   D. 9 cm

14. Les wants 3 CDs that cost $8 each. He has a coupon for $3 off the price of 1 CD. What price will he pay for all 3 CDs?

   A. $5   B. $15   **C.** $21   D. $24

15. Mariko puts ribbon around a picture. Two sides are 50 cm long, and 2 sides are 25 cm long. How many meters of ribbon does she need?

   A. 0.75 meters   B. 1 meter
   C. 1.25 meters   **D.** 1.50 meters

16. What temperature does this thermometer show?

   A. ⁻10°F
   B. 0°F
   C. 70°F
   D. 90°F

17. Which of the following temperatures is the coldest?

   A. ⁻5°F   B. 0°F
   C. 5°F   D. 10°F

18. What is the difference between the two temperatures?

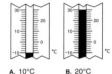

   A. 20°F   **B.** 40°F
   C. 60°F   D. 80°F

19. What is the difference between the two temperatures?

   A. 10°C   B. 20°C
   C. 30°C   **D.** 40°C

20. At sunrise the temperature was 62°F. At noon it was 18 degrees warmer. By six o'clock in the evening it had cooled off 10 degrees. What was the evening temperature?

   A. 52°F   **B.** 70°F
   C. 72°F   D. 80°F

Form A • Multiple-Choice   A94   ▶ Stop!

Bottom-left — Test • Chapters 24–26, Page 1

Name _____

TEST • CHAPTERS 24–26
PAGE 1

Choose the letter of the correct answer.

For some items, you may need an inch ruler.

1. Which of the following is a linear unit?

   A. quart   **B.** yard
   C. gallon   D. pound
   24-A.2

2. What is the reasonable unit of measure?
   Joe's new puppy is 8 __?__ long.

   A. inches   B. feet
   C. yards   D. miles
   24-A.1

3. 6 ft = __?__ in.

   A. 24   B. 36   **C.** 72   D. 96
   24-A.2

4. How long is the chalk to the nearest ¼ in.?

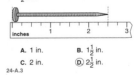

   A. 2 in.   B. 2¼ in.
   C. 2½ in.   **D.** 2¾ in.
   24-A.3

5. How long is the nail to the nearest ½ in.?

   A. 1 in.   B. 1½ in.
   C. 2 in.   **D.** 2½ in.
   24-A.3

6. To change tons to pounds, __?__.

   A. multiply by 16
   B. divide by 16
   C. multiply by 2,000
   D. divide by 2,000
   24-A.2

7. A school uses 80 bags of potatoes in one month. One bag weighs 20 pounds. How many pounds does the school use in a month?

   A. 160 lb   **B.** 1,600 lb
   C. 2,400 lb   D. 16,000 lb
   24-A.4

8. Julie is making hot chocolate for 9 people. She uses 3 oz of chocolate per person. How many ounces of chocolate should Julie use?

   A. 27 oz   B. 32 oz
   C. 36 oz   D. not here
   24-A.4

9. 10 cm = __?__ dm

   A. 0.01   B. 0.1   **C.** 1   D. 10
   25-A.1

10. The teacher's desk is 2 meters wide. A student desk is 10 decimeters wide. The teacher's desk is __?__ as the student desk.

   A. the same width
   B. 0.5 times as wide
   C. 2 times as wide
   D. not here
   25-A.1

11. Which number sentence shows how to change 30 dm to meters?

   A. 30 × 1.0 = 30
   B. 30 × 10 = 300
   C. 30 ÷ 3 = 10
   D. 30 ÷ 10 = 3
   25-A.1

Form A • Multiple-Choice   A95   Go on. ▶

Bottom-right — Test • Chapters 24–26, Page 2

Name _____

TEST • CHAPTERS 24–26
PAGE 2

12. 5 m = __?__ dm

   A. 50   B. 500   C. 550   D. 5,000
   25-A.1

For questions 13–14, use the diagram.

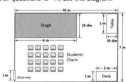

13. About how far is it from the edge of the table to the edge of the desk?

   A. 2 m   B. 3 m
   C. 4 m   D. not here
   25-A.2

14. Which of these are the same length?

   A. doorway and stage
   B. stage and table
   C. table and desk
   D. not here
   25-A.2

15. Which of these is a reasonable measurement of the amount of milk in a jug?

   A. 100 mL   **B.** 1 L
   C. 10 L   D. 50 L
   25-A.3

16. After baseball practice, Jason drinks 500 mL of water. What is the amount of water Jason will drink after 7 practices?

   A. 350 mL   B. 2 L 50 mL
   C. 2 L 200 mL   **D.** 3 L 50 mL
   25-A.3

17. What is another way to write a quarter to three?

   A. 2:15   **B.** 2:45
   C. 3:15   D. 3:45
   26-A.1

18. What is another way to write 3:15?

   A. a quarter to 3
   B. a quarter past 3
   C. a quarter to 4
   D. a quarter past 4
   26-A.1

19. Anne is sewing lace around a place mat she made. The place mat has 2 sides 15 inches long and 2 sides 10 inches long. How many inches of lace does Anne need?

   A. 40 inches   **B.** 50 inches
   C. 60 inches   D. 70 inches
   26-A.3

20. At sunrise the temperature was 43°F. At noon it was 15 degrees warmer. By six o'clock in the evening, it had cooled 9 degrees. What was the evening temperature?

   A. 40°F   B. 45°F
   C. 47°F   **D.** 49°F
   26-A.4

Form A • Multiple-Choice   A96   ▶ Stop!

Choose the letter of the correct answer.

1.
76
44
+52

A. 168
B. 171
C. 172
D. 182

1-A.2

2. There are 32 runners at the track meet. How many runners are on each of 8 relay teams?

A. 3 runners
B. 4 runners
C. 6 runners
D. not here

4-A.1

3. How many thousands are in 3,654?

A. 3 thousands
B. 4 thousands
C. 5 thousands
D. 6 thousands

5-A.2

4. In which number does the digit 7 have a value of 700?

A. 217
B. 4,871
C. 7,452
D. 8,738

6-A.1

5. In which pair of numbers do the digits differ in the hundreds position?

A. 4,629; 3,692
B. 2,756; 2,657
C. 5,312; 6,321
D. 7,832; 8,823

7-A.2

For questions 6–7, use the frequency table.

SCOUT MEMBERSHIP DRIVE

Week	Number Joined (Frequency)	Cumulative Frequency
1	12	12
2	9	21
3	7	?
4	3	?

6. How many more Scouts joined in Week 2 than in Week 3?

A. 2 more Scouts
B. 3 more Scouts
C. 4 more Scouts
D. 9 more Scouts

9-A.1

7. What is the cumulative frequency for the number of Scouts who joined in all 4 weeks?

A. 12 Scouts
B. 22 Scouts
C. 28 Scouts
D. 31 Scouts

9-A.1

For questions 8–9, use the stem-and-leaf plot.

Scores in the Bowling Tournament

Stem	Leaves
9	4 6 7
10	3 3 5 6 6 6 9
11	2 3 4 7 8

8. What number is the mode for the data?

A. 97
B. 103
C. 106
D. not here

10-A.3

9. What is the difference between the highest and the lowest score?

A. 6 points
B. 15 points
C. 24 points
D. not here

10-A.3

For questions 10–11, use the grid.

10. What are the coordinates of point x?

A. (7,8)
B. (7,7)
C. (8,8)
D. (8,7)

12-A.2

11. Which set of coordinates identifies the vertices of the rectangle marked on the grid?

A. (1,2), (4,2), (1,7), (4,7)
B. (2,1), (2,4), (7,4), (7,1)
C. (3,2), (3,5), (8,2), (8,8)
D. not here

12-A.2

12. Susie's dining room table is 4 feet by 7 feet. What is the area of the table?

A. 11 sq ft
B. 24 sq ft
C. 28 sq ft
D. 49 sq ft

14-A.2

13. Which figure shows a line of symmetry?

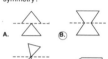

A.   B.

C.   D.

15-A.3

14.
637
× 8

A. 4,996
B. 5,016
C. 5,096
D. 5,104

16-A.2

15. Find the product by using a basic fact and a pattern of zeros.
$20 \times 900 = n$

A. $n = 18,000$
B. $n = 180,000$
C. $n = 1,800,000$
D. $n = 18,000,000$

17-A.1

16.
$59
× 46

A. $2,414
B. $2,654
C. $2,655
D. $2,714

17-A.3

17. In which place should the first digit in the quotient be placed?
$5\overline{)74}$

A. ones place
B. tens place
C. hundreds place
D. divisor

18-A.3

18. $5\overline{)325}$

A. 61
B. 63
C. 65
D. not here

19-A.4

19. A basketball team needs to score 87 points to equal its season average. How many points should the team score in each of the game's 4 quarters to be sure it reaches its season average?

A. 19 points
B. 20 points
C. 21 points
D. 22 points

19-A.4

---

20. Sharon scored 6 of her volleyball team's 18 points. What fraction of the team's points did Sharon score?

A. $\frac{6}{24}$
B. $\frac{6}{18}$
C. $\frac{12}{18}$
D. $\frac{2}{3}$

20-A.1

21. What is the fraction renamed as a mixed number?
$\frac{13}{7} = \underline{\ ?\ }$

A. $1\frac{5}{7}$
B. $1\frac{6}{7}$
C. $2\frac{1}{7}$
D. $2\frac{3}{7}$

20-A.3

22. Use the fraction bars to help you find the sum.

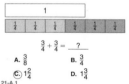

$\frac{3}{4} + \frac{3}{4} = \underline{\ ?\ }$

A. $\frac{3}{8}$
B. $\frac{3}{4}$
C. $1\frac{2}{4}$
D. $1\frac{3}{4}$

21-A.1

23. Which number sentence matches the model?

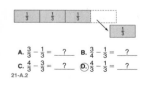

A. $\frac{3}{3} - \frac{1}{3} = \underline{\ ?\ }$
B. $\frac{3}{4} - \frac{1}{3} = \underline{\ ?\ }$
C. $\frac{4}{3} - \frac{3}{3} = \underline{\ ?\ }$
D. $\frac{4}{3} - \frac{1}{3} = \underline{\ ?\ }$

21-A.2

24. What is 0.47 written as a fraction?

A. $\frac{1}{47}$
B. $\frac{10}{47}$
C. $\frac{1}{4}$
D. $\frac{47}{100}$

22-A.1

25. Which group of decimals is written in order from least to greatest?

A. 0.6, 0.75, 0.8
B. 0.75, 0.6, 0.8
C. 0.75, 0.8, 0.6
D. 0.8, 0.75, 0.6

22-A.4

26.
2.96
+1.37

A. 3.33
B. 4.23
C. 4.33
D. 4.35

23-A.1

27.
2.12
−0.07

A. 2.05
B. 2.06
C. 2.19
D. not here

23-A.1

28. A reasonable unit of measure for the diameter of a soccer ball is about 1 __?__ .

A. inch
B. foot
C. yard
D. mile

24-A.1

29. How long is the string to the nearest $\frac{1}{4}$ in.?

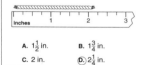

A. $1\frac{1}{4}$ in.
B. $1\frac{3}{4}$ in.
C. 2 in.
D. $2\frac{1}{4}$ in.

24-A.3

---

30. 36 in. = __?__ ft

A. 1
B. 3
C. 12
D. not here

24-A.2

For questions 31–32, use the diagram.

Stars in the Sky

1 square = 1 light year

31. How many stars are in the diagram?

A. 7 stars
B. 8 stars
C. 9 stars
D. 10 stars

24-A.3

32. How far is it from the star at A to the star at C?

A. 8 miles
B. 80 miles
C. 8 light years
D. 80 light years

24-A.3

33. 4,000 lb = __?__ tons

A. 2
B. 3
C. 4
D. 5

24-A.4

34. 8 dm = __?__ cm

A. 0.08
B. 0.8
C. 8
D. 80

25-A.1

35. 18 dm = __?__ cm

A. 18
B. 180
C. 1,800
D. not here

25-A.1

36. 7 liters = __?__ milliliters

A. 70
B. 700
C. 1,400
D. 7,000

25-A.3

37. What is another way to write a quarter to twelve?

A. 11:30
B. 11:45
C. 12:15
D. 12:30

26-A.1

38. Which is the most reasonable measure for the length of the ribbon?

A. 1 mm
B. 1 cm
C. 3 cm
D. 3 in.

26-A.2

39. A hamburger costs $2.00. Ralph buys a dozen. He uses a coupon to save $4.00. How much will Ralph pay?

A. $8
B. $20
C. $24
D. $28

26-A.4

40. What is the difference between the temperatures on the thermometers?

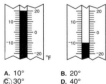

A. 10°
B. 20°
C. 30°
D. 40°

26-A.4

Multiple Choice • Test Answers   **135**

Name _____

Choose the letter of the correct answer.

1. Which numbers should you use to estimate the quotient for this division problem?

   $82 \div 18 = n$

   A. $80 \div 10 = n$
   B. $80 \div 20 = n$
   C. $90 \div 10 = n$
   D. $90 \div 20 = n$

2. What basic fact helps find these quotients?

$280 \div 70 = n$
$2{,}800 \div 70 = n$
$28{,}000 \div 70 = n$

   A. $28 \div 7 = 4$
   B. $28 \div 4 = 7$
   C. $28 \times 4 = 7$
   D. not here

For questions 3–4, find the best estimate of the quotient.

3. $598 \div 19 = n$

   A. 20   B. 30   C. 40   D. 150

4. $309 \div 54 = n$

   A. 4   B. 3   C. 6   D. 7

For questions 5–6, choose the best estimate.

5. There are 217 books. About 39 books fit in a carton. About how many cartons are needed to pack the books?

   A. about 5 cartons
   B. about 7 cartons
   C. about 9 cartons
   D. about 10 cartons

6. For a field trip, 192 students are divided into groups of 11 each. About how many groups are there?

   A. about 10 groups
   B. about 12 groups
   C. about 15 groups
   D. about 20 groups

7. Which box shows where the first digit of the quotient should be placed?

   A. $50\overline{)785}$ B. $50\overline{)785}$
   C. $50\overline{)785}$ D. not here

8. Where should the first digit in the quotient be placed?

   $60\overline{)488}$

   A. thousands place
   B. hundreds place
   C. tens place
   D. ones place

9. $30\overline{)364}$

   A. 10 r24   B. 11 r14
   C. 12 r4   D. 13 r4

10. $50\overline{)412}$

    A. 8 r12   B. 8 r42
    C. 80 r12 D. 82 r2

11. $80\overline{)580}$

    A. 7   B. 7 r20
    C. 8   D. 8 r40

Form A • Multiple-Choice   A101   Go on. ▶

Name _____

12. During one month 20 volunteers at a soup kitchen worked 440 hours. Each volunteer worked the same number of hours. How many hours did each volunteer work?

    A. 20 hours   B. 21 hours
    C. 22 hours   D. 23 hours

13. Florence must solve the division problem below. She starts by estimating. What is the next step?

    $27\overline{)306}$

    A. Check the estimate by multiplying.
    B. Divide the hundreds.
    C. Write the remainder.
    D. Decide where to place the first digit in the quotient.

14. Roger started doing the problem below. What should he do next?

    A. Divide the tens.
    B. Divide the ones.
    C. Write the remainder.
    D. Subtract 12 from 14.

15. $13\overline{)167}$

    A. 10 r37   B. 11 r4
    C. 12 r11   D. 13 r2

16. $24\overline{)180}$

    A. 5   B. 6 r16
    C. 7 r2   D. 7 r12

17. $46\overline{)756}$

    A. 16   B. 16 r20
    C. 17 r14 D. 17 r24

18. $33\overline{)689}$

    A. 20 r29 B. 21 r16
    C. 22 r29 D. 23

19. A movie video is 118 minutes long. How many hours and minutes is this?

    A. 1 hour 18 minutes
    B. 1 hour 58 minutes
    C. 2 hours 18 minutes
    D. 2 hours 38 minutes

20. Corinna walked on her hands for a distance of 105 inches. How far is this in feet and inches?

    A. 8 feet 9 inches
    B. 9 feet 8 inches
    C. 9 feet 9 inches
    D. 10 feet 5 inches

For questions 21–24, decide if each estimate is too high, too low, or just right.

21. $17\overline{)158}$ with 8
    A. too high
    B. too low
    C. just right

22. $31\overline{)184}$ with 5
    A. too high
    B. too low
    C. just right

23. $53\overline{)314}$ with 6
    A. too high
    B. too low
    C. just right

24. $78\overline{)575}$ with 7
    A. too high
    B. too low
    C. just right

Form A • Multiple-Choice   A102   ▶ Stop!

Name _____

Choose the letter of the correct answer.

For questions 1–2, use the circle graph.

1. What does the whole circle represent?

   A. the whole school
   B. all the students in grade 4, grade 5, and grade 6
   C. the 24 members of the school band
   D. high school students in the school band

2. By looking at the graph, what do you know about the number of students in each grade?

   A. There are not many students.
   B. There are fewer students in sixth grade than in other grades.
   C. There are more fourth-graders than fifth-graders.
   D. The number of students from each grade is the same.

For questions 3–6, use the circle graph.

Favorite Fruit Choices of 30 Students

3. What fraction of the 30 students chose peaches as their favorite fruit?

   A. $\frac{1}{6}$ B. $\frac{2}{6}$ C. $\frac{3}{6}$ D. $\frac{4}{6}$

4. What fraction of the 30 students chose apples as their favorite?

   A. $\frac{1}{6}$ B. $\frac{2}{6}$ C. $\frac{3}{6}$ D. $\frac{4}{6}$

5. What fraction represents all the students in the survey?

   A. $\frac{6}{30}$ B. $\frac{4}{6}$ C. $\frac{5}{6}$ D. $\frac{6}{6}$

6. Which two fruits were chosen by the most students?

   A. apples and peaches
   B. bananas and peaches
   C. oranges and apples
   D. bananas and oranges

For questions 7–8, use the circle.

7. What decimal represents 1 part of the circle?

   A. 0.25   B. 0.50
   C. 0.75   D. 1.00

8. What is the sum of the decimals that represent the 2 parts of the circle?

   A. 0.50   B. 0.80
   C. 1.00   D. 2.00

Form A • Multiple-Choice   A103   Go on. ▶

Name _____

For questions 9–12, use the graph.

Seasons When Students Were Born

9. What decimal tells how many students were born in the spring?

   A. 0.1   B. 0.2   C. 0.3   D. 0.4

10. What decimal tells how many students were born in the summer?

    A. 0.1   B. 0.2   C. 0.3   D. 0.4

11. What decimal tells how many students were born in the fall?

    A. 0.1   B. 0.2   C. 0.3   D. 0.4

12. What decimal tells how many students were born in the winter?

    A. 0.1   B. 0.2   C. 0.3   D. 0.4

For questions 13–14, use the circles.

Circle A   Circle B

13. Which circle can be used to show that $\frac{1}{2}$ the members of a chorus are boys and $\frac{1}{2}$ are girls?

    A. only Circle A
    B. only Circle B
    C. Circle A or Circle B
    D. neither Circle A nor Circle B

14. Which circle can be used to show that $\frac{1}{2}$ the school band are sixth graders, $\frac{1}{4}$ are fifth graders and $\frac{1}{3}$ are fourth graders?

    A. only Circle A
    B. only Circle B
    C. either Circle A or Circle B
    D. neither Circle A nor Circle B

For questions 15–18, choose the graph that matches the data.

Weather for 24 Days in May

Graph A   Graph B   Graph C   Graph D

15. Which graph shows that $\frac{1}{2}$ of the days were cloudy, $\frac{1}{4}$ were sunny, and $\frac{1}{4}$ were rainy?

    A. Graph A   B. Graph B
    C. Graph C   D. Graph D

16. Which graph shows that $\frac{1}{2}$ of the days were sunny, $\frac{1}{4}$ were rainy, and $\frac{1}{4}$ were cloudy?

    A. Graph A   B. Graph B
    C. Graph C   D. Graph D

17. Which graph shows that $\frac{1}{4}$ of the days were rainy and $\frac{3}{4}$ were sunny?

    A. Graph A   B. Graph B
    C. Graph C   D. Graph D

18. Which graph shows that $\frac{1}{3}$ of the days were sunny, $\frac{1}{3}$ were cloudy, and $\frac{1}{3}$ were rainy?

    A. Graph A   B. Graph B
    C. Graph C   D. Graph D

Form A • Multiple-Choice   A104   ▶ Stop!

Choose the letter of the correct answer.

1. Which numbers should you use to estimate the quotient for this problem?

$$56 ÷ 31 = n$$

A. $50 ÷ 40 = n$ B. $70 ÷ 30 = n$
C. $60 ÷ 40 = n$ D. $60 ÷ 30 = n$

27-A.1

2. Find the best estimate of the quotient.

$$411 ÷ 9 = n$$

A. 20   B. 30   C. 40   D. 360

27-A.1

3. A librarian packed 309 books in boxes, with 32 books in each box. About how many boxes were there?

A. about 10 boxes
B. about 12 boxes
C. about 15 boxes
D. about 30 boxes

27-A.1

4. $50)\overline{860}$

A. 17 r10   B. 17 r11
C. 18 r2   D. 18 r10

27-A.3

5. Lenny must solve this problem. He starts by estimating. What is the next step? $32)\overline{908}$

A. Write the remainder.
B. Divide the hundreds.
C. Check the estimate by multiplying.
D. Decide where to place the first digit in the quotient.

27-A.3

6. $15)\overline{231}$

A. 15   B. 15 r6
C. 16   D. not here

27-A.3

7. A school play is 105 minutes long. How many hours and minutes is this?

A. 1 hour 5 minutes
B. 1 hour 45 minutes
C. 2 hours 5 minutes
D. 2 hours 25 minutes

27-A.3

8. A rug is 110 inches long. How long is this in feet and inches?

A. 8 feet 10 inches
B. 8 feet 11 inches
C. 9 feet 2 inches
D. 9 feet 6 inches

27-A.3

For questions 9–10, decide whether the estimate is *too high, too low,* or *just right.*

9. $\begin{matrix}5\\75)\overline{480}\end{matrix}$

A. too high
B. too low
C. just right

27-A.4

10. $\begin{matrix}8\\45)\overline{390}\end{matrix}$

A. too high
B. too low
C. just right

27-A.4

For questions 11–12, use the circle graph.

FAVORITE BOOK CHOICES OF 80 STUDENTS

11. What fraction of the 80 students chose biographies as their favorite books?

A. $\frac{1}{4}$ B. $\frac{2}{4}$
C. $\frac{3}{4}$ D. not here

28-A.1

Form A • Multiple-Choice   A105   **Go on. ▶**

---

12. What fraction of the 80 students chose mysteries as their favorite?

A. $\frac{1}{4}$ B. $\frac{2}{4}$
C. $\frac{2}{3}$ D. $\frac{3}{4}$

28-A.1

For questions 13–14, use the circle.

13. What decimal represents 1 part of the circle?

A. 0.25   B. 0.50
C. 0.75   D. 1.00

28-A.2

14. What is the sum of the decimals that represent the 4 parts of the circle?

A. 0.150   B. 0.75
C. 0.80   D. 1.00

28-A.2

For questions 15–16, use the circle graph.

PEOPLE AT PICNIC

Boys   Girls
Women   Men

15. What decimal tells how many people at the picnic were men?

A. 0.1   B. 0.2   C. 0.3   D. 0.4

28-A.2

16. What decimal tells how many people were girls?

A. 0.2   B. 0.25   C. 0.3   D. 0.4

28-A.2

For questions 17–18, use the circle graphs.

Graph A   Graph B

17. Which graph can be used to show that $\frac{1}{2}$ of the students in a class are boys and $\frac{1}{2}$ are girls?

A. only Graph A
B. only Graph B
C. Graph A or Graph B
D. neither Graph A nor Graph B

28-A.3

18. Which graph can be used to show that $\frac{1}{2}$ of the cookies are chocolate, $\frac{1}{4}$ are peanut butter, and $\frac{1}{4}$ are oatmeal?

A. only Graph A
B. only Graph B
C. either Graph A or Graph B
D. neither Graph A nor Graph B

28-A.3

For questions 19–20, choose the graph that matches the data.

Graph A   Graph B   Graph C   Graph D

19. Which graph shows that $\frac{1}{2}$ of the students played soccer, $\frac{1}{4}$ played tennis, and $\frac{1}{4}$ ran track?

A. Graph A   B. Graph B
C. Graph C   D. Graph D

28-A.3

20. Which graph shows that $\frac{1}{3}$ of the students played soccer, $\frac{1}{3}$ played tennis, and $\frac{1}{3}$ ran track?

A. Graph A   B. Graph B
C. Graph C   D. Graph D

28-A.3

Form A • Multiple-Choice   A106   **▶ Stop!**

Choose the letter of the correct answer.

1. Choose the best estimate of the sum or difference.

$$\begin{matrix}8,762\\-1,197\end{matrix}$$

A. 6,000
B. 7,000
C. 8,000
D. 9,000

2-A.3

2. Use the model to find the quotient.

$$23 ÷ 4 = \underline{\ ?\ }$$

A. 5 r2   B. 5 r3
C. 6   D. 6 r1

4-A.3

3. What is the value of the digit 8 in the number 892?

A. $8 × 0 = 0$ B. $8 × 1 = 8$
C. $8 × 10 = 80$ D. $8 × 100 = 800$

6-A.1

4. Compare the numbers and choose the correct statement.

$$787 \bullet 778$$

A. $787 > 778$ B. $787 = 778$
C. $787 < 778$ D. not here

7-A.2

5. Which time is closest to the time that a cafeteria serves breakfast?

A. 1:00 A.M.   B. 7:00 A.M.
C. 1:00 P.M.   D. 7:00 P.M.

8-A.2

For questions 6–7, use the calendars.

June	July
Su M T W Th F Sa	Su M T W Th F Sa
1 2 3 4 5 6 7	1 2 3 4 5
8 9 10 11 12 13 14	6 7 8 9 10 11 12
15 16 17 18 19 20 21	13 14 15 16 17 18 19
22 23 24 25 26 27 28	20 21 22 23 24 25 26
29 30	27 28 29 30 31

6. How many days is it from June 25 to July 5?

A. 5 days   B. 7 days
C. 9 days   D. 10 days

8-A.4

7. Paul is going to visit his cousin for 8 days. His visit will end on June 15. On what day will it begin?

A. June 6   B. June 7
C. June 8   D. June 9

8-A.4

8. What kind of graph would be best to compare the number of home runs hit by different players on a baseball team?

A. Bar graph
B. Stem-and-leaf plot
C. Line graph
D. Double-bar graph

10-A.4

Form A • Multiple-Choice   A107   Chapters 1–28   **Go on. ▶**

For questions 9–10, use the spinner.

9. What is the probability of spinning a 3 or a 4?

A. $\frac{1}{4}$ B. $\frac{2}{4}$
C. $\frac{3}{4}$ D. not here

11-A.2

10. What is the probability of spinning a 4?

A. $\frac{0}{4}$ B. $\frac{1}{4}$ C. $\frac{2}{4}$ D. $\frac{3}{4}$

11-A.2

11. Which line segments are parallel?

A.   B.
C.   D.

13-A.1

12. A figure is drawn on 1-in. grid paper. If you copy the figure on 1.5-in. paper, it will be __?__.

A. similar but larger
B. similar but smaller
C. symmetric
D. congruent

15-A.5

13. $\begin{matrix}217\\\times\ \ 4\end{matrix}$

A. 651
B. 858
C. 868
D. 908

16-A.2

14. $6)\overline{35}$

A. 5 r3   B. 5 r5
C. 7   D. not here

18-A.1

15. $3)\overline{$14.55}$

A. $4.53   B. $4.79
C. $4.85   D. $5.83

19-A.3

16. Which group of fractions is in order from greatest to least?

A. $\frac{1}{4}, \frac{3}{8}, \frac{5}{8}$ B. $\frac{3}{8}, \frac{1}{4}, \frac{5}{8}$
C. $\frac{3}{8}, \frac{5}{8}, \frac{1}{4}$ D. $\frac{5}{8}, \frac{3}{8}, \frac{1}{4}$

20-A.2

17. $\frac{2}{7} + \frac{3}{7} = \underline{\ ?\ }$

A. $\frac{1}{7}$ B. $\frac{5}{14}$
C. $\frac{5}{7}$ D. $1\frac{6}{7}$

21-A.1

18. $\begin{matrix}0.64\\-0.47\end{matrix}$

A. 0.17
B. 0.27
C. 1.11
D. not here

23-A.1

19. Find the equivalent measurement.

8 yd = __?__ ft

A. 16   B. 20   C. 22   D. 24

24-A.2

20. To change ounces to pounds, __?__.

A. multiply by 16
B. divide by 16
C. multiply by 2,000
D. divide by 2,000

24-A.2

21. 4 dm = __?__ cm

A. 40   B. 4
C. 0.4   D. not here

25-A.1

Form A • Multiple-Choice   A108   Chapters 1–28   **Go on. ▶**

For questions 22–23, use the diagram.

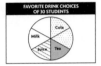

Floor Plan of Nathan's Family Room

22. About how far is it from the TV cabinet to the sofa?

   A. 1 m   B. 2 m
   C. 3 m   D. 4 m

   25-A.2

23. Which of these are the same size in width?

   A. doorway and sofa
   B. sofa and TV cabinet
   C. TV cabinet and bookcase
   D. table and sofa

   25-A.2

24. Jean's tennis racket is 33 in. long. Her dog is 33 cm long. Which is longer?

   A. the tennis racket
   B. the dog
   C. They are the same length.
   D. More information is needed.

   26-A.2

25. Which of the following temperatures is the warmest?

   A. −30°F   B. 5°F
   C. 15°F   D. 25°F

   26-A.3

For questions 26–27, find the best estimate of the quotient.

26. $409 \div 9 = n$

   A. 20   B. 30
   C. 40   D. 80

   27-A.1

27. $493 \div 49 = n$

   A. 8   B. 9
   C. 10   D. 11

   27-A.1

28. $40\overline{)299}$

   A. 6 r19   B. 6 r29
   C. 7 r9   D. 7 r19

   27-A.2

29. $70\overline{)814}$

   A. 11 r44   B. 11 r54
   C. 12 r10   D. 12 r34

   27-A.2

30. $17\overline{)219}$

   A. 12 r5   B. 12 r13
   C. 12 r15   D. 13 r5

   27-A.3

For questions 31–32, decide if each estimate is *too high, too low,* or *just right*.

31. $13\overline{)128}$ → 9

   A. too high
   B. too low
   C. just right

   27-A.4

32. $27\overline{)520}$ → 20

   A. too high
   B. too low
   C. just right

   27-A.4

33. A baseball game is 144 minutes long. How many hours and minutes is this?

   A. 1 hour 44 minutes
   B. 2 hours 4 minutes
   C. 2 hours 14 minutes
   D. 2 hours 24 minutes

   27-A.5

34. A camel is 117 inches tall. How high is this in feet and inches?

   A. 8 feet 7 inches
   B. 9 feet 3 inches
   C. 9 feet 9 inches
   D. 10 feet 2 inches

   27-A.5

For questions 35–36, use the circle graph.

FAVORITE DRINK CHOICES OF 30 STUDENTS

35. What fraction of the 30 students chose cola as their favorite drink?

   A. $\frac{1}{6}$ B. $\frac{2}{6}$
   C. $\frac{3}{6}$ D. $\frac{4}{6}$

   28-A.1

36. What fraction of the 30 students chose juice as their favorite?

   A. $\frac{1}{6}$ B. $\frac{2}{6}$
   C. $\frac{3}{6}$ D. $\frac{4}{6}$

   28-A.1

For questions 37–38, use the graph.

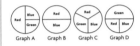

FAVORITE SUBJECTS OF 50 STUDENTS

37. What decimal tells how many students like history best?

   A. 0.1   B. 0.2   C. 0.3   D. 0.4

   28-A.2

38. What decimal tells how many students like math best?

   A. 0.1   B. 0.2   C. 0.3   D. 0.4

   28-A.2

For questions 39–40, choose the graph that matches the data on cars in 4 lots.

Graph A   Graph B   Graph C   Graph D

39. Which graph shows that $\frac{1}{4}$ of the cars were red and $\frac{2}{4}$ were green?

   A. Graph A   B. Graph B
   C. Graph C   D. Graph D

   28-A.3

40. Which graph shows that $\frac{1}{4}$ of the cars were blue, $\frac{1}{4}$ were green, and $\frac{1}{2}$ were red?

   A. Graph A   B. Graph B
   C. Graph C   D. Graph D

   28-A.3

Free-Response Format Tests

The free-response format tests are useful as diagnostic tools. The work the student performs provides information about what the student understands about the concepts and/or procedures so that appropriate reteaching can be chosen from the many options in the program.

There is an Inventory Test which tests the learning goals from the previous grade level. This can be used at the beginning of the year or as a placement test when a new student enters your class.

There is a Chapter Test for each chapter and a Multi-Chapter Test to be used as review after several chapters in a content cluster. Also, there are Cumulative Tests at the same point as the Multi-Chapter Tests. The Cumulative Test reviews content from Chapter 1 through the current chapter.

Math Advantage also provides multiple-choice format tests that parallel the free-response format tests. You may wish to use one form as a pretest and one form as a posttest.

Write the correct answer.

1.   5
      +2
    ____

2. Write a subtraction fact that is related to this addition fact.

$4 + 7 = 11$

_____

For question 3, estimate the sum by rounding.

3.   31
      +42
    ____

4. Sam has 18 pennies in his pocket and 24 pennies in his bank. How many pennies does he have in all?

_____

5.   62
      −17
    ____

For questions 6–7, tell what time it is.

6.

_____

7.

_____

8. Mr. Ash spent $12.00 for a shirt and $32.50 for slacks. He gave the clerk $50.00. How much change did he receive?

_____

For questions 9 and 10, use the calendar.

April						
Su	M	T	W	Th	F	Sa
		1	2	3	4	5
6	7	8	9	10	11	12
13	14	15	16	17	18	19
20	21	22	23	24	25	26
27	28	29	30			

9. How many Mondays are there in the month?

_____

10. What is the date of the third Wednesday?

_____

For question 11, round the number to the nearest hundred.

11. 910

_____

12. A cabinet had 4 shelves with 5 plates on each shelf. How many plates were there in all?

_____

13. $1 \times 6 = \underline{\ ?\ }$

14. $\begin{array}{r} 9 \\ \times 4 \\ \hline \end{array}$

15. $35 \div 5 = \underline{\ ?\ }$

_____

16. Sally bought 16 turtles. She placed an equal number of turtles in each of 4 bowls. How many turtles were in each bowl?

_____

For questions 17–18, use the table.

STUDENTS' FAVORITE VACATION	
Place	**Votes**
Beach	卌 卌 卌
Theme Park	卌 IIII
Campground	卌 III
Home with Friends	卌 II

17. How many students answered the survey?

_____

18. How many more students liked a theme park than liked a campground?

_____

For questions 19–20, identify the solid figure that is like the object shown.

19.

_____

20.

_____

21. Lee drew this figure. She matched it to make the other half. Draw the completed figure.

_____

For questions 22–23, use the picture.

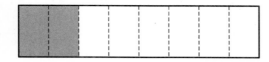

22. How many parts make up the whole?

_____

23. How many parts are shaded?

_____

For question 24, write the numbers or words that name the part of the group that is shaded.

24.

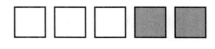

_____

25. Mrs. Green has 3 cars to wash. She has washed 2 cars so far. What part of the cars has been washed?

_____

For question 26, measure the length to the nearest half-inch.

26.

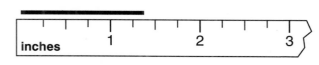

_____

For question 27, find the perimeter of the figure.

27.

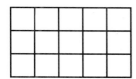

_____

28. The canopy over Glen's patio is 4 meters long and 3 meters wide. How many square meters of material does Glen need to replace the canopy?

_____

29. A party table has 6 pizzas on it. Each pizza has 12 slices. How many pizza slices are on the table?

_____

30.   22
         $\times\ 7$

31. $8 \times 62 =$ ___?___

_____

32. $58 \div 7 =$ ___?___

_____

33. Mrs. Wong had 50 party prizes. She gave the same number to 7 children at the party. How many prizes did each child get and how many prizes were left over?

_____

34. A paintbox has 54 tubes of paint. If 6 children share the paints, how many tubes will each child have?

_____

Solve. Then write the correct answer.

1. $8 + 2 = \underline{\ ?\ } + 4$

_____

2. $7 - 3 = 9 - \underline{\ ?\ }$

_____

3. $\underline{\ ?\ } + 0 = 6 - 2$

_____

4. $12 - 3 = \underline{\ ?\ } + 1$

_____

For questions 5–6, find the perimeter.

5.
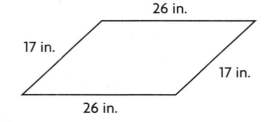
26 in.
17 in.
17 in.
26 in.

_____

6.
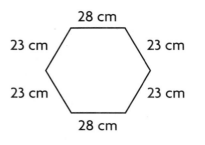
28 cm
23 cm   23 cm
23 cm   23 cm
28 cm

_____

7.
```
  22
  15
+ 11
```

8.
```
  68
  12
+ 44
```

9.
```
  63
  27
+ 80
```

10.
```
  93
  28
+ 36
```

11. A rectangular room has a perimeter of 100 feet. The room is 30 feet long. How wide is it?

_____

12. Paco made a rectangular rabbit cage. He used 4 feet of wire each for the north and south sides, and 3 feet each for the east and west sides of the cage. How many feet of wire did he use in all?

_____

Form B • Free-Response   **B145**   **Go on.** ▶

13. What is 277 rounded to the nearest hundred?

_____

14. What is $53.75 rounded to the nearest ten dollars?

_____

15. Estimate the sum to the nearest hundred.

119
196
+305

16. Estimate the difference to the nearest ten dollars.

$67.88
− 32.35

For questions 17–18, use the price list.

Pizza	$1.75 a slice
Burgers	$2.80 each
Salad	$1.08 each

17. About how much change will Kimi receive from a $10 bill if she buys a slice of pizza and a salad?

_____

18. Leon bought 2 burgers and 2 salads. About how much did he spend?

_____

19. $7.46
− 3.87

20. $3.72
2.98
+ 4.10

21. $10.59
− 7.78

22. $25.46
+ 16.37

23. Theo bought chicken for $3.68, iced tea for $1.03, and dessert for $2.20. How much did he spend in all?

_____

24. Marty uses a $20 bill to buy lunch. He gets a burger for $2.50, a soda for $1.25, and yogurt for $1.50. How much change should he get?

_____

Name _____

Solve. Then write the correct answer.

1. The perimeter of this figure is 636 feet. Find the missing length.

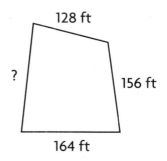

128 ft

? 156 ft

164 ft

_____

2. The perimeter of this figure is 1,177 feet. Find the missing length.

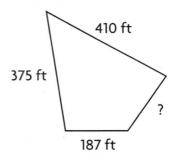

410 ft

375 ft

?

187 ft

_____

3. There are 182 street lights around the park. There are 46 lights on the west side, 39 on the north side, and 53 on the east side. How many lights are on the south side?

_____

4. A rectangular painting has a perimeter of 356 inches. If two sides of the painting are each 96 inches, what is the length of each of the other two sides?

_____

5. Which place-value positions should be regrouped to solve this problem?

$$\begin{array}{r} 5,020 \\ -2,007 \\ \hline \end{array}$$

_____

Find the difference.

6. $\begin{array}{r} 700 \\ -519 \\ \hline \end{array}$

7. $\begin{array}{r} 400 \\ -208 \\ \hline \end{array}$

8. $\begin{array}{r} 6,000 \\ -4,937 \\ \hline \end{array}$

9. $\begin{array}{r} 60,000 \\ -48,253 \\ \hline \end{array}$

10. There are 4,000 students at the high school. There are 1,400 students at the middle school. How many more students are at the high school?

_____

11. The store sold 3,800 books and 1,950 tapes. How many more books than tapes were sold?

_____

12. A chess player won 6 matches, lost 3 matches, and tied 2 matches. Each player plays 19 matches. How many matches does this player have left to play?

_____

13. Kyle chose a number. He added 5. Then, he subtracted 9. Last, he added 7. The result was 15. What number did Kyle start with?

_____

14. What is 461 rounded to the nearest hundred?

_____

15. What is 8,389 rounded to the nearest thousand?

_____

For questions 16–20, give an estimate of the sum or difference.

16.   576
    +141

17.   8,998
    −4,002

18.   5,679
    +2,892

For questions 19–20, use the table.

RECYCLED ALUMINUM CANS	
Month	**Cans**
March	2,311
April	1,935
May	3,014
June	1,720
July	1,447

19. How many cans were collected in March and April?

_____

20. How many fewer cans were collected in April than in March?

_____

Name _____

Write the correct answer.

1. The number line shows how many dance lessons Gina takes in 4 weeks.

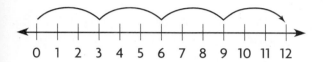

0 1 2 3 4 5 6 7 8 9 10 11 12

Write a number sentence that matches the number line.

_____

2. Buddy has 2 plates with 7 cookies on each plate. Write a number sentence that shows how many cookies Buddy has in all.

_____

3. Write a number sentence that tells how many eggs are in the nests.

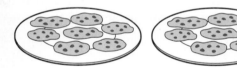

_____

4. Ted is collecting seashells in 2 pails. He put 6 shells in each pail. Write how many shells Ted has in all.

_____

5. Rosa takes music lessons 3 times each week. Write how many lessons Rosa takes in 3 weeks.

_____

6. Using the numbers 5 and 2, write a number sentence that shows the Order Property of Multiplication.

_____

7. Using the number 3, write a number sentence that shows the Zero Property for Multiplication.

_____

8. Using the number 6, write a number sentence that shows the Property of One for Multiplication.

_____

9. $146 \times 1 = $ ___?___

_____

10. $0 \times 8 = $ ___?___

_____

11. $7 \times 8 = 56$, so $8 \times 7 = \underline{}$

_____

12. $(3 \times 3) \times 2 = \underline{}$

_____

13. $5 \times (5 \times 1) = \underline{}$

_____

14. $8 \times (2 \times 2) = \underline{}$

_____

15. $4 \times (1 \times 4) = \underline{}$

_____

16. Len has a photo album. It has 5 pages. Each page has 2 rows, with 3 photos in each row. Write how many photos Len has in all.

_____

17. Suki has 3 shelves in her room. There are 7 books on each shelf. Write how many books she has in all.

_____

For questions 18–20, choose the operation that can be used to solve the problem. Then write a number sentence and solve.

18. Tina slept 9 hours one night and 8 hours the next night. How many hours did Tina sleep in all?

_____

19. Tim has 3 pets. Donna has 5 pets. How many more pets does Donna have than Tim?

_____

20. Mrs. Garza's classroom has 5 rows of desks. There are 7 desks in each row. How many desks are there in all?

_____

Write the correct answer.

1. There are 24 students in Mrs. Lee's class. She divides them into 4 teams for a game. How many students are on each team?

_____

2. Jane's mom is baking cookies. She puts 8 cookies in each pan. She bakes 4 pans of cookies. How many cookies does she have in all?

_____

3. Name the operation that is the inverse of multiplication.

_____

4. Write a number sentence that is in the same fact family as this:

$5 \times 7 = 35$

_____

For questions 5–6, use the multiplication fact to help you find the quotient.

5. $4 \times 7 = 28$

$28 \div 7 =$ _____

6. $5 \times 3 = 15$

$15 \div 3 =$ _____

For questions 7–8, use the model to find the quotient.

7. $28 \div 9 =$ _?_

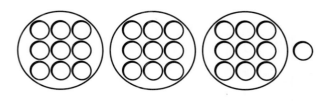

_____

8. $11 \div 4 =$ _?_

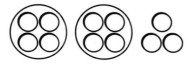

_____

9. There are 36 students in math class, and there are 6 rows of desks. How many students sit in each row?

_____

10. The librarian received 64 new paperbacks. She put 8 books in each fourth-grade classroom. How many classes received books?

_____

Form B • Free-Response   **Go on.** ▶

Name _____

For questions 11–14, use the
multiplication table to find the quotient.

x	0	1	2	3	4	5
0	0	0	0	0	0	0
1	0	1	2	3	4	5
2	0	2	4	6	8	10
3	0	3	6	9	12	15
4	0	4	8	12	16	20
5	0	5	10	15	20	25

11. $25 \div 5 = \underline{?}$

_____

12. $12 \div 3 = \underline{?}$

_____

13. $8 \div 4 = \underline{?}$

_____

14. $9 \div 3 = \underline{?}$

_____

15. $9\overline{)81}$

16. $7\overline{)49}$

For questions 17–18, use the table.

USED-BOOK DRIVE	NUMBER BROUGHT IN
Mystery	40
Humor	30
Biography	63
Nonfiction	54

17. Eight students each brought the
same number of mystery books to
the Used-Book Drive. How many
mystery books did each student
bring?

_____

18. An equal number of biography
books were placed on 7 shelves.
How many biographies were put
on each shelf?

_____

For questions 19–20, solve each problem.

19. Joe earned $56 raking lawns for his
neighbors. He was paid $8 for each
lawn he raked. How many lawns
were raked in all?

_____

20. Frank is putting 72 new stamps into
his stamp book. He puts 9 stamps
on each page. How many pages did
he use in all?

_____

Write the correct answer.

1. $9 - 4 = 7 - \underline{\ ?\ }$

_____

2.   87
   14
 + 25

_____

3. A rectangular field has a perimeter of 200 yards. The field is 60 yards long. How wide is it?

_____

4. Estimate the sum to the nearest hundred.
   365
   105
 + 213

_____

5. $12.45
 −   5.62

_____

6. Kara bought a sandwich for $2.89, juice for $1.07, and pretzels for $1.19. How much did she spend in all?

_____

7. The perimeter of this figure is 1,810 feet. Find the missing length.

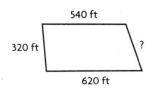

540 ft
320 ft   ?
620 ft

_____

8.   400
 − 218

_____

9. There are 1,560 girls and 2,100 boys in the school. How many more boys than girls are in the school?

_____

10. What is 824 rounded to the nearest hundred?

_____

For questions 11–12, use the table.

ATTENDANCE AT SOCCER GAMES	
Game	Attendance
1	1,905
2	2,122
3	1,896
4	2,483
5	2,061

11. How many people were at Games 1 and 2?

_____

12. How many fewer people were at Game 5 than at Game 4?

_____

13. Write a number sentence that tells how many flowers in all are in the flower pots.

_____

14. Use the numbers 8 and 0 to write a number sentence that shows the Zero Property for Multiplication.

_____

15. $5 \times 9 = 45$, so $9 \times 5 =$ ___

_____

16. $(2 \times 2) \times 6 =$ ___

_____

17. A pet store has 7 fish tanks. Each tank has 9 fish. How many fish are there in all?

_____

18. Write a number sentence that can be used to solve the problem.

Eddie read 14 chapters in his book. Sarah read 22 chapters in her book. How many more chapters did Sarah read than Eddie?

_____

19. The Lions basketball team will play 31 games in all. They have 9 games left to play. How many games have they played so far?

_____

20. Write a number sentence that is in the same fact family as $27 \div 9 = 3$.

_____

21. Use the model to find the quotient.
$17 \div 5 =$ __?__

_____

22. The Smithfield baseball league has 32 new players. Each of the 8 teams gets the same number of players. How many new players will each team get?

_____

23. $8\overline{)64}$

_____

24. Dennis earns money by delivering newspapers. In the past 9 weeks, he has earned $54.00. How much does he earn per week?

_____

Write the correct answer.

1. $6 + 3 =$ ___?___ $+ 4$

_____

2. $8 - 5 = 7 -$ ___?___

_____

3.
```
  12
  37
+14
```

4.
```
  57
  62
+49
```

5. What is 389 rounded to the nearest hundred?

_____

6. Use the price list.

Cap	$5.99
Gloves	$4.12
Socks	$1.89

About how much change from a $10 bill will Raymond receive if he buys a cap and socks?

_____

7.
```
  $9.27
- 4.59
```

8.
```
  $4.19
  3.27
+ 5.54
```

9. Nick paid $5.75 for a movie ticket, $2.25 for lemonade, and $1.99 for popcorn. How much change did he get from a $10 bill?

_____

10. The perimeter of the figure is 789 feet. What is the missing length?

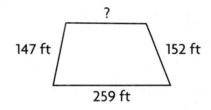

11. A rectangular sports field has a perimeter of 488 feet. Two sides of the field are each 164 feet. What is the length of each of the other two sides?

_____

12. $\begin{array}{r} 600 \\ -179 \\ \hline \end{array}$

13. $\begin{array}{r} 7,000 \\ -2,156 \\ \hline \end{array}$

14. What is 643 rounded to the nearest hundred?

    _____

15. What is the sum estimated to the nearest thousand?

    $\begin{array}{r} 3,877 \\ +4,753 \\ \hline \end{array}$

For questions 16–18, use the table.

HOT DOGS SOLD AT THE BALL PARK	
May	2,672
June	2,514
July	2,973
August	2,814
September	2,767

16. How many hot dogs were sold in June and July?

    _____

17. How many fewer hot dogs were sold in September than in August?

    _____

18. How many fewer hot dogs were sold in June than in July?

    _____

19. Write a number sentence that tells how many rolls are on the plates.

    _____

20. Use the number 7 to write a number sentence that shows the Property of One for multiplication.

    _____

21. $3 \times 9 = 27$ $9 \times 3 = $ __?__

_____

22. $(8 \times 5) \times 2 = $ __?__

_____

23. $3 \times (2 \times 6) = $ __?__

_____

24. On a fishing trip, Tommy put 5 fish into each of 3 containers. How many fish does Tommy have in all?

_____

For questions 25–27, tell what operation can be used to solve the problem. Then write a number sentence and solve.

25. Karen learned to spell 7 new words one week. The following week she learned to spell 12 new words. How many words did Karen learn to spell during the two weeks?

_____

26. Ben ran 6 laps around the track. Molly ran 3 laps. How many more laps did Ben run than Molly?

_____

27. A parking lot has 4 rows, with 8 cars parked in each row. How many cars are there in all?

_____

28. At a school library, 28 students were working on a class project. They sat at 4 tables with the same number of students at each table. How many students were at each table?

_____

29. At a pool, 5 friends swam in a relay race. Each friend swam 2 laps. How many laps did they swim in all?

_____

30. Write a number sentence that is in the same fact family as $4 \times 9 = 36$.

_____

31. Use the multiplication fact $5 \times 6 = 30$ to help you find the quotient.

$$30 \div 6 = \underline{\quad ? \quad}$$

_____

32. Use the model to find the quotient.

$$31 \div 7 = \underline{\quad ? \quad}$$

_____

33. The Oakdale Softball League has 4 teams. The teams got 51 softballs to share equally. How many softballs did each team get? How many softballs will be left over?

_____

For questions 34–35, use the multiplication table to find the quotient.

×	3	4	5
3	9	12	15
4	12	16	20
5	15	20	25

34. $16 \div 4 = \underline{\quad ? \quad}$

35. $20 \div 5 = \underline{\quad ? \quad}$

_____

36. $7\overline{)42}$

_____

37. $5\overline{)45}$

_____

For questions 38–40, use the table.

Pie	Number Sold
Lemon	48
Cherry	34
Apple	59
Peach	27

38. There were 9 people who each bought the same number of peach pies. How many peach pies did each person buy?

_____

39. The same number of lemon pies was placed on each of 4 tables. How many lemon pies were on each table?

_____

40. Mrs. Jensen bought the first 12 apple pies for a family reunion. How many apple pies were left?

_____

Name _____

Write the correct answer.

1. Write whether this is a cardinal, ordinal, or nominal number.

_____

2. Write whether this is a cardinal, ordinal, or nominal number.

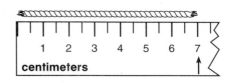

_____

For questions 3–6, use the coordinate grid.

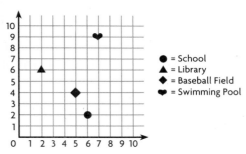

● = School
▲ = Library
◆ = Baseball Field
♥ = Swimming Pool

3. Which ordered pair shows the location of the school?

_____

4. What is located at (5, 4)?

_____

5. Which ordered pair shows the location of the swimming pool?

_____

6. What is located at (2,6)?

_____

For questions 7–8, use the base-ten blocks.

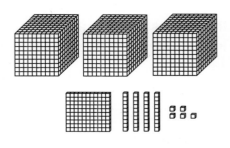

7. What does the stand for?

_____

8. Which number is shown by all these base-ten blocks?

_____

9. How many thousands are in 5,280?

_____

10. How many hundreds are in 3,095?

_____

11. Which number is in the tens place in 4,162?

_____

12. Put the comma in the number where it belongs. Write the number.

8427

_____

13. Al has English class first. Then he goes to gym class. His next class is science. After that he has math class. Then it's time for lunch. What is Al's third class?

_____

14. Mr. Clark is 3 times as old as Tina. Tina is 9 years old. How old is Mr. Clark?

_____

15. Which benchmark number can you use to estimate the number of crackers in Box B?

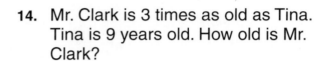

Box A   Box B

_____

16. About how many stamps are on Page B?

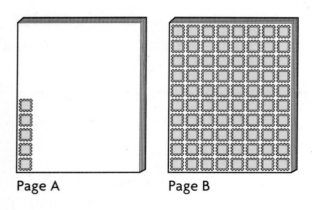

Page A   Page B

_____

17. About how many squares are in Quilt B?

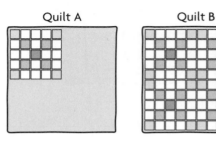

Quilt A   Quilt B

_____

18. About how many peppermints are in Jar B?

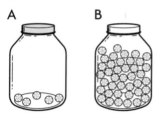

A   B

_____

19. A half gallon of milk costs $1.01. About how much should a gallon cost?

_____

20. There are 200 marbles in the jar now. About how many could the jar hold?

_____

Write the correct answer.

1. What is the value of the digit 2 in the number 723?

_____

2. Write the number with the digit 8 in the hundreds place, 0 in the ones place, and 4 in the tens place.

_____

3. Is this number written in standard form, expanded form, or written form?

$$2,000 + 600 + 10 + 9$$

_____

4. Write in standard form the number that is shown in this place-value chart.

Thousands	Hundreds	Tens	Ones
3,	**4**	**8**	**5**
$3 \times 1,000 = 3,000$	$4 \times 100 = 400$	$8 \times 10 = 80$	$5 \times 1 = 5$

_____

5. Write *six hundred forty-three* in standard form.

_____

6. Write *nine thousand, thirty-seven* in standard form.

_____

7. Write $8,000 + 500 + 2$ in written form.

_____

8. Write 5,360 in expanded form.

_____

9. What is another name for 2,000?

_____

10. Write the sum in standard form.

$$\begin{array}{r} 6 \text{ hundreds} \\ + \ 7 \text{ hundreds} \\ \hline 13 \text{ hundreds} \end{array}$$

_____

For questions 11–12, solve by using mental math.

11. $\begin{array}{r} 900 \\ +500 \\ \hline \end{array}$

12. $\begin{array}{r} 6,000 \\ +5,000 \\ \hline \end{array}$

13. Rewrite the number, placing the commas correctly to separate the periods.

24704612

_____

14. Could the number of people living in the United States be counted in the millions, thousands, hundreds, or tens?

_____

15. Write *six million, three hundred forty-six thousand, seven hundred twenty-five* in standard form.

_____

16. Write *four hundred two million, sixty-three thousand, five hundred nineteen* in standard form.

_____

17. Write 230,657,489 as you would say it with period names.

230 _?_ , 657 _?_ , 489

_____

18 Write 701,005,300 as you would say it with period names.

701 _?_ , 5 _?_ , 300

_____

For questions 19–20, use the table.

SPRINGTOWN SLUGGERS ATTENDANCE		
Year	Number of People	Increase from Previous Year
1994	335,974	–
1995	520,028	184,054
1996	642,905	122,877
1997	916,263	273,358

19. Between which two years did attendance increase the most?

_____

20. How many more people attended the games in 1997 than in 1994?

_____

Write the correct answer.

1. Use the number line to compare 30 and 50. Then complete the sentence below. Write <, >, or =.

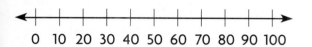

50 ◯ 30

_____

2. Use the number line to compare 700 and 900. Then complete the sentence below. Write <, >, or =.

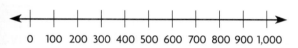

700 ◯ 900

_____

3. Compare 625 and 652.

_____>_____

4. Compare 9,118 and 9,181.

_____<_____

5. Write the number that completes the statement.

6,402 = __?__

_____

6. Write the greatest place-value position in which the digits differ in 64 and 85.

_____

7. Write the greatest place-value position in which the digits differ in 3,427 and 3,526.

_____

For questions 8–9, compare the numbers. Write <, >, or = for each ◯.

8. 521 ◯ 512

_____

9. 7,892 ◯ 7,982

_____

10. There are 24 players on the team. There are twice as many right-handed players as left-handed players. How many left-handed players are there?

_____

11. Mrs. Ortiz has 8 bills that total $48.00. She has at least 1 one-dollar bill, 1 five-dollar bill, 1 ten-dollar bill, and 1 twenty-dollar bill. How many five-dollar bills does she have?

_____

12. Write the numbers in order from least to greatest: 460, 406, 466.

_____

13. Write the numbers in order from the greatest to the least: 7,756; 7,776; 7,765.

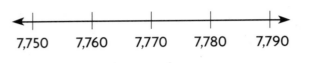

7,750   7,760   7,770   7,780   7,790

_____

14. Write the numbers in order from the greatest to the least: 450; 504; 455.

_____

15. Write the numbers in order from the least to the greatest: 5,618; 8,165; 5,815.

_____

For questions 16–17, use the table.

STUDENT ATTENDANCE AT COLE MIDDLE SCHOOL	
Day of Week	**Number of Students**
Monday	1,403
Tuesday	1,341
Wednesday	1,430
Thursday	1,195
Friday	1,340

16. On which day were the most students in school?

_____

17. On which day were the fewest students in school?

_____

For questions 18–20, use the Venn diagram.

Sports Played by Boys and Girls

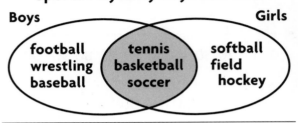

_____

18. In which sports are there only girls' teams?

_____

19. In which sports are there only boys' teams?

_____

20. In which sports are there both girls' teams and boys' teams?

_____

Write the correct answer.

1. Which unit of time would you use to measure how long it takes to pop popcorn in a microwave?

_____

2. Which unit of time would you use to measure how long it takes to dial a telephone number?

_____

3. Show 25 minutes past six on the digital clock below.

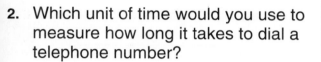

4. Write the time shown on the clock.

_____

5. Kevin leaves for school every day at the time shown on the clock. Write the time Kevin leaves.

_____

6. Mrs. Wu is taking her family to a movie at the time shown on the clock. Write the time that the movie begins.

_____

7. The first star was seen at 9:00. Was this A.M. or P.M.?

_____

8. Peggy eats breakfast at 8 o'clock. Is this A.M. or P.M.?

_____

9. Patty practiced the piano from 7:30 P.M. to 8:10 P.M. How many minutes did she practice?

_____

10. The movie began at 9:00 A.M. and ended at 10:35 A.M. How many minutes elapsed from the time the movie began until it ended?

_____

For questions 11–16, use the schedule.

NEW YORK – WASHINGTON, D.C.		
Flight	Leave NY	Arrive D.C.
A	7:10 A.M.	8:30 A.M.
B	10:30 A.M.	?
C	4:15 P.M.	?
D	6:45 P.M.	8:05 P.M.
All flights last 1 hour 20 minutes.		

11. What time does Flight B arrive in Washington, D.C.?

_____

12. What time does Flight C arrive in Washington, D.C.?

_____

13. Mr. Gomez has to attend a meeting at 11:00 A.M. in Washington, D.C. What flight should he take?

_____

14. It takes Mrs. Paul 45 min to drive from her house to the airport. What is the latest she can leave and still catch Flight B?

_____

15. The Stuarts take Flight A to begin an early tour. Their tour ends at 6:45 P.M. How long is the tour?

_____

16. It takes Mrs. Poski 35 minutes to drive from the Washington airport to her home. If she takes Flight D, what is the earliest she will arrive home?

_____

For questions 17–20, use the calendars.

August

Su	M	T	W	Th	F	Sa
				1	2	3
4	5	6	7	8	9	10
11	12	13	14	15	16	17
18	19	20	21	22	23	24
25	26	27	28	29	30	31

school starts ↘ **September**

Su	M	T	W	Th	F	Sa
1	2	③	4	5	6	7
8	9	10	11	12	13	14
15	16	17	18	19	20	21
22	23	24	25	26	27	28
29	30					

17. Super Buys department store is having a 3-day back-to-school sale starting on August 23. On what date will the sale end?

_____

18. Charles will attend camp from August 4 to August 18. How many weeks will he spend there?

_____

19. Charles returns from camp on August 18. How many days will he have before school starts?

_____

20. The Pirates played their last home game two weeks before school started. What was the date?

_____

Name _____

Write the correct answer.

For questions 1–2, use the grid.

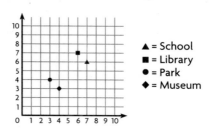

▲ = School
■ = Library
● = Park
◆ = Museum

1. Which ordered pair shows the location of the library?

   _____

2. What is located at (3,4)?

   _____

3. How many thousands are in 4,987?

   _____

4. During vacation Mayra read 4 times as many books as Kirk. Kirk read 6 books. How many books did Mayra read?

   _____

5. Which benchmark number can you use to estimate the number of pogs on Side 1 and Side 2?

   Side 1   Side 2

   _____

6. A 3-pack of yogurt costs $1.79. About how much should a 9-pack cost?

   _____

7. Write *seven hundred fourteen* in standard form.

   _____

8. Write 4,161 in expanded form.

   _____

9. What is another name for 7,200?

   _____

For questions 10–11, use the table.

SALES AT STEVE'S PIZZA SHOP	
Year	Sales
1994	14,163
1995	15,476
1996	16,597
1997	17,779

10. Between which two years did the number of sales increase the most?

   _____

11. How many more pizzas were sold in 1997 than in 1996?

   _____

12. Use the numbers 714 and 741 to complete the statement correctly.

   _____ > _____

Form B • Free-Response   B167   **Go on.** ▶

13. Write the greatest place-value position in which the digits differ in these numbers.

5,534
5,543

_____

14. Write the numbers in order from the greatest to the least.

1,561; 1,591; 1,516

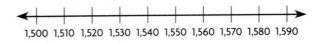

1,500 1,510 1,520 1,530 1,540 1,550 1,560 1,570 1,580 1,590

_____

For questions 15–16, use the Venn diagram.

Students Who Play Sports
Basketball   Track

Bill   Jena   Tom
Craig   Scott   Lisa
Pam   Leon   Brian

15. Which students play only basketball?

_____

16. Which students participate in both basketball and track?

_____

17. Show 14 minutes past twelve on the digital clock.

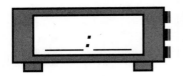

18. Bobby rode the school bus from 2:55 P.M. to 3:25 P.M. How many minutes was he on the bus?

_____

For questions 19–20, use the calendars.

January

Su	M	T	W	Th	F	Sa
				1	2	3	4
5	6	7	8	9	10	11
12	13	14	15	16	17	18
19	20	21	22	23	24	25
26	27	28	29	30	31	

February

Su	M	T	W	Th	F	Sa
						1
2	3	4	5	6	7	8
9	10	11	12	13	14	15
16	17	18	19	20	21	22
23	24	25	26	27	28	

19. How many days is it from January 29 to the first Friday in February?

_____

20. How many days are there from the first day of school on January 6 until the first test on January 27?

_____

Name _____

Write the correct answer.

1. $\begin{array}{r} 59 \\ 17 \\ +25 \\ \hline \end{array}$

2. Estimate the difference to the nearest ten dollars.

    $\begin{array}{r} \$58.25 \\ -\ 33.79 \\ \hline \end{array}$

3. $\begin{array}{r} \$3.56 \\ 3.93 \\ +\ 2.11 \\ \hline \end{array}$

4. $\begin{array}{r} 700 \\ -116 \\ \hline \end{array}$

5. Estimate the difference to the nearest hundred.

    $\begin{array}{r} 611 \\ -209 \\ \hline \end{array}$

6. Jill has 3 jars with 4 marbles in each jar. Write a number sentence that shows how many marbles Jill has in all.

    _____

7. Use the numbers 7 and 5 to write a number sentence that shows the Order Property of Multiplication.

    _____

8. $(5 \times 3) \times 2 = \underline{\quad ? \quad}$

    _____

9. A library has 9 rows of bookcases. There are 8 bookcases in each row. Write a number sentence and find how many bookcases there are in all.

    _____

10. On Saturday 3 friends went fishing. Each of the 3 friends caught 6 fish. How many fish did they catch in all?

    _____

11. What is a number sentence that is in the same fact family as $3 \times 9 = 27$?

    _____

12. Use the model to find the quotient.

$$25 \div 7 = \underline{\quad ? \quad}$$

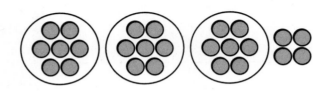

_____

For questions 13–14, use the multiplication table to find the quotient.

×	3	4	5
3	9	12	15
4	12	16	20
5	15	20	25

13. $12 \div 4 = \underline{\quad ? \quad}$

_____

14. $15 \div 3 = \underline{\quad ? \quad}$

_____

15. $6\overline{)30}$

_____

16. Mrs. Kaufman's students earned $63 at a car wash. They were paid $3 for each car they washed. How many cars in all did the students wash?

_____

17. Write whether the number is a *cardinal, ordinal,* or *nominal* number.

_____

18. What digit is in the tens place in 2,876?

_____

19. There are 30 marbles in a jar now. About how many marbles could the jar hold?

_____

20. What is the value of the digit 5 in the number 543?

_____

21. What is *five hundred ninety-two* written in standard form?

_____

22. What is *seven million, three hundred thirty-five thousand, nine hundred seventy-four* written in standard form?

_____

23. How do you write 8,463,587 with period names?

_____

For questions 24–25, use mental math.

24.   800
         +300

_____

25.   9,000
         +3,000

_____

26. Use the number line to compare. Write < or > for the ●.

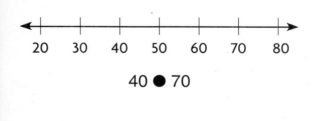

40 ● 70

_____

27. Use the numbers 756 and 765 to complete the statement.

_____ > _____

28. Write < or > for the ●.

432 ● 423

_____

For questions 29–30, use the table.

VISITORS TO THE SCIENCE MUSEUM	
Week	**Number of Visitors**
1	1,291
2	1,452
3	1,312
4	1,276
5	1,495

29. During which week did the most visitors go to the Science Museum?

_____

30. During which week did the fewest visitors go to the Science Museum?

_____

For questions 31–32, use the Venn diagram.

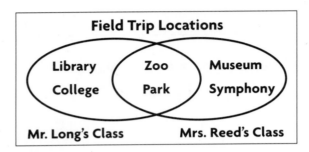

Field Trip Locations

Library
College
Zoo
Park
Museum
Symphony

Mr. Long's Class   Mrs. Reed's Class

31. To which locations did only Mr. Long's class go?

_____

32. To which locations did both classes go?

_____

33. Show 45 minutes past eight on the digital clock.

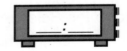

34. You look in the sky and see a rainbow at 10:00. Is this A.M. or P.M.?

_____

For questions 35–36, use the schedule.

CITY SIGHTSEEING TOUR		
Tour	Start Time	Finish Time
A	11:15 A.M.	1:45 P.M.
B	11:45 A.M.	?
C	12:15 P.M.	2:45 P.M.
D	?	6:15 P.M.
All tours last 2 hours 30 minutes.		

35. At what time does Tour B finish?

_____

36. At what time does Tour D start?

_____

For questions 37–38, use the calendars.

May						
Su	M	T	W	Th	F	Sa
				1	2	3
4	5	6	7	8	9	10
11	12	13	14	15	16	17
18	19	20	21	22	23	24
25	26	27	28	29	30	31

June						
Su	M	T	W	Th	F	Sa
1	2	3	4	5	6	7
8	9	10	11	12	13	14
15	16	17	18	19	20	21
22	23	24	25	26	27	28
29	30					

37. The circus will be in town for 6 days starting on June 4. What date will be the last day for the circus to be in town?

_____

38. Caroline is going to visit her cousin from May 24 to June 7. How many weeks will she spend with her cousin?

_____

Name _____

Write the correct answer.

For questions 1–3, use the frequency table.

NUMBER OF MILES TERESA JOGGED

Week	Miles (Frequency)	Cumulative Frequency
1	14	14
2	11	25
3	20	?
4	18	?

1. During which week did Teresa jog farthest?

_____

2. How many more miles did Teresa jog in Week 1 than in Week 2?

_____

3. What is the cumulative frequency for the miles jogged in all 4 weeks?

_____

4. You can order a turkey, tuna, peanut butter, or cheese sandwich on white bread or on rye bread. How many sandwich choices are there?

_____

5. Bob can play with his toy trucks, cars, motorcycles, and vans in a toy garage, roadway, or car wash or in a sandbox. How many ways can he spend his time playing?

_____

6. Mr. Eng is having a picnic. He must decide if he should prepare beef, chicken, lamb, or veal. What survey question should he ask his guests?

_____

For questions 7–8, use the data in the table.

FAVORITE JUICE	
Choice	**Votes**
Orange	卌 卌 IIII
Apple	卌 II
Grape	卌 I
Pineapple	卌 IIII

7. Which juice was chosen as the favorite by the greatest number of people?

_____

8. Which juice was the favorite of the fewest people?

_____

For questions 9–11, use the graph.

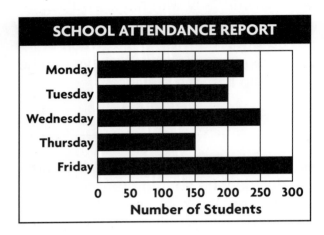

SCHOOL ATTENDANCE REPORT

Monday
Tuesday
Wednesday
Thursday
Friday

0   50   100 150 200 250 300
Number of Students

For questions 12–15, use the graph.

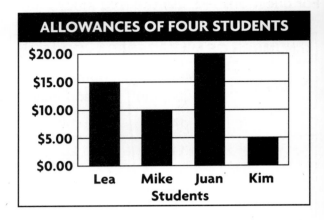

ALLOWANCES OF FOUR STUDENTS

$20.00
$15.00
$10.00
$5.00
$0.00

Lea   Mike   Juan   Kim
Students

9. How many students were in school on Thursday?

   _____

10. What interval is used in the scale of the graph?

   _____

11. How many more students were in school on Wednesday than on Monday?

   _____

12. What interval is used in the scale of the graph?

   _____

13. How would the length of the bars change if an interval of $1.00 were used in the graph?

   _____

14. How much more is Lea's allowance than Kim's?

   _____

15. How much do all 4 students combined receive each week?

   _____

Name _____

Write the correct answer.

For questions 1–6, use the line graph.

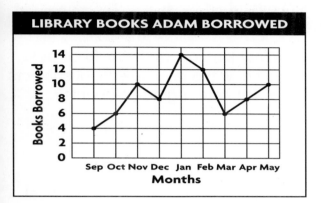

LIBRARY BOOKS ADAM BORROWED

1. Why is a line graph a good choice for showing this information?

   _____

2. What interval is used on the scale of this graph?

   _____

3. How many books did Adam borrow in November?

   _____

4. In which month did Adam borrow the most books?

   _____

5. In how many months did Adam borrow exactly 6 books?

   _____

6. How many more books did Adam borrow in February than in April?

   _____

For questions 7–11, use the line plot. There is one X for each student.

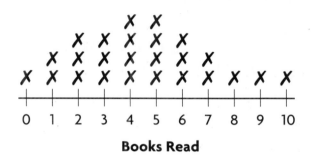

Books Read

7. What do the numbers on the line plot represent?

   _____

8. What is the range of data used in this line plot?

   _____

9. How many students read 6 books?

   _____

10. What was the greatest number of books read?

   _____

11. How many books were read in all by students who read 4 books?

   _____

Form B • Free-Response   **Go on.** ▶

For questions 12–16, use the stem-and-leaf plot.

SCORES ON SCIENCE TEST	
Stem	Leaves
6	2 6 8
7	0 0 2 2 4 4 6 6
8	0 1 2 2 2 4 4 8 8
9	0 2 4 4 6

12. How would you find the highest score on the test?

_____

13. What is the middle number in this set of data called?

_____

14. What is the mode for this data?

_____

15. What is the median for this data?

_____

16. What is the difference between the highest score and the lowest score?

_____

For questions 17–20, choose the type of graph that would be best to display the data described.

17. What kind of graph would be best to show the favorite school subjects of 100 fourth-grade students?

_____

18. What kind of graph would be best to show how much a baby has grown over time?

_____

19. Would a bar graph or a stem-and-leaf plot be better to compare the heights in inches of 30 fourth-grade students?

_____

20. What kind of graph would be best to display the data in the table?

FAVORITE RADIO STATIONS OF FOURTH-GRADE BOYS AND GIRLS		
Station	Boys	Girls
103 AM	11	6
107.5 FM	9	18
98.9 FM	3	7

_____

Write the correct answer.

1. An event is _?_ if it never happens.

    _____

2. A bag contains pennies and dimes. It is _?_ to pull a quarter out of the bag.

    _____

For questions 3–4, use the spinner.

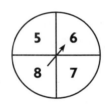

3. Using this spinner, you are certain to spin a number less than _?_ .

    _____

4. Using this spinner it is impossible to spin a number greater than _?_ .

    _____

For questions 5–6, use the tally table.

NUMBER OF MARBLES IN A BAG	
Red	ЖЖ ЖЖ ЖЖ II
Blue	III
Yellow	ЖЖ II
Green	ЖЖ ЖЖ ЖЖ ЖЖ III

5. Which outcome is most likely if a marble is pulled from the bag?

    _____

6. Which color are you unlikely to pull?

    _____

For questions 7–8, use the spinner.

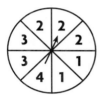

7. Which number are you most likely to spin on this spinner?

    _____

8. Which number are you unlikely to spin?

    _____

For questions 9–10, use the box.

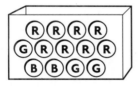

9. If you pull a counter from the box ten times, which color counter are you most likely to pull?

    _____

10. If you pull a counter from the box ten times, which color counter are you unlikely to pull?

    _____

For questions 11–12, use a number cube that has 6 sides, labeled 1, 2, 3, 4, 5, and 6.

11. What is the probability of rolling a 3?

_____

12. What is the probability of rolling an even number?

_____

For questions 13–14, use the spinner.

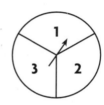

13. What is the probability of spinning a 2 or a 3?

_____

14. What is the probability of spinning a 4?

_____

15. If each player has an equal chance of winning a game, the game is _?_ .

_____

For questions 16–17, use the spinners.

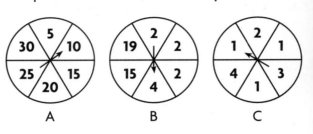

A   B   C

In this game, the "odd" player gets points for odd numbers and the "even" player gets points for even numbers.

16. Which spinner gives both players an equal chance to win?

_____

17. If you were the "even" player, which spinner would give you the greatest probability of winning?

_____

18. Lupe's spinner is divided into 3 equal sections. There is 1 red section, 1 white section, and 1 blue section. Tell why the spinner is fair or not fair.

_____

Form B • Free-Response   B178   ▶ **Stop!**

Name _____

Write the correct answer.

For questions 1–2, use the table.

INCHES OF SNOW IN JANUARY		
Week	Inches	Cumulative Inches
1	6	6
2	3	9
3	19	?
4	6	?

1. During which week did the most snow fall?

_____

2. What was the cumulative amount of snowfall in all 4 weeks?

_____

For questions 3–4, use the table.

FAVORITE FOOD	
Choice	Votes
Pizza	JHT JHT JHT III
Hamburger	JHT JHT II
Spaghetti	JHT JHT JHT
Hot dog	JHT JHT

3. Which food was chosen as their favorite by the most students?

_____

4. Which food was the favorite of the fewest students?

_____

For questions 5–6, use the bar graph.

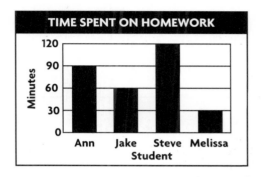

5. What interval is used on the scale of the graph?

_____

6. How would the length of the bars change if four intervals of 60 were used on the graph?

_____

For questions 7–8, use the line graph.

7. What interval is used on the scale of the graph?

_____

8. Which month had the lowest number of sales?

_____

For questions 9–10, use the line plot. There is one X for each student.

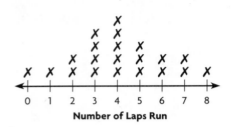

Number of Laps Run

9. What is the range of data used in the line plot?

_____

10. How many students ran 4 laps?

_____

For questions 11–12, use the stem-and-leaf plot.

Stem	Leaves
6	7 8 8
7	4 4 7 8
8	3 6 7 7 7
9	2 5 8

Bowling Scores

11. What number is the median for the data?

_____

12. What is the difference between the highest score and the lowest score?

_____

For questions 13–14, use the box.

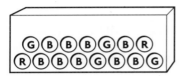

13. Which color counter is it impossible for you to pull—blue, yellow, red, or green?

_____

14. If you pull a counter from the box ten times, which color counter are you unlikely to pull?

_____

For questions 15–16, use the spinners.

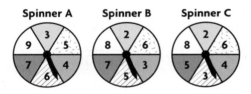

In this game, the "odd" player gets points for odd numbers and the "even" player gets points for even numbers.

15. Which spinner gives both players an equal chance to win?

_____

16. If you were the "even" player, which spinner would give you the greatest probability of winning?

_____

Write the correct answer.

1. What is a reasonable estimate of the sum?

$$\begin{array}{r} 212 \\ 396 \\ +101 \\ \hline \end{array}$$

_____

2. $$\begin{array}{r} 6,000 \\ -3,987 \\ \hline \end{array}$$

_____

3. A farmer has 3 barns. He has 5 cows in each barn. How many cows does he have in all?

_____

4. $(4 \times 2) \times 7 = \underline{\ ?\ }$

_____

5. There are 54 students taking a trip. They will go in 6 vans. How many students will ride in each van?

_____

6. What number sentence is in the same fact family as these number sentences?

$$3 \times 4 = 12$$
$$4 \times 3 = 12$$
$$12 \div 3 = 4$$

_____

7. $14 \div 3 = \underline{\ ?\ }$

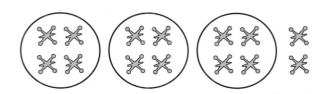

_____

For questions 8–9, use the multiplication table to find the quotient.

×	2	3	4
2	4	6	8
3	6	9	12
4	8	12	16

8. $16 \div 4 = \underline{\ ?\ }$

_____

9. $9 \div 3 = \underline{\ ?\ }$

_____

10. Earl has 18 books stored on 3 shelves. He put the same number on each shelf. How many books are on each shelf?

_____

11. Sue Ellen is 25 years old. Is the number 25 *cardinal, ordinal,* or *nominal?*

_____

12. How many tens are in 9,265?

_____

13. In the number 400, what is the value of 4?

_____

14. What are these numbers in order from the least to the greatest?

872, 869, 857

_____

For questions 15–16, use the Venn diagram.

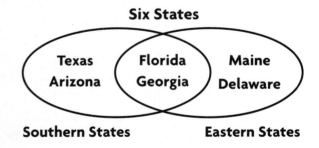

Six States

Texas
Arizona

Florida
Georgia

Maine
Delaware

Southern States   **Eastern States**

15. Which states are eastern states only?

_____

16. Which states are both southern states and eastern states?

_____

17. What unit of time would you use to measure how long it takes to prepare a bowl of cereal?

_____

18. Which time is closer to the time that school starts—8:00 A.M. or 8:00 P.M.?

_____

For questions 19–20, use the schedule.

Bus	Leave Johnson City	Arrive Fosterville
A	8:00 A.M.	9:50 A.M.
B	9:30 A.M.	?
C	11:10 A.M.	?
D	1:45 P.M.	?
Each trip lasts 1 hour and 50 minutes.		

19. At what time does Bus B arrive in Fosterville?

_____

20. Mr. Lorenzo has a meeting in Fosterville at 2:00 P.M. Which is the latest bus he could take to arrive at the meeting on time?

_____

For questions 21–22, use the table.

BOXES OF COOKIES SOLD		
Week	Number Sold (Frequency)	Cumulative Frequency
1	235	235
2	175	410
3	150	?

21. During which week were the most boxes of cookies sold?

_____

22. What was the total number of boxes of cookies sold during the 3 weeks?

_____

23. A teacher will survey students to find out whether they want to play soccer, basketball, or baseball on Sports Day. What survey question would be the most useful for the teacher to ask?

_____

For questions 24–25, use the graph.

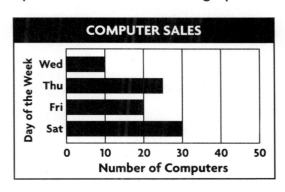

24. What interval is used in the scale of the graph?

_____

25. How many more computers were sold on Saturday than were sold on Friday?

_____

For questions 26–27, use the line graph.

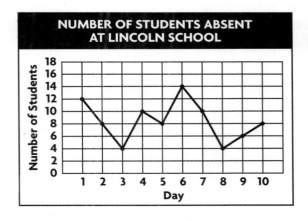

26. How many students were absent on Day 4?

_____

27. On which days were the fewest students absent?

_____

For questions 28–29, use the line plot. There is one X for each student.

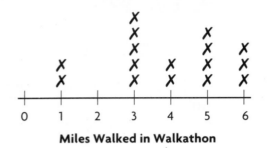

Miles Walked in Walkathon

28. How many students walked 3 miles?

_____

29. What was the greatest number of miles walked by any student?

_____

For questions 30–31, use the stem-and-leaf plot.

Stem	Leaves
7	2 4 6 6
8	4 6 6 8 8
9	2 4 4 4 4 6 8

**Scores on a Spelling Test
for 16 Students**

30. What number is the mode for these data?

_____

31. What number is the median for these data?

_____

32. What graph would be best to show how many girls were absent and how many boys were absent each day for a week?

_____

For questions 33–36, use the spinner.

33. Using this spinner, it is impossible to spin a number greater than __?__.

_____

34. What number are you most likely to spin on this spinner?

_____

35. What is the probability of spinning a 1?

_____

36. What is the probability of spinning a 3?

_____

Name _____

Write the correct answer.

For questions 1–2, tell whether the figure is one-dimensional, two-dimensional, or three-dimensional.

1.

_____

2.

_____

3. What unit would be used to measure the area of a large blackboard?

_____

4. What unit would be used to measure the volume of a refrigerator?

_____

For questions 5–6, use the figure.

5. How many faces are on this figure?

_____

6. What two plane figures are the faces of this figure?

_____

For questions 7–8, use this figure.

7. How many faces does this figure have?

_____

8. Each face on this figure is a ? .

_____

For questions 9–11, use the figure.

9. How many faces does this figure have?

_____

10. How many edges does this figure have?

_____

11. How many vertices does this figure have?

_____

For questions 12–15, use the grid.

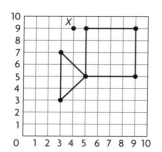

12. Write the ordered pair for point *x*.

_____

13. Write the ordered pairs of the vertices of the square marked on the grid.

_____

14. Write the ordered pairs of the vertices of the triangle marked on the grid.

_____

15. Which ordered pair identifies the vertex that is shared by the square *and* the triangle?

_____

16. Ralph placed a can of beans, a roll of mints, and a can of soda in his grocery basket. Which term best describes the shapes of these objects?

_____

17. What is the shape of a globe, a round balloon, and a marble?

_____

18. Circle the figure that belongs in the overlapped section of this Venn diagram.

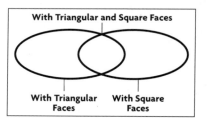

 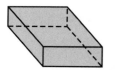

For questions 19–20, use the organized list.

19. Which heading can be used for the last column?

Rectangular Prisms	Cylinders	?
book candy box ?	lipstick straw pen	party hat ice-cream cone

_____

20. Which figure listed below could be listed under **Rectangular Prisms**?

pencil shoe box	soup can basketball

_____

Write the correct answer.

1. The part of a line between point *A* and point *B* is called a __?__ .

_____

2. Is a flat surface with no end called a plane, a line segment, a line, or a point?

_____

3. Are line segments that never cross and are the same distance apart called *parallel lines* or *perpendicular lines*?

_____

4. What term names these figures?

_____

5. What kind of angle is the following?

_____

6. What is the name of this figure?

_____

7. Are lines that cross each other called *parallel lines* or *intersecting lines*?

_____

8. Are lines that intersect to form four right angles called *parallel lines* or *perpendicular lines*?

_____

For questions 9–10, use the map.

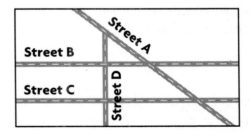

9. Which street is perpendicular to Streets B and C?

_____

10. Which street is parallel to Street B?

_____

11. Do all polygons have straight sides or curved sides?

_____

12. What is this figure called?

_____

13. An octagon has 8 sides. How many angles does it have?

_____

14. A hexagon has 6 angles. How many sides does it have?

_____

15. How many angles does a quadrilateral have?

_____

16. I am a 4-sided polygon. I have 2 pairs of parallel sides. I have 2 congruent acute angles and 2 congruent obtuse angles. What am I?

_____

17. What is the name of this figure?

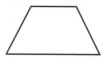

_____

18. What is the name of this figure?

_____

19. Circle the figure that does *not* have 4 right angles.

20. Martin drew a 4-sided figure. It had 4 right angles and 2 sets of parallel lines of equal length. What shape was his figure?

_____

Write the correct answer.

1. Write a number sentence to find the perimeter of this figure.

_____

2. Write a number sentence to find the perimeter of this figure.

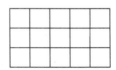

_____

For questions 3–4, find the perimeter.

3.

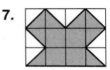

4m

6m

_____

4.

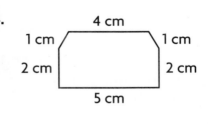

4 cm
1 cm   1 cm
2 cm   2 cm
5 cm

_____

5. A garden is 62 feet long and 25 feet wide. How many feet of fencing are needed to go around the garden?

_____

6. Students are hanging a banner all the way around the four walls of their classroom. Each wall is 40 feet long. How long is the banner?

_____

For questions 7–8, find the area.

7.

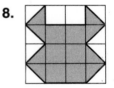

_____

8.

_____

9. Estimate the area.

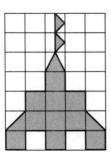

_____

10. Estimate the area.

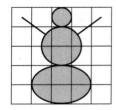

_____

11. Find the area.

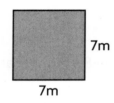

7m

7m

_____

12. Find the area.

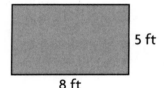

5 ft

8 ft

_____

13. How many square feet of wallpaper do you need to cover a wall that is 8 feet high and 10 feet wide?

_____

14. The dog's pen is 7 yards by 9 yards. How much area does the dog have?

_____

For questions 15–18, use the shaded figures below.

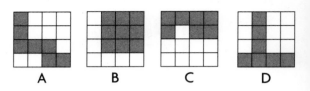

A   B   C   D

15. What is the perimeter of Figure B?

_____

16. What is the area of Figure C?

_____

17. Which figure has the same area as Figure D but a different perimeter?

_____

18. Which two figures have the same area and the same perimeter?

_____

19. Screen costs $2.00 per square foot. The screen door is 7 feet by 3 feet. How much does screen for the door cost?

_____

20. Pia has a rope that is 48 feet long. What is the greatest square area she can rope off?

_____

Name _____

Write the correct answer.

1. A figure that has been turned around a point or vertex is called a __?__.

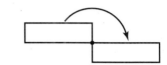

_____

For questions 2–3, use the figures.

2. Figure A is an example of a __?__.

_____

3. Figure B is an example of a __?__.

_____

4. If two figures have the same size and shape, they are __?__.

_____

5. Circle the two figures that are congruent.

6. Draw a figure that is congruent to the figure shown.

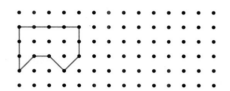

7. Circle the figure that has point symmetry.

8. Draw a line of symmetry through this figure.

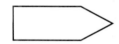

9. Circle the figure that has line symmetry.

Form B • Free-Response   B191   **Go on.** ▶

10. A pattern of repeated polygons with no gaps or overlaps is called a _?_.

_____

11. Draw the figure that tessellates in this design.

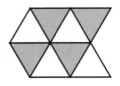 _____

12. Circle the figure that will tessellate.

13. What figures are used in this tessellation?

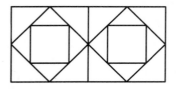

_____

14. A figure is drawn on 1-cm grid paper. If you copy the figure on 2-cm paper, it will be the same but _?_.

_____

For questions 15–17, use the pairs of figures.

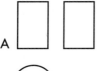

15. In which pair are the figures congruent?

_____

16. In which pair are the figures similar but not congruent?

_____

17. You could describe the figures in pair B as neither similar nor _?_.

_____

18. Luz has a design on grid paper. How can she reduce the size of the design and be sure it is the same as the original design?

_____

_____

Name _____

Write the correct answer.

1. Tell whether the figure is one-dimensional, two-dimensional, or three-dimensional.

_____

For questions 2–3, use the figure.

2. How many faces are on the figure?

_____

3. What plane figure is each face of the figure?

_____

For questions 4–6, use the grid.

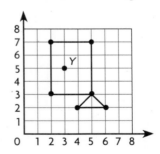

4. What is the ordered pair for point Y?

_____

5. What ordered pairs identify the three vertices of the triangle?

_____

6. Which ordered pair identifies the point that is a vertex shared by the rectangle and the triangle?

_____

7. What is Figure XY called?

_____

For questions 8–9, use the map.

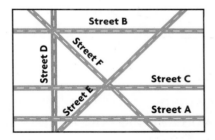

8. Which street is perpendicular to Streets B and C?

_____

9. Which streets are parallel to Street A?

_____

Form B • Free-Response   B193   **Go on.** ▶

10. What is the figure called?

_____

11. A rectangle has sides 7 cm long and 5 cm long. What is the perimeter of the rectangle?

_____

12. A patio is 25 feet long and 15 feet wide. How many feet is the border?

_____

13. Find the area of the shaded figure.

_____

14. How many square feet of carpet do you need to cover a floor that is 10 feet long and 12 feet wide?

_____

For questions 15–16, use the shaded figures.

15. What is the perimeter of Figure C?

_____

16. Which figures have the same area?

_____

17. When you flip a figure over a line, it is called a __?__ .

_____

18. Which two figures are congruent?

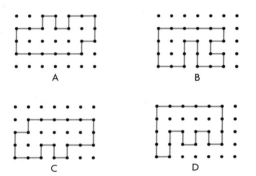

19. Which figure has point symmetry?

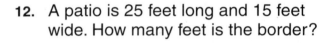

_____

20. What figure is used in the tessellation?

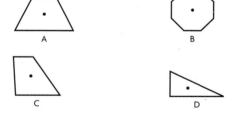

_____

Name _____

Write the correct answer.

1. $9 - 7 = 6 -$ ___?___

_____

2. There are 136 people holding the ropes of a blimp. There are 42 people on the left side, 45 on the right side, and 31 at the front. How many people are holding the ropes at the back?

_____

3. Choose the operation that can be used to solve the problem. Then write a number sentence and solve.

   Val wrote 7 pages in one day and 6 pages the next day. How many pages did Val write in all?

_____

4. $9\overline{)81}$

_____

5. Write whether this number is a *cardinal, ordinal,* or *nominal* number.

SPEED LIMIT
55
Miles Per Hour

_____

6. A 6-pack of soda costs $1.49. About how much should a 12-pack cost?

_____

7. Write the number with the digit 6 in the hundreds place, 0 in the ones place, and 3 in the tens place.

_____

8. $\begin{array}{r} 700 \\ +400 \\ \hline \end{array}$

_____

9. Compare 3,225 and 3,252. Use the numbers to complete the statement.

_____ $<$ _____

10. Compare the numbers. Write $<$, $>$, or $=$ for ◯.

    479 ◯ 497

11. You can join the band, drama club, or choir. Each activity has a beginners, intermediate, and advanced group. How many choices are there?

_____

12. Mr. Gold is renting a video for the movie club. He must decide whether to rent a comedy, a musical, a drama, or an action movie. What survey question should he ask the club members?

_____

For questions 13–14, use the graph.

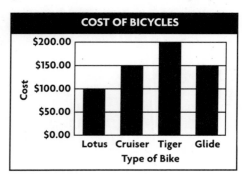

COST OF BICYCLES

13. What interval is used in the scale of the graph?

_____

14. How much more is a Tiger than a Lotus?

_____

For questions 15–16, use the line plot. There is one X for each student.

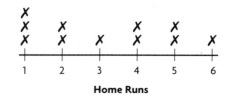

Home Runs

15. What is the range of data used in the line plot?

_____

16. How many students hit 4 home runs?

_____

For questions 17–18, choose the kind of graph that would be best to display the data described.

17. What kind of graph would be best to compare favorite movie choices of boys to favorite movie choices of girls?

_____

18. What kind of graph would best show how much the population of a city has changed over time?

_____

19. A bag contains nickels, dimes, quarters, and pennies. You are ___?___ to pull a coin out of the bag.

_____

20. Which unit would be used to measure the area of a dance floor?

_____

For questions 21–22, use the figure.

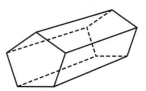

21. How many faces are on the figure?

_____

22. What two plane figures are the faces of the figure?

_____

For questions 23–24, use the grid.

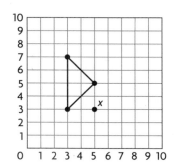

23. What is the ordered pair for point *x*?

_____

24. What set of ordered pairs identifies the vertices of the triangle marked on the grid?

_____

For questions 25–26, use the organized list.

Cubes	?	Cones
ice cube ? box	food can drinking straw telephone pole	ice-cream cone drink cups

25. Which heading can be used for the middle column?

_____

26. Which object listed below could be listed under **Cubes**?

pen	toy block
shoe box	football
	sheet of paper

_____

27. What is the name of the figure?

_____

28. What is the name of the figure?

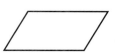

_____

29. An octagon has 8 sides. How many angles does it have?

_____

30. What is the name of the figure?

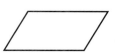

_____

31. What is the perimeter?

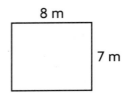

8 m

7 m

_____

32. What is the area of the shaded part? Each square is one unit.

_____

33. Tile costs $4.00 per square foot. The hallway is 8 feet by 3 feet. How much does tile for the hallway cost?

_____

34. A figure that has been moved from one point to another is called a ___?___ .

_____

35. Two figures that are congruent have the same shape and ___?___ .

_____

36. Circle the figure that has point symmetry.

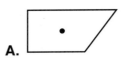

A.

B.

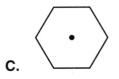

C.

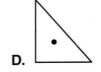

D.

37. What plane figures are used in the tessellation?

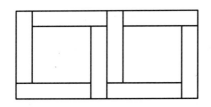

_____

38. In which pair are the figures similar and congruent?

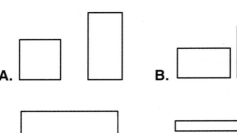

A.

B.

C.

D.

_____

Name _____

Write the correct answer.

1. Write the number that completes the pattern.

   $6 \times 40 = 240$

   $6 \times 400 = 2,400$

   $6 \times \underline{\ ?\ } = 24,000$

   _____

2. Write the number that completes the pattern.

   $2 \times 80 = 160$

   $2 \times \underline{\ ?\ } = 1,600$

   $2 \times 8,000 = 16,000$

   _____

3. $7 \times 40 = n$

   _____

4. $\begin{array}{r} 50 \\ \times\ 9 \\ \hline \end{array}$

5. $\begin{array}{r} 400 \\ \times\ \ 8 \\ \hline \end{array}$

6. $3 \times 5,000 = n$

   _____

For questions 7–8, use the model place-value chart.

Tens	Ones

7. Write the multiplication sentence that the base-ten blocks show.

   _____

8. Solve the multiplication problem shown by the model. Write the product.

   _____ tens _____ ones, or _____

For questions 9–10, use the following student work.

9. How did Pilar get the partial product 36?

   _____

10. What should Pilar record as the product?

    _____

11. 221
    × 4

12. 108
    × 7

13. 514
    × 3

14. 623
    × 8

15. There are 175 toothpicks in a box. How many toothpicks are there in 5 boxes?

_____

16. A machine makes 625 bottle caps in 1 minute. How many bottle caps does it make in 4 minutes?

_____

17. $7.29
    × 2

18. $6 \times \$5.27 = n$

_____

For questions 19–20, write a number sentence that can be used to solve the problem and solve.

19. Sarah spends $2.95 for lunch each day. How much does she spend in 5 days?

_____

20. Peter spent $6.50 to wash his car. He paid with a $10 bill. How much change did he get?

_____

Write the correct answer.

For questions 1–3, find the product by using a basic fact and a pattern of zeros.

1. $5 \times 7 = 35$

$5 \times 70 = 350$

$50 \times 70 = 3{,}500$

$50 \times 700 = n$

_____

2. $80 \times 60 = n$

_____

3. $40 \times 500 = n$

_____

4. A building has 20 sets of stairs. Each set of stairs has 30 steps. How many steps does the building have?

_____

5. Debra has a puzzle. When she says 5, the answer is 150. When she says 10, the answer is 300. When she says 20, the answer is 600. What is the pattern?

_____

6. Write a number sentence to estimate the product of 57×31.

_____

For questions 7–8, write a reasonable estimate for the product.

7. $82 \times 23 = n;$

_____

8. $\begin{array}{r} 493 \\ \times\ 71 \\ \hline \end{array}$

_____

9. An airplane makes 12 flights a week and carries 103 people on each flight. What is a reasonable estimate of the number of people the airplane carries?

_____

10. A rain forest averages 39 inches of rain per month. What is a reasonable estimate of the amount of rain that would fall in 12 months?

_____

Form B • Free-Response

Go on. ▶

11. Sarah is using the partial-products method to multiply 73 and 48. Her next step should be to multiply __?__ by 40.

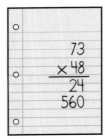

$$\begin{array}{r} 73 \\ \times\ 48 \\ \hline 24 \\ 560 \end{array}$$

_____

12. John is using a shorter way to multiply 73 and 48. His next step should be to multiply __?__ by 40.

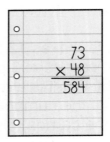

$$\begin{array}{r} 73 \\ \times\ 48 \\ \hline 584 \end{array}$$

_____

13. $\begin{array}{r} 53 \\ \times\ 76 \\ \hline \end{array}$

_____

14. $\begin{array}{r} \$39 \\ \times\ 26 \\ \hline \end{array}$

_____

15. $55 \times 82 = n$

_____

16. Carol is multiplying 219 by 18. Which operation should she perform next?

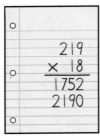

$$\begin{array}{r} 219 \\ \times\ 18 \\ \hline 1752 \\ 2190 \end{array}$$

_____

17. $\begin{array}{r} 456 \\ \times\ 38 \\ \hline \end{array}$

_____

18. $\begin{array}{r} \$2.38 \\ \times\ 59 \\ \hline \end{array}$

_____

19. A bicycle wheel has 112 spokes. How many spokes are on 6 bicycle wheels?

_____

20. A telephone book has 270 names on each page. How many names are on 95 pages?

_____

Write the correct answer.

1. To check the quotient for this division problem, first multiply 5 times __?__ .

$$\frac{5\ r1}{8)\overline{41}}$$

_____

2. An even number can be divided by 2 with no __?__ .

_____

3. $7)\overline{47}$

4. $4)\overline{29}$

5. When you divide by 7, what is the largest possible remainder?

_____

6. The next step in solving this problem is to divide __?__ by 4.

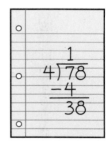

_____

7. $7)\overline{85}$

8. $5)\overline{93}$

9. The first digit in the quotient should be placed in the __?__ place.

$5)\overline{76}$

_____

10. How many digits will be in the quotient?

$4)\overline{93}$

_____

11. Six friends are having a bake sale. They want a total of 120 cookies to sell. How many cookies should each person bake?

_____

12. There were 266 crackers in a carton. They were divided equally among 7 people. How many crackers did each person receive?

_____

13. At the end of art class, the students put an equal number of crayons into each box. All but 1 of the 118 crayons fit into the boxes. How many boxes were used?

_____

14. The first digit of the quotient should be placed over the __?__ .

$8\overline{)753}$

_____

Divide.

15. $7\overline{)58}$

_____

16. $374 \div 4 = n$

_____

17. $319 \div 6 = n$

_____

18. A table in the lunchroom has space for 6 students. How many tables are needed to hold 126 students?

_____

19. A gallon of milk contains 8 pints. If 128 students each drink 1 pint of milk, how many gallons will they drink?

_____

20. Mike has 528 baseball cards. He has an equal number in each of 4 shoe boxes. How many baseball cards are in each shoe box?

_____

Write the correct answer.

For questions 1–2, use a basic fact and a pattern of zeros to find the quotient.

1. $24 \div 6 = 4$

$2,400 \div 6 = n$

_____

2. $21 \div 7 = 3$

$21,000 \div 7 = n$

_____

For questions 3–4, estimate. Use a basic fact and a pattern of zeros to estimate the quotient.

3. $63,017 \div 9 = n$

_____

4. $4,123 \div 7 = n$

_____

5. What number belongs in the tens place of the quotient?

_____

6. $4\overline{)824}$

_____

7. $7\overline{)985}$

_____

8. A farmer picks 125 pumpkins in 5 days. How many pumpkins does he pick each day?

_____

9. On sports day the P.E. teacher separated 176 students into teams of 8. How many teams were there?

_____

10. $3\overline{)\$18.03}$

_____

11. $6\overline{)\$13.80}$

_____

12. $9\overline{)\$7.29}$

_____

13. Baseball cards cost $4.50 for 6. What is the cost for each card?

_____

14. Mr. Waller is buying 3 bags of sand for $25.50. What is the cost for each bag?

_____

For questions 15–16, tell how you interpret the remainder.

15. Larry has 250 pieces of candy and 3 bags. He wants to put an equal amount of candy in each bag. How many pieces of candy will he put in each bag?

_____

16. Mrs. Fox needs 135 pencils for her class. There are 6 pencils in a package. How many packages does she need to buy?

_____

17. Mr. Robinson bought 475 feet of rope. He will cut the rope into 6-foot lengths. How many 6-foot lengths can he cut?

_____

18. Sue Ellen has to do 144 math problems. How many problems should she do each day to be sure she finishes in 5 days?

_____

19. Sandra can make 1 bracelet in 7 minutes. How many bracelets can she make in 130 minutes?

_____

20. Pete can make a key chain in 9 minutes. How many key chains can he make in 162 minutes?

_____

For questions 21–24, solve. Name the operation you used.

21. Jose's family recycled 120 pounds of newspaper in June, 136 pounds in July, and 163 pounds in August. How many pounds did they recycle in all?

_____

22. The basketball game lasts 48 minutes. Each of the 4 quarters takes the same amount of time. How long is each quarter?

_____

23. Josh is climbing a mountain that is 953 feet high. He has climbed 208 feet. How many more feet does he have to climb?

_____

24. Delia does 45 minutes of home-work each night after school. How many minutes of homework will she do in 20 school nights?

_____

Name _____

Write the correct answer.

1. Write the number that completes the pattern.
$3 \times 40 = 120$
$3 \times 400 = 1,200$
$3 \times \underline{\ ?\ } = 12,000$

_____

2. 500
    $\times\ \ 6$

_____

3. 278
    $\times\ \ 4$

_____

4. There are 150 seats in each section of a ball park. How many seats are in 7 sections?

_____

5. $5 \times \$4.95 = \underline{\ ?\ }$

_____

6. Write a number sentence that can be used to solve the problem and solve.

Bobby saves $1.75 of his allowance each week. How much does he save in 3 weeks?

_____

7. $20 \times 600 = n$

_____

8. Lauren was putting pennies in penny wrappers. Each penny wrapper held 50 pennies. Lauren filled 20 penny wrappers. How many pennies did Lauren have?

_____

9. A truck makes 7 trips a month and carries 53 packages on each trip. What is a reasonable estimate of the number of packages the truck carries each month?

_____

10. 35
    $\times 58$

_____

11. $4.37
    $\times\ \ 26$

_____

12. A library has 175 books on each shelf. How many books are on 80 shelves?

_____

Form B • Free-Response   B207   **Go on.** ▶

13. $6\overline{)39}$

_____

14. When you divide by 6, what is the largest possible remainder?

_____

15. $8\overline{)62}$

_____

16. At the end of computer class, the students put an equal number of diskettes into each box. All but 2 of the 121 diskettes fit into the boxes. How many boxes were used?

_____

17. $172 \div 5 = n$

_____

18. A school plans to use 4 buses for a field trip. If 220 students go on the field trip, how many will ride in each bus?

_____

19. Use a basic fact and a pattern of zeros to find the quotient.
$27 \div 9 = 3$
$270 \div 9 = 30$
$2,700 \div 9 = n$
$27,000 \div 9 = 3,000$

_____

20. $2\overline{)416}$

_____

21. $3\overline{)572}$

_____

22. $6\overline{)\$4.38}$

_____

23. A farmer bought 225 gallons of fertilizer. He will pour the fertilizer into 8-gallon containers. How many 8-gallon containers can he fill? How much fertilizer will be left over?

_____

24. Solve and name the operation you used.

A school play lasts 42 minutes. Each of the 6 scenes takes the same amount of time. How long is each scene?

_____

Form B • Free-Response ▶ **Stop!**

Name _____

Write the correct answer.

1. The perimeter of the figure is 706 feet. What is the missing length?

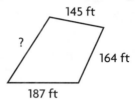

145 ft

?

164 ft

187 ft

_____

2. Use the multiplication fact to help you find the quotient.

$$3 \times 9 = 27$$
$$27 \div 9 = \underline{\ ?\ }$$

_____

3. How many hundreds are in 6,942?

_____

4. What are these numbers in order from the least to the greatest?
8,273; 9,134; 8,749.

_____

For questions 5–7, use the graph.

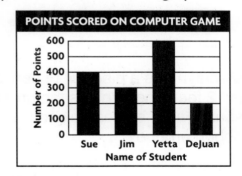

POINTS SCORED ON COMPUTER GAME

Number of Points: 600, 500, 400, 300, 200, 100, 0

Sue   Jim   Yetta   DeJuan
Name of Student

5. What interval is used in the scale of the graph?

_____

6. How much more is Yetta's score than Sue's score?

_____

7. How many points did all 4 students combined score?

_____

For questions 8–9, use the stem-and-leaf plot.

High Temperatures for One Month

Stem	Leaves
6	7, 8, 8, 8, 9, 9, 9
7	0, 1, 2, 3, 3, 6, 7, 8
8	0, 2, 2, 2, 2, 5, 6, 7, 8, 9
9	0, 0, 1, 1, 1

8. What number is the mode for the data?

_____

9. What is the difference between the highest temperature and the lowest temperature?

_____

For questions 10–11, use the tally table.

NUMBER OF DISKS IN A BAG	
Gold	卌 ||
Silver	卌 卌 卌 |
Bronze	卌 卌
Copper	卌 ||||

10. What outcome is most likely if a disk is pulled from the bag?

_____

11. What color disk are you least likely to pull?

_____

12. What unit would be used to measure the area of a television screen?

_____

For questions 13–14, use the organized list.

Spheres	?	Cubes
ball	pencil	ice cubes
orange	lipstick	dice
marble	marker	?

13. What heading can be used for the middle column?

_____

14. Which object listed below could be listed under **Cubes**?

toy block   baseball
party hat
a sheet of notebook paper

_____

15. What is a flat surface with no end called?

_____

16. I am a 4-sided polygon. My opposite sides are parallel, and all of my angles are equal. What am I?

_____

17. What is the area of the shaded section?

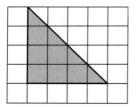

_____

18. Madelyn has a piece of ribbon that is 12 feet long. What is the greatest square area she can place the ribbon around?

_____

19. Draw a figure that is congruent to the figure shown.

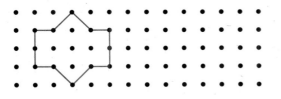

_____

20. Will the figure tessellate?

_____

21. $4 \times 60 = \underline{\ ?\ }$

_____

22. $5 \times 2,000 = \underline{\ ?\ }$

_____

For questions 23–24, use the model place-value chart.

Tens	Ones

23. What multiplication sentence do the base-ten blocks show?

_____

24. Solve the multiplication problem shown by the model. Write the product.

_?_ tens _?_ ones, or _?_

_____

25. $3 \times \$8.25 = \underline{\ ?\ }$

_____

26. $20 \times 80 = n$

_____

27. Estimate by rounding to the nearest ten.

$$\begin{array}{r} 798 \\ \times\ 41 \\ \hline \end{array}$$

_____

28.
$$\begin{array}{r} 34 \\ \times 85 \\ \hline \end{array}$$

_____

29.
$$\begin{array}{r} 49 \\ \times 23 \\ \hline \end{array}$$

_____

30. A box of candy contains 24 pieces. How many pieces are in 17 boxes?

_____

31. $4\overline{)31}$

_____

32. $9\overline{)59}$

_____

33. After lunch the cooks put an equal number of leftover hot dogs into the fewest number of boxes possible. All but 2 of the 53 hot dogs fit into the boxes. How many boxes were used?

_____

34. $624 \div 9 = n$

_____

For questions 35–36, use a basic fact and a pattern of zeros to find the quotient.

35. $28 \div 7 = 4$

$2,800 \div 7 = n$

_____

36. $36 \div 6 = 6$

$36,000 \div 6 = n$

_____

37. $2\overline{)416}$

_____

38. $5\overline{)\$10.60}$

_____

39. How would you interpret the remainder?

Billy needs 150 seeds for a science project. The seeds are sold in bags of 60. How many bags does Billy need?

_____

40. Solve and name the operation you used.

Richard works on his computer 30 minutes each day before school starts. How many minutes will he work on his computer in one week?

_____

Write the correct answer.

1. What fraction of the circle is shaded?

_____

2. What fraction of the bar is shaded?

_____

3. What fraction of the rectangle is shaded?

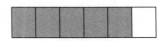

_____

4. What fraction means the same as three out of four?

_____

For questions 5–6, use the figure.

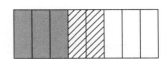

5. What fraction of the figure is striped?

_____

6. What fraction of the figure is *not* striped or shaded?

_____

For questions 7–10, write the fraction that represents the group that is shaded.

7.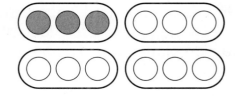

_____

8.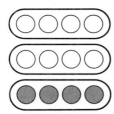

_____

9.

_____

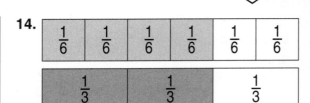
10.

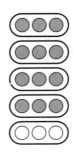

_____

11. Mrs. Sentra bought 12 eggs. She used 4 of them for breakfast. What fraction of the eggs did she use?

_____

12. Kendal bought a six-pack of soda. He kept one can and gave the rest to his mother. What fraction did he keep?

_____

For questions 13–14, use the fraction bars to compare the fractions. Write $<$, $>$, or $=$.

13.

| $\frac{1}{10}$ | $\frac{1}{10}$ | $\frac{1}{10}$ | $\frac{1}{10}$ | $\frac{1}{10}$ | $\frac{1}{10}$ | $\frac{1}{10}$ | $\frac{1}{10}$ | $\frac{1}{10}$ | $\frac{1}{10}$ |

| $\frac{1}{4}$ | $\frac{1}{4}$ | $\frac{1}{4}$ | $\frac{1}{4}$ |

$\frac{8}{10}$ ◯ $\frac{3}{4}$

_____

14.

| $\frac{1}{6}$ | $\frac{1}{6}$ | $\frac{1}{6}$ | $\frac{1}{6}$ | $\frac{1}{6}$ | $\frac{1}{6}$ |

| $\frac{1}{3}$ | $\frac{1}{3}$ | $\frac{1}{3}$ |

$\frac{4}{6}$ ◯ $\frac{2}{3}$

_____

15. Arrange the fractions in order from least to greatest.

$$\frac{2}{3}, \frac{1}{2}, \frac{1}{3}$$

_____

16. Arrange the fractions in order from greatest to least.

$$\frac{1}{4}, \frac{3}{8}, \frac{3}{4}$$

_____

17. Shawna bought $\frac{1}{8}$ pound of peanuts, $\frac{3}{8}$ pound of almonds, and $\frac{3}{4}$ pound of cashews. List the nuts she bought in order from greatest to least.

_____

18. A spinner has 8 equal sections. Of the sections, 1 is blue, 3 are yellow, 1 is white, and 3 are red. Which two colors together cover more than $\frac{1}{2}$ of the spinner?

_____

For questions 19–20, write the mixed number for the shaded part of the picture.

19.

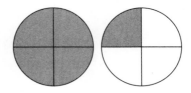

_____

20.

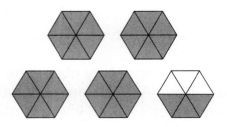

_____

For questions 21–24, rename each fraction as a mixed number.

21. $\frac{7}{5} = $ __?__

_____

22. $\frac{9}{4} = $ __?__

_____

23. $\frac{8}{3} = $ __?__

_____

24. $\frac{11}{8} = $ __?__

_____

Write the correct answer.

1. Use the fraction bars to help you find the sum.

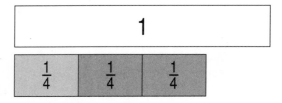

$\frac{1}{3} + \frac{2}{3} = n$

_____

2. Use the fraction bars to help you find the sum.

1

| $\frac{1}{4}$ | $\frac{1}{4}$ | $\frac{1}{4}$ |

$\frac{1}{4} + \frac{2}{4} = n$

_____

3. Write the number sentence for the problem and solve.

two sixths plus three sixths

_____

4. Is the sum greater than 1 or less than 1?

$\frac{6}{8} + \frac{3}{8} = \underline{\ ?\ }$

_____

5. $\frac{1}{5} + \frac{3}{5} = n$

_____

6. $\frac{4}{10} + \frac{3}{10} = n$

_____

7. Felix ate $\frac{2}{5}$ cup of raisins before the game. He ate $\frac{1}{5}$ cup of raisins after the game. How much of a cup of raisins did Felix eat?

_____

8. Before dinner Mary played outside for $\frac{1}{3}$ hour. After dinner she played outside for $\frac{1}{3}$ hour. How long did Mary play outside in all?

_____

9. Use the model to help you find the difference.

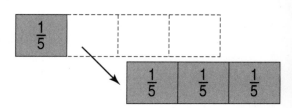

$\frac{4}{5} - \frac{3}{5} = n$

_____

Form B • Free-Response

Go on. ▶

10. Use the model to help you find the difference.

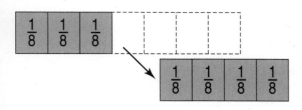

$$\frac{7}{8} - \frac{4}{8} = n$$

_____

11. Betty has read $\frac{2}{3}$ of her book. How much is left to read?

_____

12. Julio ate $\frac{3}{8}$ of a pizza. What fraction of the pizza is left?

_____

13. Use the model to help you find the sum.

$$3\frac{1}{4}$$
$$+1\frac{2}{4}$$

14.
$$7\frac{1}{9}$$
$$+2\frac{3}{9}$$

15.
$$5\frac{7}{12}$$
$$+4\frac{4}{12}$$

16. $3\frac{4}{6} + 2\frac{1}{6} = n$

_____

17. Jason did homework for $1\frac{1}{4}$ hours before dinner and $1\frac{3}{4}$ after dinner. How much time did Jason spend on homework?

_____

18. Shelly jogged $1\frac{1}{5}$ miles on Tuesday and $2\frac{2}{5}$ miles on Wednesday. How far did Shelly jog in all?

_____

19. Use the model to help you find the difference.

$$2\frac{3}{4}$$
$$-1\frac{1}{4}$$

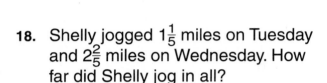

20.
$$9\frac{3}{6}$$
$$-1\frac{2}{6}$$

21.
$$6\frac{7}{10}$$
$$-5\frac{2}{10}$$

22. $3\frac{6}{8} - 1\frac{3}{8} = n$

_____

23. Oscar grew $5\frac{3}{4}$ inches in one year. His sister Shawna grew $2\frac{1}{4}$ inches. How much more did Oscar grow than Shawna?

_____

24. The trail up the mountain is $6\frac{4}{10}$ miles. The trail down is $5\frac{2}{10}$ miles. How much shorter is the trail down?

_____

Write the correct answer.

1. The model shows 0.6. Write the fraction for the shaded part.

_____

2. The model shows $\frac{75}{100}$. Write the decimal for the shaded part.

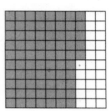

_____

3. Write $\frac{7}{10}$ as a decimal.

_____

4. Write 0.35 as a fraction.

_____

5. Write the decimal name for the shaded part of the model.

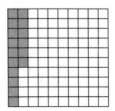

_____

6. Write the decimal name for the shaded part of the model.

_____

7. Write 8 pennies as a money amount.

_____

8. Write 5 dimes as a money amount.

_____

9. Trey has 83 pennies. Write that amount as a decimal.

_____

10. Dina has $\frac{25}{100}$ of a dollar. How many pennies is that?

_____

For questions 11–12, use the number line.

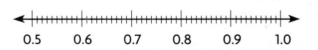

11. The number line has small ticks and large ticks. Do the large ticks show hundreds, tens, ones, or tenths?

_____

Name _____

12. Write another decimal number that would be at the same place on the number line as 0.40.

_____

13. Write the number that is greater.

0.41, 0.2

_____

14. Write the number that is greater.

0.8, 0.18

_____

15. Write 0.5, 0.21, 0.9, and 0.62 in order from least to greatest.

_____

16. Write 0.08, 0.01, 0.19, and 0.70 in order from greatest to least.

_____

17. Write the mixed decimal shown by the model.

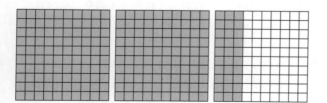

_____

18. Write an equivalent mixed decimal for 4.10.

_____

19. Write an equivalent mixed decimal for 6.30.

_____

20. Write $5\frac{5}{10}$ as a mixed decimal.

_____

21. Write 14.07 as a mixed number.

_____

22. Write 8.32 as a mixed number.

_____

23. In a swimming race, Phil finished in 20.09 seconds. Raj finished in 22.10 seconds, Jorge finished in 19.75 seconds, and Chal finished in 21.60 seconds. Who finished the race in the least amount of time?

_____

24. Four girls counted their money. Samara has $2.91, Gina has $2.56, Carmen has $2.73, and Patty has $2.65. Which girl has the least amount of money?

_____

Name _____

Write the correct answer.

For questions 1–2, use the decimal-square model.

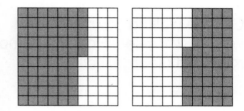

1. Write a number sentence that matches the model.

_____

2. What is the sum of the shaded parts of the model?

_____

3. 0.8
      +0.5

_____

4. 0.23
      +0.72

_____

5. 2.65
      +0.54

_____

6. Bill has 2.5 pounds of bananas and 2.3 pounds of grapes. How many pounds of fruit does he have in all?

_____

7. Becky runs the first half of a race in 1.35 minutes and the second half in 1.70 minutes. What is her total time?

_____

8. Use the model to find the difference.

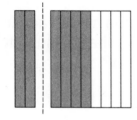

$$0.6 - 0.4 = n$$

_____

9. Use the model to find the difference.

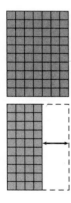

$$0.70 - 0.40 = n$$

_____

10. 1.5
       −0.7

_____

11.
$$\begin{array}{r} 0.83 \\ -0.19 \\ \hline \end{array}$$

_____

12.
$$\begin{array}{r} 3.02 \\ -0.75 \\ \hline \end{array}$$

_____

13. Ruth ran a race in 1.85 minutes. Jan ran the same race in 1.63 minutes. What is the difference in their times?

_____

14. Drew lives 1.8 miles from school. Mark lives 0.9 miles from school. How many miles farther from school does Drew live?

_____

15.
$$\begin{array}{r} 0.77 \\ +0.57 \\ \hline \end{array}$$

_____

16.
$$\begin{array}{r} 0.60 \\ -0.35 \\ \hline \end{array}$$

_____

17.
$$\begin{array}{r} 1.90 \\ -0.06 \\ \hline \end{array}$$

_____

18. $0.43 + 0.2 = n$

_____

For questions 19–20, write a number sentence that shows how to solve the problem.

19. George walked 3.5 miles. Bert walked 2.1 miles. How many more miles did George walk?

_____

20. Alice practiced her guitar for 1.7 hours on Saturday and 1.2 hours on Sunday. How many hours did she practice in all?

_____

21. What is 8.8 rounded to the nearest whole number?

_____

For questions 22–24, estimate the sum or difference by rounding to the nearest whole number.

22.
$$\begin{array}{r} 2.8 \\ +1.9 \\ \hline \end{array}$$

_____

23.
$$\begin{array}{r} 5.7 \\ -2.3 \\ \hline \end{array}$$

_____

24. Alonzo and Marci worked on a puzzle for 2.9 hours on Saturday, 2.8 hours on Sunday, and 1.7 hours on Monday. About how many hours in all did they work on the puzzle?

_____

Write the correct answer.

1. What fraction of the circle is shaded?

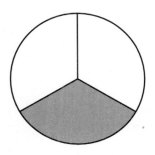

_____

2. What fraction represents the group that is shaded?

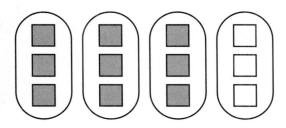

_____

3. Donald checked out 4 books from the library. He read 2 of them. What fraction of the books did he read?

_____

4. Write the fractions in order from greatest to least.

$\frac{1}{6}, \frac{1}{4}, \frac{3}{4}$

_____

5. What is the mixed number for the shaded part of the picture?

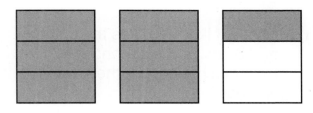

_____

6. $\frac{3}{5} + \frac{4}{5} = $ ___?___

_____

7. $4\frac{2}{7} + 2\frac{3}{7} = $ ___?___

_____

8. Barbara went swimming for $1\frac{2}{4}$ hours in the morning. She went swimming for $1\frac{1}{4}$ hours in the afternoon. How many hours in all did Barbara go swimming?

_____

9. A recipe uses $1\frac{1}{8}$ cups of wheat flour and $2\frac{3}{8}$ cups of white flour. How much flour does the recipe use?

_____

10. $5\frac{4}{5} - 2\frac{1}{5} = $ ____?____

_____

11. Scouts hiked $8\frac{5}{8}$ miles the first day and $6\frac{3}{8}$ miles the second day. How much more did they hike the first day?

_____

12. Write $\frac{43}{100}$ as a decimal.

_____

13. Write 4 nickels as a money amount.

_____

14. Write 5.37 as a mixed number.

_____

15. Write 0.29, 0.5, 0.73, and 0.4 in order from greatest to least.

_____

16. What is a mixed decimal equivalent to 2.50?

_____

17. In a track meet, Julio finished in 40.09 seconds, Ricky finished in 39.85 seconds, Brent finished in 42.26 seconds, and Andy finished in 41.70 seconds. Who finished the race in the least amount of time?

_____

18. Write a number sentence that matches the model.

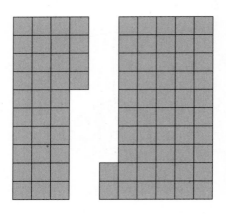

_____

19.   1.74
    $+2.53$

_____

20.   1.3
    -0.8

_____

21. What is 6.7 rounded to the nearest whole number?

_____

Estimate the sum or difference by rounding to the nearest whole number.

22. Rebecca collected 2.1 lb of cans on Friday, 4.8 lb of cans on Saturday, and 3.9 lb of cans on Sunday. About how many pounds did she collect on the three days?

_____

Name _____

Write the correct answer.

1. Use the number 9 to write a number sentence that shows the Zero Property for Multiplication.

_____

2. Is the number a *cardinal, ordinal,* or *nominal* number?

_____

3. A 32-oz drink costs $0.98. About how much should a 16-oz drink cost?

_____

4. What is *six hundred eighty million, seven hundred thirteen thousand, six hundred sixteen* written in standard form?

_____

5. You can choose chocolate, vanilla, strawberry, or pecan ice cream. You can choose chocolate, vanilla, or caramel topping. How many choices are there?

_____

For questions 6–7, use the line plot. There is one X for each student.

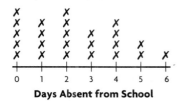

Days Absent from School

6. What is the range of data used in the line plot?

_____

7. How many students were absent 2 days?

_____

8. A bag contains marbles and rocks. How likely is it that a golf ball will be pulled out?

_____

For questions 9–10, use the spinners.

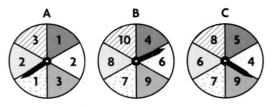

In this game, the "odd" player gets points for odd numbers and the "even" player gets points for even numbers.

9. Which spinner gives both players an equal chance to win?

_____

10. If you were the "even" player, which spinner would give you the greatest probability of winning?

_____

11. Use the figure.

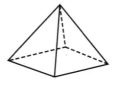

How many faces are on the figure?

_____

12. What are lines that cross each other at right angles called?

_____

13. What is the perimeter?

7 ft

2 ft

_____

14. What is a figure that has been moved to a new location called?

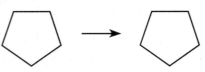

_____

15. Circle the figure that has point symmetry.

16.   60
       $\times$ 3

_____

17. Use the model place-value chart. Write the multiplication sentence that the base-ten blocks show.

Tens	Ones

_____

18. $3.72
        $\times$ 6

_____

19. What is a reasonable estimate for the product?

$$58 \times 39 = n$$

_____

20.
$$\begin{array}{r} 23 \\ \times 47 \\ \hline \end{array}$$

_____

21. $5\overline{)92}$

_____

22. $315 \div 4 = n$

_____

23. Use a basic fact and a pattern of zeros to estimate the quotient.

$2,689 \div 9 = n$

_____

24. $6\overline{)\$4.14}$

_____

25. What fraction means the same as *three out of seven*?

_____

26. What fraction represents the group that is shaded?

_____

27. What is the fraction renamed as a mixed number?

$$\frac{12}{5} = \underline{\ ?\ }$$

_____

28. Use the fraction bars to help you find the sum.

1

$\frac{1}{5}$	$\frac{1}{5}$	$\frac{1}{5}$	$\frac{1}{5}$

$$\frac{1}{5} + \frac{3}{5} = \underline{\ ?\ }$$

_____

29. $\frac{1}{7} + \frac{4}{7} = \underline{\ ?\ }$

_____

30. Owen spent $\frac{5}{8}$ of his allowance on a model airplane. What fraction of his allowance is left?

_____

31. $4\frac{3}{9}$
$+2\frac{5}{9}$

_____

32. $7\frac{7}{9}$
$-3\frac{3}{9}$

_____

33. What is 0.42 written as a fraction?

_____

34. What is 7 nickels written as a money amount?

_____

35. Which number is greatest?

0.07, 0.7, 0.17

_____

36. What is 7.21 written as a mixed number?

_____

37. Myra practiced her music lessons for 1.2 hours on Monday, 2.1 hours on Wednesday, and 2.8 hours on Saturday. On which day did she practice the longest?

_____

38. 0.56
$+0.73$

_____

39. 0.78
-0.59

_____

40. What is 5.3 rounded to the nearest whole number?

_____

Name _____

Write the correct answer.
For some items, an inch ruler may be needed.

1. Name a linear unit of measurement.

   _____

2. Use a ruler to measure the length of this ribbon.

   _____

For questions 3–4, write the reasonable unit of measure.

3. A new pencil is about 6 _?_ long.

   _____

4. A baseball bat is about 1 _?_ long.

   _____

5. The Amazon is the longest river in South America. Which unit is best for describing its length?

   _____

6. Mr. Black is buying some rope. Which unit is best for describing the length of the rope?

   _____

For questions 7–9, find the equivalent measurement.

7. 60 ft = ___ yd

   _____

8. 5 yd = ___ ft

   _____

9. 33 ft = ___ yd

   _____

For questions 10–11, use the diagram.

Mrs. Garcia's Yard

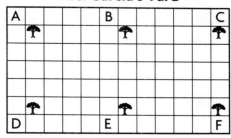

1 square = 1 yard

10. How many trees are in Mrs. Garcia's yard?

    _____

11. About how far is it from the tree at D to the tree at F?

    _____

12. How long is the crayon to the nearest $\frac{1}{4}$ in.?

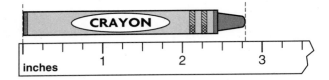

_____

13. How long is the string to the nearest $\frac{1}{2}$ in.?

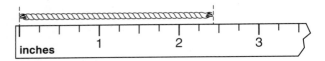

_____

For questions 14–16, use an inch ruler to measure length.

14. How long is this paper clip to the nearest $\frac{1}{4}$ in.?

_____

15. How long is this pencil to the nearest $\frac{1}{2}$ in.?

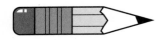

_____

16. How long is this line to the nearest $\frac{1}{4}$ in.?

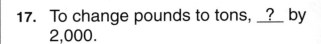

_____

17. To change pounds to tons, __?__ by 2,000.

_____

18. A good estimate of the weight of a medium-size turkey is about 10 __?__ .

_____

19. A good estimate of the weight of a small car is about 1 __?__ .

_____

20. Find the equivalent measure.

2 pounds = __?__ oz

_____

21. Mrs. Slotsky bought a case of 24 cans of soda. Each can contains 12 ounces. How many ounces of soda are in the whole case?

_____

22. Kim bought 3 lb of birdseed for her feeder. Her feeder holds 8 oz. How many times can she fill her feeder?

_____

Form B • Free-Response   B230   ▶ **Stop!**

Name _____

Write the correct answer.

1. Arrange the metric units in order from largest to smallest.

cm, m, dm

_____

For questions 2–8, write the equivalent measurement.

2. 1 dm = _____ cm

_____

3. 1 m = _____ dm

_____

4. 1 dm = _____ m

_____

5. 2 cm = _____ dm

_____

6. 5 dm = _____ m

_____

7. Darla's poster is 2 times longer than Cassie's poster. Cassie's poster is 6 dm long. How long is Darla's poster in meters?

_____

8. Frank needs 1 m of rope. He has 4 dm of rope. How much more rope does he need?

_____

9. To change 2 m to cm, multiply 2 by _____ .

_____

10. Write a number sentence that shows how to change 3 m to dm.

_____

For questions 11–14, write the equivalent measurement.

11. 8 dm = _____ cm

_____

12. 5 m = _____ dm

_____

13. 15 m = _____ cm

_____

14. 9 m = _____ dm

_____

For questions 15–16, use the diagram.

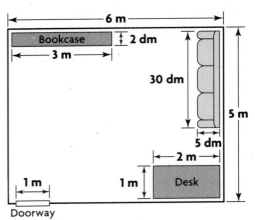

Floor Plan of Mrs. Bell's Office

15. About how far is the desk from the door?

_____

16. How much wider is the bookcase than the doorway?

_____

17. What is a common metric unit of measure of capacity?

_____

18. A good estimate of the amount of water in the glass is 250 __?__.

19. A good estimate of the amount of medicine in an eyedropper is 5 __?__.

_____

For questions 20–21, find the equivalent measure.

20. 10 liters = _____ milliliters

_____

21. 8 metric cups = _____ L

_____

22. After practice, each of 8 tennis players drank 3 cups of water. How many quarts of water did all the players drink?

_____

23. Soda costs $0.89 for a 2-L bottle and $0.59 for a 1-L bottle. Janie bought two 2-L bottles and one 1-L bottle. How much money did she spend?

_____

24. A soccer player's water bottle holds 500 mL. How many liters are needed to fill the water bottles of 6 players?

_____

Name _____

Write the correct answer.

For questions 1–2, draw the minute hand and hour hand to show the correct time.

1. a quarter to three

2. half past ten

3. What is another way to write *a quarter past five*?

_____

4. What is another way to write *half past twelve*?

_____

5. What is another way to write 4:45?

_____

6. What is another way to write 2:15?

_____

7. The perimeter of a square is 50 cm. If the same square is measured in inches, would the number of units be *greater than* or *less than* 50?

_____

8. A reasonable estimate for the length of this line is 2 __?__ .

▬▬▬▬▬▬▬▬

_____

9. A reasonable estimate for the length of the rope is 5 __?__ .

_____

10. A reasonable estimate for the length of the ribbon is 6 __?__ .

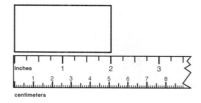

_____

11. Use the ruler to find the perimeter of the rectangle in inches.

_____

12. Sonia caught a fish 6 in. long. Fran caught one 6 cm long. Who caught the longer fish?

_____

13. Marco's book is 4 cm longer than Billy's book. Billy's book is 34 cm long. How long is Marco's book?

_____

14. Henry wants to buy 4 books that cost $5.00 each. The store is having a sale of $1.00 off each book purchased. What price will he pay for all 4 books?

_____

15. Sally is putting a border around her flower bed. Two sides are 24 ft long, and two sides are 12 ft long. How many yards of border does she need?

_____

16. What temperature does this thermometer show?

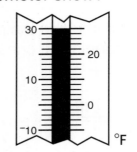

17. Which temperature is colder: 8°F or −8°F?

_____

18. What is the difference between the temperatures?

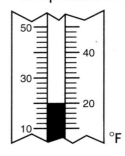 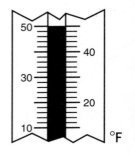

_____

19. What is the difference between the temperatures?

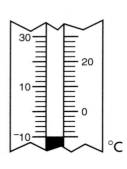 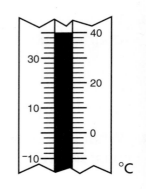

_____

20. At sunrise the temperature was 35°F. At noon it was 20 degrees warmer. By six o'clock in the evening, it had cooled off 15 degrees. What was the evening temperature?

_____

Name _____

Write the correct answer.

For some items, an inch ruler may be needed.

1. An inch is a ___?___ unit of measurement.

_____

2. What unit of measure is reasonable to measure the distance from one end of town to the other?

_____

3. 36 in. = ___?___ ft

_____

4. How long is the leaf to the nearest $\frac{1}{4}$ in.?

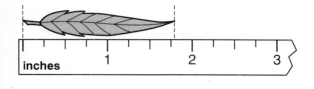

_____

5. How long is the string to the nearest $\frac{1}{2}$ in.?

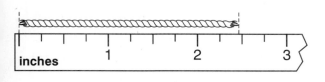

_____

6. To change pounds to tons, divide the number of pounds by ___?___.

_____

7. Mr. Rey used 30 bags of mulch in his garden. One bag weighs 20 pounds. How many pounds of mulch did Mr. Rey use?

_____

8. Jill bought 3 lb of bread for a party. Each loaf of bread weighed 8 oz. How many loaves did she buy?

_____

9. 1 cm = ___?___ m

_____

10. Lenno's older brother is 20 dm tall. His younger brother is one half as tall. How tall is Lenno's younger brother in centimeters?

_____

11. To change 3 m to dm, multiply 3 by ___?___.

_____

Form B • Free-Response   **Go on.** ▶

12. 4 m = ___?___ cm

_____

For questions 13–14, use the diagram.

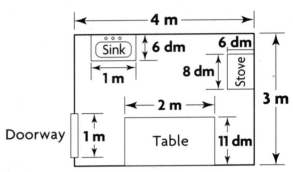

The Bryants' Kitchen

13. The stove is 8 dm long. How much longer is the sink than the stove?

_____

14. The table is 11 dm wide. How long is the table in decimeters?

_____

15. A reasonable estimate of the amount of soda in a can is 350 ___?___.

_____

16. A cup holds 250 mL. How many liters are needed to fill 4 cups?

_____

17. What is another way to write a quarter to six?

_____

18. What is another way to write 2:30?

_____

19. Raul's picture is 5 cm wide and 9 cm long. He wants to glue a border of yarn around the picture. How many centimeters of yarn does Raul need?

_____

20. At sunrise the temperature was 60°F. At noon it was 20 degrees warmer. By six o'clock in the evening, it had cooled off 15 degrees. What was the evening temperature?

_____

Write the correct answer.

1. 67
    26
    +39
    _____

2. A bakery puts 8 donuts in each box. The bakery has 16 boxes of donuts. How many donuts does the bakery have in all?

3. How many thousands are in 8,615?

4. What number has the digit 3 in the hundreds place, 8 in the ones place, and 1 in the tens place?

5. What is the greatest place-value position in which the digits are different?

    5,673
    5,764

For questions 6–7, use the frequency table.

INCHES OF SNOWFALL DURING JANUARY		
Week	Inches (Frequency)	Cumulative Frequency
1	11	14
2	8	22
3	17	?
4	15	?

6. How much more snow fell in Week 3 than in Week 1?

7. What is the cumulative frequency for the snow that fell in all 4 weeks?

For questions 8–9, use the stem-and-leaf plot.

High Temperatures

Stem	Leaves
7	4 5 5 7 8 9 9
8	3 3 4 5 6 6 8 8 8
9	1 1 2 3 4 4

8. What number is the mode for the data?

9. What is the difference between the highest and the lowest temperature?

_____

For questions 10–11, use the grid.

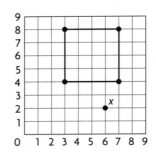

10. What is the ordered pair for point *x*?

_____

11. What is the set of ordered pairs that identifies the vertices of the square marked on the grid?

_____

12. A large painting is 5 feet by 7 feet. What is the area of the painting?

_____

13. Draw a line of symmetry through the figure.

14.   453
      $\times$ 7

_____

15. Find the product by using a basic fact and a pattern of zeros.
$$90 \times 300 = n$$

_____

16. $53
      $\times$ 32

_____

17. In which place should the first digit in the quotient be placed?

$7\overline{)63}$

_____

18. $8\overline{)537}$

_____

19. A train has to travel 179 miles in 3 hours. How many miles should it travel each hour to reach its destination on time?

_____

20. A car had a flat tire. What fraction of the car's 4 tires was flat?

_____

21. What is the fraction renamed as a mixed number?

$$\frac{11}{3} = \underline{\quad?\quad}$$

_____

22. Use the fraction bars to help you find the sum.

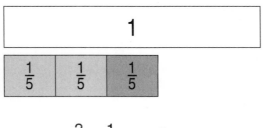

$$\frac{2}{5} + \frac{1}{5} = \underline{\quad?\quad}$$

_____

23. Use the model to help you find the difference.

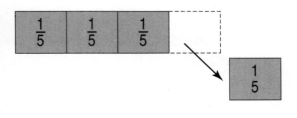

$$\frac{4}{5} - \frac{1}{5} = \underline{\quad?\quad}$$

_____

24. What is 0.55 written as a fraction?

_____

25. What are 0.44, 0.7, 0.64, and 0.5 written in order from least to greatest?

_____

26. 1.71
    +1.52

_____

27. 3.19
    −1.42

_____

28. A reasonable unit of measure for a hot dog is about 5 ___?___.

_____

29. How long is the string to the nearest $\frac{1}{2}$ in.?

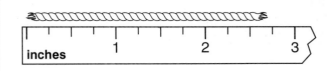

_____

30. 36 in. = ___?___ yd

_____

For questions 31–32, use the diagram.

Darts on a Dartboard

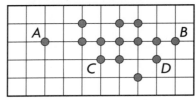

1 square = 1 inch

31. How many darts are on the dart board?

_____

32. How far is it from the dart at *A* to the dart at *B*?

_____

33. 4 lb = __?__ oz

_____

34. 0.07 m = __?__ cm

_____

35. 90 cm = __?__ dm

_____

36. 3,000 milliliters = __?__ liters

_____

37. What is another way to write *half past seven*?

_____

38. A reasonable estimate for the length of the string is 3 __?__.

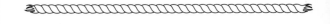

_____

39. Tickets to a movie theater cost $5. The price is reduced by $2 for tickets bought before 6 P.M. How much would 3 tickets bought at 5 P.M. cost?

_____

40. What is the difference between the temperatures on the thermometers?

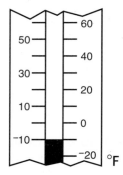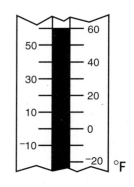

_____

Write the correct answer.

1. What numbers should you use to estimate the quotient for this division problem?

   $415 \div 48 = n$

   _____

2. What basic fact helps find these quotients?

$360 \div 40 = n$
$3,600 \div 40 = n$
$36,000 \div 40 = n$

   _____

For questions 3–4, estimate the quotient by rounding to the nearest ten.

3. $796 \div 38 = n$

   _____

4. $203 \div 52 = n$

   _____

For questions 5–6, estimate by rounding to the nearest ten or hundred.

5. There are 302 CDs. About 58 CDs fit in a box. About how many boxes are needed to pack the CDs?

   _____

6. At a basketball camp, 107 players are divided into groups of 12. About how many groups are there?

   _____

7. Should the first digit in the quotient be placed in the hundreds, tens, or ones place?

   $21\overline{)480}$

   _____

8. Should the first digit in the quotient be placed in the hundreds, tens, or ones place?

   $70\overline{)258}$

   _____

9. $60\overline{)686}$

   _____

10. $30\overline{)215}$

   _____

11. $90\overline{)847}$

   _____

12. A troop of 30 Scouts sold 630 boxes of popcorn. Each Scout sold the same number of boxes. How many boxes did each Scout sell?

_____

13. Tim must solve the division problem below. What is the first step he should take after estimating the quotient?

$42\overline{)506}$

_____

14. Mary started doing the problem below. What should she do next?

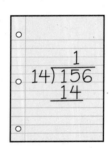

_____

15. $21\overline{)257}$

_____

16. $36\overline{)184}$

_____

17. $72\overline{)890}$

_____

18. $55\overline{)739}$

_____

19. Celine swam one lap in 124 seconds. How many minutes and seconds is this?

_____

20. Eric's bed is 77 inches long. How long is his bed in feet and inches?

_____

For questions 21–24, decide if each estimate is *too high, too low,* or *just right.*

21. $19\overline{)178}$ with 8 above

_____

22. $21\overline{)162}$ with 9 above

_____

23. $82\overline{)193}$ with 2 above

_____

24. $59\overline{)183}$ with 4 above

_____

Name _____

Write the correct answer.

For questions 1–2, use the circle graph.

28 Pets at the Pet Fair

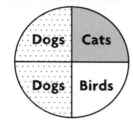

1. What does the whole circle represent?

_____

2. What is something you can tell by looking at the graph?

_____

For questions 3–6, use the circle graph.

Favorite Sport Choices of 25 Students

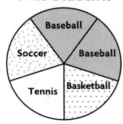

3. What fraction of the 25 students chose baseball as their favorite sport?

_____

4. What fraction of the 25 students chose soccer as their favorite sport?

_____

5. What fraction represents all the students in the survey?

_____

6. Which sport was chosen by the most students?

_____

For questions 7–8, use the circle.

7. What decimal represents 1 part of the circle?

_____

8. What is the sum of the decimals that represents 3 parts of the circle?

_____

Form B • Free-Response   B243   **Go on.** ▶

For questions 9–12, use the graph.

Favorite Colors of Fourth Graders

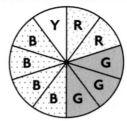

9. What decimal tells how many students chose green?

_____

10. What decimal tells how many students chose blue?

_____

11. What decimal tells how many students chose red?

_____

12. What decimal tells how many students chose yellow?

_____

For questions 13–14, use the graphs.

Graph A   Graph B   Graph C

13. Which graph can be used to show that $\frac{1}{2}$ of the students in a class are boys and $\frac{1}{2}$ are girls?

_____

14. Which graph can be used to show that $\frac{1}{2}$ the members of the school band are sixth graders, $\frac{1}{4}$ are fifth graders, and $\frac{1}{4}$ are fourth graders?

_____

For questions 15–18, choose the graph that matches the data.

Work Lin Did in Her Garden

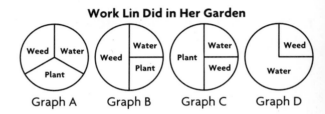

Graph A   Graph B   Graph C   Graph D

15. Which graph shows that Lin spent $\frac{1}{3}$ of her time planting, $\frac{1}{3}$ weeding, and $\frac{1}{3}$ watering?

_____

16. Which graph shows that Lin spent $\frac{1}{4}$ of her time weeding and $\frac{3}{4}$ watering?

_____

17. Which graph shows that Lin spent $\frac{1}{2}$ of her time weeding, $\frac{1}{4}$ planting, and $\frac{1}{4}$ watering?

_____

18. Which graph shows that Lin spent $\frac{1}{4}$ of her time weeding, $\frac{1}{2}$ planting, and $\frac{1}{4}$ watering?

_____

Write the correct answer.

1. What numbers should you use to estimate the quotient?

   $811 \div 79 = n$

   _____

2. Estimate the quotient by rounding to the nearest ten or hundred.

   $603 \div 19 = n$

   _____

3. At a recreation center, 39 players are divided into groups of 9. About how many groups are there?

   _____

4. $80\overline{)752}$

   _____

5. Luisa must solve this problem. She starts by estimating. What is the next step?

   $19\overline{)212}$

   _____

6. $16\overline{)249}$

   _____

7. Riley likes a song that plays for 207 seconds. How many minutes and seconds is this?

   _____

8. Nova can jump a distance of 59 inches. How long is this in feet and inches?

   _____

For questions 9–10, decide whether the estimate is *too high, too low,* or *just right.*

9. $39\overline{)248}$ with 7 above

   _____

10. $19\overline{)212}$ with 9 above

    _____

For questions 11–12, use the circle graph.

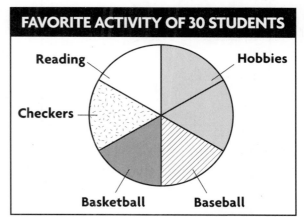

FAVORITE ACTIVITY OF 30 STUDENTS

Reading   Hobbies

Checkers

Basketball   Baseball

11. What fraction of the 30 students chose basketball as their favorite activity?

    _____

12. What fraction of the 30 students chose hobbies as their favorite?

_____

For questions 13–14, use the circle.

13. What decimal represents 1 part of the circle?

_____

14. What is the sum of the decimals that represent 4 parts of the circle?

_____

For questions 15–16, use the circle graph.

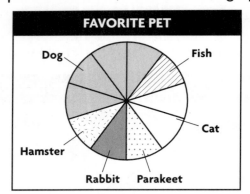

FAVORITE PET

Dog · Fish · Cat · Parakeet · Rabbit · Hamster

15. What decimal tells how many chose a dog as their favorite pet?

_____

16. What decimal tells how many chose a cat as their favorite pet?

_____

For questions 17–18, use the circle graphs.

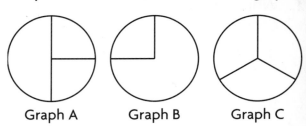

Graph A   Graph B   Graph C

17. Which graph can be used to show that $\frac{3}{4}$ of the students play baseball and $\frac{1}{4}$ play football?

_____

18. Which graph can be used to show that $\frac{1}{4}$ of the students prefer pizza, $\frac{1}{2}$ prefer hamburgers, and $\frac{1}{4}$ prefer peanut butter sandwiches?

_____

For questions 19–20, choose the graph that matches the data.

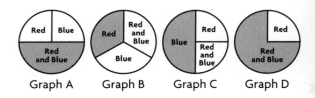

Graph A   Graph B   Graph C   Graph D

19. Which graph shows that $\frac{1}{4}$ of the students like red cars and $\frac{3}{4}$ like both red cars and blue cars?

_____

20. Which graph shows that $\frac{1}{3}$ of the students like red cars, $\frac{1}{3}$ like blue cars, and $\frac{1}{3}$ like both red cars and blue cars?

_____

Write the correct answer.

1. Estimate the difference to the nearest thousand.

6,281
−4,873

_____

2. Use the model to find the quotient.

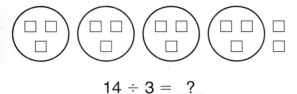

$14 ÷ 3 =$ ___?___

_____

3. What is the value of the digit 6 in the number 861?

_____

Compare the numbers and write $<$, $>$, or $=$.

4. 923 ● 932

_____

5. The flag at many schools is raised every day at about 8:00. Is this A.M. or P.M.?

_____

For questions 6–7, use the calendar.

July

Su	M	T	W	Th	F	Sa
		1	2	3	4	5
6	7	8	9	10	11	12
13	14	15	16	17	18	19
20	21	22	23	24	25	26
27	28	29	30	31		

6. If a space shuttle is launched on July 4 and returns 7 days later, on what date will it land?

_____

7. On July 15 Laura will sign up for swimming lessons that begin on July 26. How many days will she have to wait for the lessons to start?

_____

8. What kind of graph would be best to compare the changing times at which the sun sets each day during a month?

_____

For questions 9–10, use the spinner.

9. What is the probability of spinning a 2?

_____

10. What is the probability of spinning a 1 or a 3?

_____

11. Parallel lines are lines that are the same distance apart and that never __?__ .

_____

12. If a figure on 0.5-cm grid paper is copied onto another page of 0.5-cm paper, the two figures will be __?__ .

_____

13. $\begin{array}{r} 329 \\ \times \quad 3 \\ \hline \end{array}$

_____

14. $7\overline{)41}$

_____

15. $4\overline{)\$19.72}$

_____

16. Arrange the fractions in order from least to greatest.

$\dfrac{5}{6}, \dfrac{1}{3}, \dfrac{3}{6}$

_____

17. $\dfrac{2}{9} + \dfrac{5}{9} =$ __?__

_____

18. $\begin{array}{r} 0.81 \\ -0.26 \\ \hline \end{array}$

_____

19. Find the equivalent measurement.

2 mi = __?__ ft

_____

20. To change tons to pounds, __?__ the number of tons by 2,000.

_____

21. 190 cm = __?__ dm

_____

For questions 22–23, use the diagram.

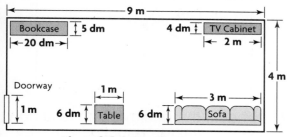

Plan of Flo's Family Room

22. About how far is it from the
     bookcase to the TV cabinet?

_____

23. Which piece of furniture is the
     longest?

_____

24. Wendy saw a bird that was 18 in.
     long. Edra saw a bird that was
     18 cm long. Who saw the longer
     bird?

_____

25. Which temperature is warmer: 2°F
     or ⁻2°F?

_____

For questions 26–27, write the best
estimate of the quotient.

26. $889 \div 29 = n$

_____

27. $298 \div 62 = n$

_____

28. $50\overline{)847}$

_____

29. $20\overline{)546}$

_____

30. $19\overline{)263}$

_____

For questions 31–32, write whether each estimate is *too high, too low,* or *just right.*

31. $15\overline{)139}$ with 9 above

_____

32. $34\overline{)199}$ with 6 above

_____

33. A visit to a museum lasts 126 minutes. How long is this in hours and minutes?

_____

34. A tennis ball bounced 73 inches. How far is this in feet and inches?

_____

For questions 35–36, use the circle graph.

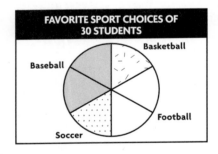

35. Write the fraction of the 30 students who chose baseball as their favorite sport.

_____

36. Write the fraction of the 30 students who chose soccer as their favorite sport.

_____

For questions 37–38, use the graph.

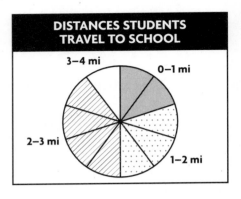

37. What is the decimal that tells how many students travel 2–3 miles?

_____

38. What is the decimal that tells how many students travel 3–4 miles?

_____

For questions 39–40, choose the graph that matches the data.

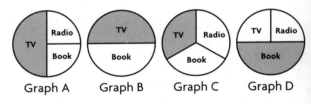

Graph A   Graph B   Graph C   Graph D

39. Which graph shows that $\frac{1}{3}$ chose TV, $\frac{1}{3}$ chose Radio, and $\frac{1}{3}$ chose Book?

_____

40. Which graph shows that $\frac{1}{2}$ chose TV and $\frac{1}{2}$ chose Book?

_____

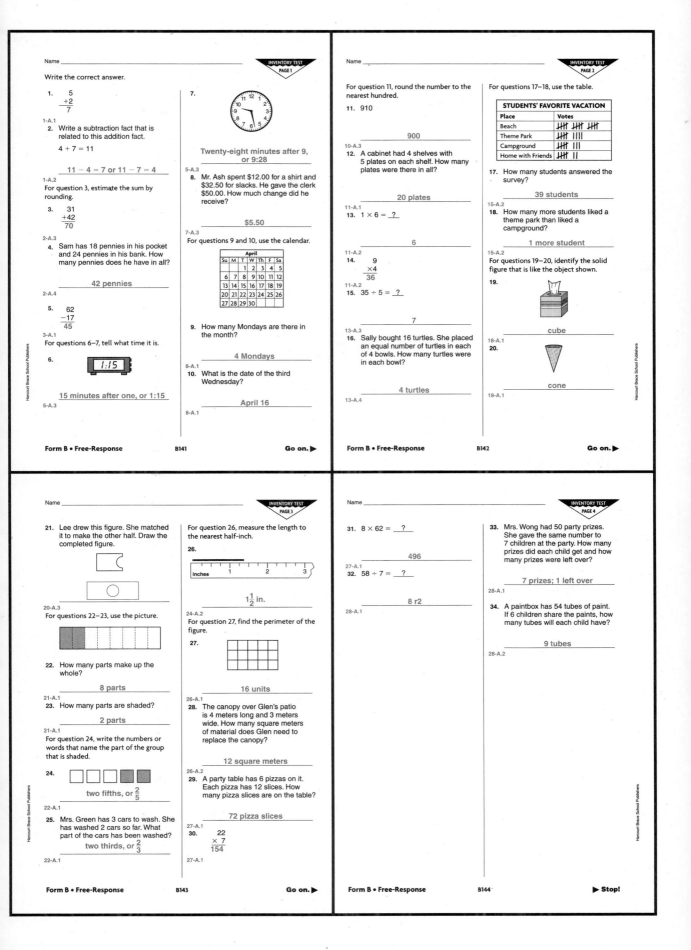

Write the correct answer.

1. $\begin{array}{r} 5 \\ +2 \\ \hline 7 \end{array}$

1-A.1

2. Write a subtraction fact that is related to this addition fact.

$4 + 7 = 11$

$11 - 4 = 7$ or $11 - 7 = 4$

1-A.2

For question 3, estimate the sum by rounding.

3. $\begin{array}{r} 31 \\ +42 \\ \hline 70 \end{array}$

2-A.3

4. Sam has 18 pennies in his pocket and 24 pennies in his bank. How many pennies does he have in all?

42 pennies

2-A.4

5. $\begin{array}{r} 62 \\ -17 \\ \hline 45 \end{array}$

3-A.1

For questions 6–7, tell what time it is.

6.

1:15

15 minutes after one, or 1:15

5-A.3

7.

Twenty-eight minutes after 9, or 9:28

5-A.3

8. Mr. Ash spent $12.00 for a shirt and $32.50 for slacks. He gave the clerk $50.00. How much change did he receive?

$5.50

7-A.3

For questions 9 and 10, use the calendar.

April						
Su	M	T	W	Th	F	Sa
		1	2	3	4	5
6	7	8	9	10	11	12
13	14	15	16	17	18	19
20	21	22	23	24	25	26
27	28	29	30			

9. How many Mondays are there in the month?

4 Mondays

8-A.1

10. What is the date of the third Wednesday?

April 16

8-A.1

Form B • Free-Response   B141   **Go on. ▶**

For question 11, round the number to the nearest hundred.

11. 910

900

10-A.3

12. A cabinet had 4 shelves with 5 plates on each shelf. How many plates were there in all?

20 plates

11-A.1

13. $1 \times 6 = \underline{\ ?\ }$

6

11-A.2

14. $\begin{array}{r} 9 \\ \times 4 \\ \hline 36 \end{array}$

11-A.2

15. $35 \div 5 = \underline{\ ?\ }$

7

13-A.3

16. Sally bought 16 turtles. She placed an equal number of turtles in each of 4 bowls. How many turtles were in each bowl?

4 turtles

13-A.4

For questions 17–18, use the table.

STUDENTS' FAVORITE VACATION	
Place	**Votes**
Beach	ⵜⵜⵜ ⵜⵜⵜ ⵜⵜⵜ
Theme Park	ⵜⵜⵜ IIII
Campground	ⵜⵜⵜ III
Home with Friends	ⵜⵜⵜ II

17. How many students answered the survey?

39 students

15-A.1

18. How many more students liked a theme park than liked a campground?

1 more student

15-A.2

For questions 19–20, identify the solid figure that is like the object shown.

19.

cube

18-A.1

20.

cone

18-A.1

Form B • Free-Response   B142   **Go on. ▶**

21. Lee drew this figure. She matched it to make the other half. Draw the completed figure.

20-A.3

For questions 22–23, use the picture.

22. How many parts make up the whole?

8 parts

21-A.1

23. How many parts are shaded?

2 parts

21-A.1

For question 24, write the numbers or words that name the part of the group that is shaded.

24.

two fifths, or $\frac{2}{5}$

22-A.1

25. Mrs. Green has 3 cars to wash. She has washed 2 cars so far. What part of the cars has been washed?

two thirds, or $\frac{2}{3}$

22-A.1

For question 26, measure the length to the nearest half-inch.

26.

$1\frac{1}{2}$ in.

24-A.2

For question 27, find the perimeter of the figure.

27.

16 units

26-A.1

28. The canopy over Glen's patio is 4 meters long and 3 meters wide. How many square meters of material does Glen need to replace the canopy?

12 square meters

26-A.2

29. A party table has 6 pizzas on it. Each pizza has 12 slices. How many pizza slices are on the table?

72 pizza slices

27-A.1

30. $\begin{array}{r} 22 \\ \times 7 \\ \hline 154 \end{array}$

27-A.1

Form B • Free-Response   B143   **Go on. ▶**

31. $8 \times 62 = \underline{\ ?\ }$

496

27-A.1

32. $58 \div 7 = \underline{\ ?\ }$

8 r2

28-A.1

33. Mrs. Wong had 50 party prizes. She gave the same number to 7 children at the party. How many prizes did each child get and how many prizes were left over?

7 prizes; 1 left over

28-A.1

34. A paintbox has 54 tubes of paint. If 6 children share the paints, how many tubes will each child have?

9 tubes

28-A.2

Form B • Free-Response   B144   **▶ Stop!**

Free-Response Format • Test Answers

Harcourt Brace School Publishers

Solve. Then write the correct answer.

1. $8 + 2 = \underline{\,?\,} + 4$

_____ 6 _____

2. $7 - 3 = 9 - \underline{\,?\,}$

_____ 5 _____

3. $\underline{\,?\,} + 0 = 6 - 2$

_____ 4 _____

4. $12 - 3 = \underline{\,?\,} + 1$

_____ 8 _____

For questions 5–6, find the perimeter.

5.

26 in.
17 in.   17 in.
26 in.

_____ 86 in. _____

6.

28 cm
23 cm   23 cm
23 cm   23 cm
28 cm

_____ 148 cm _____

7.
$$\begin{array}{r} 22 \\ 15 \\ +11 \\ \hline 48 \end{array}$$

8.
$$\begin{array}{r} 68 \\ 12 \\ +44 \\ \hline 124 \end{array}$$

9.
$$\begin{array}{r} 63 \\ 27 \\ +80 \\ \hline 170 \end{array}$$

10.
$$\begin{array}{r} 93 \\ 28 \\ +36 \\ \hline 157 \end{array}$$

11. A rectangular room has a perimeter of 100 feet. The room is 30 feet long. How wide is it?

_____ 20 ft _____

12. Paco made a rectangular rabbit cage. He used 4 feet of wire each for the north and south sides, and 3 feet each for the east and west sides of the cage. How many feet of wire did he use in all?

_____ 14 ft of wire _____

13. What is 277 rounded to the nearest hundred?

_____ 300 _____

14. What is $53.75 rounded to the nearest ten dollars?

_____ $50.00 _____

15. Estimate the sum to the nearest hundred.

$$\begin{array}{r} 119 \\ 196 \\ +305 \\ \hline 600 \end{array}$$

16. Estimate the difference to the nearest ten dollars.

$$\begin{array}{r} \$67.88 \\ -\ 32.35 \\ \hline \$40.00 \end{array}$$

For questions 17–18, use the price list.

Pizza	$1.75 a slice
Burgers	$2.80 each
Salad	$1.08 each

17. About how much change will Kimi receive from a $10 bill if she buys a slice of pizza and a salad?

_____ about $7.00 _____

18. Leon bought 2 burgers and 2 salads. About how much did he spend?

_____ about $8.00 _____

19.
$$\begin{array}{r} \$7.46 \\ -\ 3.87 \\ \hline \$3.59 \end{array}$$

20.
$$\begin{array}{r} \$3.72 \\ 2.98 \\ +\ 4.10 \\ \hline \$10.80 \end{array}$$

21.
$$\begin{array}{r} \$10.59 \\ -\ 7.78 \\ \hline \$2.81 \end{array}$$

22.
$$\begin{array}{r} \$25.46 \\ +\ 16.37 \\ \hline \$41.83 \end{array}$$

23. Theo bought chicken for $3.68, iced tea for $1.03, and dessert for $2.20. How much did he spend in all?

_____ $6.91 _____

24. Marty uses a $20 bill to buy lunch. He gets a burger for $2.50, a soda for $1.25, and yogurt for $1.50. How much change should he get?

_____ $14.75 _____

Solve. Then write the correct answer.

1. The perimeter of this figure is 636 feet. Find the missing length.

128 ft
?   156 ft
164 ft

_____ 188 ft _____

2. The perimeter of this figure is 1,177 feet. Find the missing length.

410 ft
375 ft
?
187 ft

_____ 205 ft _____

3. There are 182 street lights around the park. There are 46 lights on the west side, 39 on the north side, and 53 on the east side. How many lights are on the south side?

_____ 44 lights _____

4. A rectangular painting has a perimeter of 356 inches. If two sides of the painting are each 96 inches, what is the length of each of the other two sides?

_____ 82 in. _____

5. Which place-value positions should be regrouped to solve this problem?

$$\begin{array}{r} 5,020 \\ -2,007 \end{array}$$

_____ tens and ones _____

Find the difference.

6.
$$\begin{array}{r} 700 \\ -519 \\ \hline 181 \end{array}$$

7.
$$\begin{array}{r} 400 \\ -208 \\ \hline 192 \end{array}$$

8.
$$\begin{array}{r} 6,000 \\ -4,937 \\ \hline 1,063 \end{array}$$

9.
$$\begin{array}{r} 60,000 \\ -48,253 \\ \hline 11,747 \end{array}$$

10. There are 4,000 students at the high school. There are 1,400 students at the middle school. How many more students are at the high school?

_____ 2,600 students _____

11. The store sold 3,800 books and 1,950 tapes. How many more books than tapes were sold?

_____ 1,850 books _____

12. A chess player won 6 matches, lost 3 matches, and tied 2 matches. Each player plays 19 matches. How many matches does this player have left to play?

_____ 8 matches _____

13. Kyle chose a number. He added 5. Then, he subtracted 9. Last, he added 7. The result was 15. What number did Kyle start with?

_____ 12 _____

14. What is 461 rounded to the nearest hundred?

_____ 500 _____

15. What is 8,389 rounded to the nearest thousand?

_____ 8,000 _____

For questions 16–20, give an estimate of the sum or difference.

16.
$$\begin{array}{r} 576 \\ +141 \\ \hline 700 \end{array}$$

17.
$$\begin{array}{r} 8,998 \\ -4,002 \\ \hline 5,000 \end{array}$$

18.
$$\begin{array}{r} 5,679 \\ +2,892 \\ \hline 9,000 \end{array}$$

For questions 19–20, use the table.

| RECYCLED ALUMINUM CANS | |
Month	Cans
March	2,311
April	1,935
May	3,014
June	1,720
July	1,447

19. How many cans were collected in March and April?

_____ 4,246 cans _____

20. How many fewer cans were collected in April than in March?

_____ 376 fewer cans _____

Write the correct answer.

1. The number line shows how many dance lessons Gina takes in 4 weeks.

0 1 2 3 4 5 6 7 8 9 10 11 12

Write a number sentence that matches the number line.

_____ $4 \times 3 = 12$ _____

2. Buddy has 2 plates with 7 cookies on each plate. Write a number sentence that shows how many cookies Buddy has in all.

_____ $2 \times 7 = 14$ _____

3. Write a number sentence that tells how many eggs are in the nests.

_____ $3 \times 8 = 24$ _____

4. Ted is collecting seashells in 2 pails. He put 6 shells in each pail. Write how many shells Ted has in all.

_____ 12 shells _____

5. Rosa takes music lessons 3 times each week. Write how many lessons Rosa takes in 3 weeks.

_____ 9 lessons _____

6. Using the numbers 5 and 2, write a number sentence that shows the Order Property of Multiplication.

$5 \times 2 = 10$ (or $2 \times 5 = 10$, or $5 \times 2 = 2 \times 5$)

7. Using the number 3, write a number sentence that shows the Zero Property for Multiplication.

$3 \times 0 = 0$ (or $0 \times 3 = 0$)

8. Using the number 6, write a number sentence that shows the Property of One for Multiplication.

$6 \times 1 = 6$ (or $1 \times 6 = 6$)

9. $146 \times 1 = \underline{\ ?\ }$

_____ 146 _____

10. $0 \times 8 = \underline{\ ?\ }$

_____ 0 _____

---

11. $7 \times 8 = 56$, so $8 \times 7 = \underline{\ ?\ }$

_____ 56 _____

12. $(3 \times 3) \times 2 = \underline{\ ?\ }$

_____ 18 _____

13. $5 \times (5 \times 1) = \underline{\ ?\ }$

_____ 25 _____

14. $8 \times (2 \times 2) = \underline{\ ?\ }$

_____ 32 _____

15. $4 \times (1 \times 4) = \underline{\ ?\ }$

_____ 16 _____

16. Len has a photo album. It has 5 pages. Each page has 2 rows, with 3 photos in each row. Write how many photos Len has in all.

_____ 30 photos _____

17. Suki has 3 shelves in her room. There are 7 books on each shelf. Write how many books she has in all.

_____ 21 books _____

For questions 18–20, choose the operation that can be used to solve the problem. Then write a number sentence and solve.

18. Tina slept 9 hours one night and 8 hours the next night. How many hours did Tina sleep in all?

_____ $9 + 8 = 17$, 17 hours _____

19. Tim has 3 pets. Donna has 5 pets. How many more pets does Donna have than Tim?

_____ $5 - 3 = 2$, 2 more pets _____

20. Mrs. Garza's classroom has 5 rows of desks. There are 7 desks in each row. How many desks are there in all?

$5 \times 7 = 35$ (or $7 \times 5 = 35$),
35 desks

Write the correct answer.

1. There are 24 students in Mrs. Lee's class. She divides them into 4 teams for a game. How many students are on each team?

_____ 6 students _____

2. Jane's mom is baking cookies. She puts 8 cookies in each pan. She bakes 4 pans of cookies. How many cookies does she have in all?

_____ 32 cookies _____

3. Name the operation that is the inverse of multiplication.

_____ division _____

4. Write a number sentence that is in the same fact family as this:

$5 \times 7 = 35$ Possible answers:
$7 \times 5 = 35$; $35 \div 7 = 5$;
$35 \div 5 = 7$

For questions 5–6, use the multiplication fact to help you find the quotient.

5. $4 \times 7 = 28$

$28 \div 7 = \underline{\quad 4 \quad}$

6. $5 \times 3 = 15$

$15 \div 3 = \underline{\quad 5 \quad}$

For questions 7–8, use the model to find the quotient.

7. $28 \div 9 = \underline{\ ?\ }$

_____ 3 r1 _____

8. $11 \div 4 = \underline{\ ?\ }$

_____ 2 r3 _____

9. There are 36 students in math class, and there are 6 rows of desks. How many students sit in each row?

_____ 6 students _____

10. The librarian received 64 new paperbacks. She put 8 books in each fourth-grade classroom. How many classes received books?

_____ 8 classes _____

For questions 11–14, use the multiplication table to find the quotient.

x	0	1	2	3	4	5
0	0	0	0	0	0	0
1	0	1	2	3	4	5
2	0	2	4	6	8	10
3	0	3	6	9	12	15
4	0	4	8	12	16	20
5	0	5	10	15	20	25

11. $25 \div 5 = \underline{\ ?\ }$

_____ 5 _____

12. $12 \div 3 = \underline{\ ?\ }$

_____ 4 _____

13. $8 \div 4 = \underline{\ ?\ }$

_____ 2 _____

14. $9 \div 3 = \underline{\ ?\ }$

_____ 3 _____

15. $9\overline{)81}$ — 9

16. $7\overline{)49}$ — 7

For questions 17–18, use the table.

USED-BOOK DRIVE	NUMBER BROUGHT IN
Mystery	40
Humor	30
Biography	63
Nonfiction	54

17. Eight students each brought the same number of mystery books to the Used-Book Drive. How many mystery books did each student bring?

_____ 5 books _____

18. An equal number of biography books were placed on 7 shelves. How many biographies were put on each shelf?

_____ 9 biographies _____

For questions 19–20, solve each problem.

19. Joe earned $56 raking lawns for his neighbors. He was paid $8 for each lawn he raked. How many lawns were raked in all?

_____ 7 lawns _____

20. Frank is putting 72 new stamps into his stamp book. He puts 9 stamps on each page. How many pages did he use in all?

_____ 8 pages _____

Free-Response Format • Test Answers   **253**

TEST • CHAPTERS 1-4
PAGE 1

Write the correct answer.

1. $9 - 4 = 7 - \underline{?}$

    __2__

1-A.1

2. 87
    14
    + 25
    _____
    126

1-A.2

3. A rectangular field has a perimeter of 200 yards. The field is 60 yards long. How wide is it?

    __40 yd__

1-A.2

4. Estimate the sum to the nearest hundred.
    365
    105
    + 213
    _____
    700

1-A.3

5. $12.45
    − 5.62
    _____
    $6.83

1-A.4

6. Kara bought a sandwich for $2.89, juice for $1.07, and pretzels for $1.19. How much did she spend in all?

    __$5.15__

1-A.4

7. The perimeter of this figure is 1,810 feet. Find the missing length.

540 ft
320 ft
620 ft

    __330 ft__

2-A.1

8.   400
    − 218
    _____
    182

2-A.2

9. There are 1,560 girls and 2,100 boys in the school. How many more boys than girls are in the school?

    __540 more boys__

2-A.2

10. What is 824 rounded to the nearest hundred?

    __800__

2-A.3

For questions 11–12, use the table.

ATTENDANCE AT SOCCER GAMES

Game	Attendance
1	1,905
2	2,122
3	1,896
4	2,483
5	2,061

11. How many people were at Games 1 and 2?

    __4,027 people__

2-A.4

12. How many fewer people were at Game 5 than at Game 4?

    __422 fewer people__

2-A.4

Form B • Free-Response   B153   **Go on. ▶**

TEST • CHAPTERS 1-4
PAGE 2

13. Write a number sentence that tells how many flowers in all are in the flower pots.

    __$3 \times 6 = 18$__

3-A.1

14. Use the numbers 8 and 0 to write a number sentence that shows the Zero Property for Multiplication.

    __$8 \times 0 = 0$, or $0 \times 8 = 0$__

3-A.2

15. $5 \times 9 = 45$, so $9 \times 5 =$ ___

    __45__

3-A.2

16. $(2 \times 2) \times 6 =$ ___

    __24__

3-A.3

17. A pet store has 7 fish tanks. Each tank has 9 fish. How many fish are there in all?

    __63 fish__

3-A.3

18. Write a number sentence that can be used to solve the problem.

Eddie read 14 chapters in his book. Sarah read 22 chapters in her book. How many more chapters did Sarah read than Eddie?

    __$22 − 14 = 8$__

3-A.4

19. The Lions basketball team will play 31 games in all. They have 9 games left to play. How many games have they played so far?

    __22 games__

3-A.4

20. Write a number sentence that is in the same fact family as $27 \div 9 = 3$.

    Possible answer: $27 \div 3 = 9$,
    $9 \times 3 = 27$, or $3 \times 9 = 27$

4-A.2

21. Use the model to find the quotient.
    $17 \div 5 = \underline{?}$

    __3 r2__

4-A.3

22. The Smithfield baseball league has 32 new players. Each of the 8 teams gets the same number of players. How many new players will each team get?

    __4 new players__

4-A.3

23. $8\overline{)64}$

    __8__

4-A.5

24. Dennis earns money by delivering newspapers. In the past 9 weeks, he has earned $54.00. How much does he earn per week?

    __$6.00__

4-A.6

Form B • Free-Response   B154   **▶ Stop!**

CUMULATIVE TEST
PAGE 1

Write the correct answer.

1. $6 + 3 = \underline{?} + 4$

    __5__

1-A.1

2. $8 − 5 = 7 − \underline{?}$

    __4__

1-A.1

3.   12
     37
    +14
    _____
     63

1-A.2

4.   57
     62
    +49
    _____
    168

1-A.2

5. What is 389 rounded to the nearest hundred?

    __400__

1-A.3

6. Use the price list.

Cap	$5.99
Gloves	$4.12
Socks	$1.89

About how much change from a $10 bill will Raymond receive if he buys a cap and socks?

    __about $2__

1-A.3

7. $9.27
    − 4.59
    _____
    $4.68

1-A.4

8. $4.19
     3.27
    + 5.54
    _____
    $13.00

1-A.4

9. Nick paid $5.75 for a movie ticket, $2.25 for lemonade, and $1.99 for popcorn. How much change did he get from a $10 bill?

    __$0.01__

1-A.4

10. The perimeter of the figure is 789 feet. What is the missing length?

?
147 ft   152 ft
259 ft

    __231 ft__

2-A.2

11. A rectangular sports field has a perimeter of 488 feet. Two sides of the field are each 164 feet. What is the length of each of the other two sides?

    __80 ft__

2-A.1

Form B • Free-Response   B155   **Chapters 1–4**   **Go on. ▶**

CUMULATIVE TEST
PAGE 2

12. 600
    −179
    _____
    421

2-A.2

13. 7,000
    −2,156
    _____
    4,844

2-A.2

14. What is 643 rounded to the nearest hundred?

    __600__

2-A.3

15. What is the sum estimated to the nearest thousand?

    3,877
    +4,753
    _____
    9,000

2-A.3

For questions 16–18, use the table.

HOT DOGS SOLD AT THE BALL PARK	
May	2,672
June	2,514
July	2,973
August	2,814
September	2,767

16. How many hot dogs were sold in June and July?

    __5,487 hot dogs__

2-A.4

17. How many fewer hot dogs were sold in September than in August?

    __47 fewer hot dogs__

2-A.4

18. How many fewer hot dogs were sold in June than in July?

    __459 fewer hot dogs__

2-A.4

19. Write a number sentence that tells how many rolls are on the plates.

    Possible answer: $4 \times 6 = 24$

3-A.1

20. Use the number 7 to write a number sentence that shows the Property of One for multiplication.

    __$7 \times 1 = 7$, or $1 \times 7 = 7$__

3-A.2

Form B • Free-Response   B156   **Chapters 1–4**   **Go on. ▶**

Harcourt Brace School Publishers

21. $3 \times 9 = 27$ $9 \times 3 = $ __?__

_____ 27

3-A.2

22. $(8 \times 5) \times 2 = $ __?__

_____ 80

3-A.3

23. $3 \times (2 \times 6) = $ __?__

_____ 36

3-A.3

24. On a fishing trip, Tommy put 5 fish into each of 3 containers. How many fish does Tommy have in all?

_____ 15 fish

3-A.4

For questions 25–27, tell what operation can be used to solve the problem. Then write a number sentence and solve.

25. Karen learned to spell 7 new words one week. The following week she learned to spell 12 new words. How many words did Karen learn to spell during the two weeks?

addition; $7 + 12 = 19$;
19 new words

3-A.4

26. Ben ran 6 laps around the track. Molly ran 3 laps. How many more laps did Ben run than Molly?

subtraction; $6 - 3 = 3$;
3 more laps

3-A.4

27. A parking lot has 4 rows, with 8 cars parked in each row. How many cars are there in all?

multiplication; $4 \times 8 = 32$;
32 cars

3-A.4

28. At a school library, 28 students were working on a class project. They sat at 4 tables with the same number of students at each table. How many students were at each table?

7 students

4-A.1

29. At a pool, 5 friends swam in a relay race. Each friend swam 2 laps. How many laps did they swim in all?

10 laps

4-A.1

30. Write a number sentence that is in the same fact family as $4 \times 9 = 36$.

$9 \times 4 = 36, 36 \div 4 = 9$,
or $36 \div 9 = 4$

4-A.2

---

31. Use the multiplication fact $5 \times 6 = 30$ to help you find the quotient.

$30 \div 6 = $ __?__

_____ 5

4-A.2

32. Use the model to find the quotient.

$31 \div 7 = $ __?__

4 r3

4-A.3

33. The Oakdale Softball League has 4 teams. The teams got 51 softballs to share equally. How many softballs did each team get? How many softballs will be left over?

12 softballs, with 3 softballs left over

4-A.3

For questions 34–35, use the multiplication table to find the quotient.

×	3	4	5
3	9	12	15
4	12	16	20
5	15	20	25

34. $16 \div 4 = $ __?__

_____ 4

4-A.4

35. $20 \div 5 = $ __?__

_____ 4

4-A.4

36. $7 \overline{)42}$

_____ 6

4-A.5

37. $5 \overline{)45}$

_____ 9

4-A.5

For questions 38–40, use the table.

Pie	Number Sold
Lemon	48
Cherry	34
Apple	59
Peach	27

38. There were 9 people who each bought the same number of peach pies. How many peach pies did each person buy?

3 peach pies

4-A.6

39. The same number of lemon pies was placed on each of 4 tables. How many lemon pies were on each table?

12 lemon pies

4-A.6

40. Mrs. Jensen bought the first 12 apple pies for a family reunion. How many apple pies were left?

47 apple pies

4-A.6

Write the correct answer.

1. Write whether this is a cardinal, ordinal, or nominal number.

nominal number

2. Write whether this is a cardinal, ordinal, or nominal number.

cardinal number

For questions 3–6, use the coordinate grid.

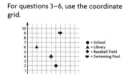

● = School
▲ = Library
◆ = Baseball Field
● = Swimming Pool

3. Which ordered pair shows the location of the school?

(6, 2)

4. What is located at (5, 4)?

Baseball Field

5. Which ordered pair shows the location of the swimming pool?

(7, 9)

6. What is located at (2,6)?

Library

For questions 7–8, use the base-ten blocks.

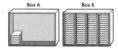

7. What does the [image] stand for?

1 hundred

8. Which number is shown by all these base-ten blocks?

3,145

9. How many thousands are in 5,280?

5 thousands

10. How many hundreds are in 3,095?

0 hundreds

11. Which number is in the tens place in 4,162?

6

12. Put the comma in the number where it belongs. Write the number.
8427

8,427

---

13. Al has English class first. Then he goes to gym class. His next class is science. After that he has math class. Then it's time for lunch. What is Al's third class?

science

14. Mr. Clark is 3 times as old as Tina. Tina is 9 years old. How old is Mr. Clark?

27 years old

15. Which benchmark number can you use to estimate the number of crackers in Box B?

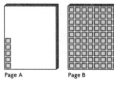

Box A   Box B

Possible answer: 5 crackers

16. About how many stamps are on Page B?

Page A   Page B

Possible answer: 80 stamps

17. About how many squares are in Quilt B?

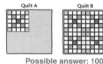

Quilt A   Quilt B

Possible answer: 100 squares

18. About how many peppermints are in Jar B?

A   B

Possible answer: 40 peppermints

19. A half gallon of milk costs $1.01. About how much should a gallon cost?

Possible answer: About $2.00

20. There are 200 marbles in the jar now. About how many could the jar hold?

Possible answer: About 600 marbles

Free-Response Format • Test Answers

Write the correct answer.

1. What is the value of the digit 2 in the number 723?

   _____ 2 × 10, or 20 _____

2. Write the number with the digit 8 in the hundreds place, 0 in the ones place, and 4 in the tens place.

   _____ 840 _____

3. Is this number written in standard form, expanded form, or written form?

   2,000 + 600 + 10 + 9

   _____ expanded form _____

4. Write in standard form the number that is shown in this place-value chart.

Thousands	Hundreds	Tens	Ones
3,	4	8	5
3 × 1,000 = 3,000	4 × 100 = 400	8 × 10 = 80	5 × 1 = 5

   _____ 3,485 _____

5. Write six hundred forty-three in standard form.

   _____ 643 _____

6. Write nine thousand, thirty-seven in standard form.

   _____ 9,037 _____

7. Write 8,000 + 500 + 2 in written form.

   _____ eight thousand, five hundred two _____

8. Write 5,360 in expanded form.

   _____ 5,000 + 300 + 60 _____

9. What is another name for 2,000?

   _____ Possible answer: 20 hundreds _____

10. Write the sum in standard form.

    6 hundreds
    + 7 hundreds
    13 hundreds

    _____ 1,300 _____

For questions 11–12, solve by using mental math.

11. 900
    +500
    1,400

12. 6,000
    +5,000
    11,000

Form B • Free-Response   B161   **Go on.** ▶

---

13. Rewrite the number, placing the commas correctly to separate the periods.

    24704612

    _____ 24,704,612 _____

14. Could the number of people living in the United States be counted in the millions, thousands, hundreds, or tens?

    _____ millions _____

15. Write six million, three hundred forty-six thousand, seven hundred twenty-five in standard form.

    _____ 6,346,725 _____

16. Write four hundred two million, sixty-three thousand, five hundred nineteen in standard form.

    _____ 402,063,519 _____

17. Write 230,657,489 as you would say it with period names.

    230 _?_, 657 _?_, 489

    _____ 230 million, 657 thousand, 489 _____

18. Write 701,005,300 as you would say it with period names.

    701 _?_, 5 _?_, 300

    _____ 701 million, 5 thousand, 300 _____

For questions 19–20, use the table.

SPRINGTOWN SLUGGERS ATTENDANCE		
Year	Number of People	Increase from Previous Year
1994	335,974	–
1995	520,028	184,054
1996	642,905	122,877
1997	916,263	273,358

19. Between which two years did attendance increase the most?

    _____ 1996–1997 _____

20. How many more people attended the games in 1997 than in 1994?

    _____ 580,289 more people _____

Form B • Free-Response   B162   ▶ **Stop!**

Write the correct answer.

1. Use the number line to compare 30 and 50. Then complete the sentence below. Write <, >, or =.

   |+-+-+-+-+-+-+-+-+-+-+|
   0 10 20 30 40 50 60 70 80 90 100

   50 ○ 30

   _____ > _____

2. Use the number line to compare 700 and 900. Then complete the sentence below. Write <, >, or =.

   |+-+-+-+-+-+-+-+-+-+-+|
   0 100 200 300 400 500 600 700 800 900 1,000

   700 ○ 900

   _____ < _____

3. Compare 625 and 652.

   _____ 652 > 625 _____

4. Compare 9,118 and 9,181.

   _____ 9,118 < 9,181 _____

5. Write the number that completes the statement.

   6,402 = _?_

   _____ 6,402 _____

6. Write the greatest place-value position in which the digits differ in 64 and 85.

   _____ tens position _____

7. Write the greatest place-value position in which the digits differ in 3,427 and 3,526.

   _____ hundreds position _____

For questions 8–9, compare the numbers. Write <, >, or = for each ○.

8. 521 ○ 512

   _____ > _____

9. 7,892 ○ 7,982

   _____ < _____

10. There are 24 players on the team. There are twice as many right-handed players as left-handed players. How many left-handed players are there?

    _____ 8 left-handed players _____

11. Mrs. Ortiz has 8 bills that total $48.00. She has at least 1 one-dollar bill, 1 five-dollar bill, 1 ten-dollar bill, and 1 twenty-dollar bill. How many five-dollar bills does she have?

    _____ 3 five-dollar bills _____

12. Write the numbers in order from least to greatest: 460, 406, 466.

    |+-+-+-+-+-+-+-+-+-+-+|
    400 410 420 430 440 450 460 470 480 490 500

    _____ 406, 460, 466 _____

Form B • Free-Response   B163   **Go on.** ▶

---

13. Write the numbers in order from the greatest to the least: 7,756; 7,776; 7,765.

    |+-+-+-+-+-+|
    7,750 7,760 7,770 7,780 7,790

    _____ 7,776; 7,765; 7,756 _____

14. Write the numbers in order from the greatest to the least: 450; 504; 455.

    _____ 504; 455; 450 _____

15. Write the numbers in order from the least to the greatest: 5,618; 8,165; 5,815.

    _____ 5,618; 5,815; 8,165 _____

For questions 16–17, use the table.

STUDENT ATTENDANCE AT COLE MIDDLE SCHOOL	
Day of Week	Number of Students
Monday	1,403
Tuesday	1,341
Wednesday	1,430
Thursday	1,195
Friday	1,340

16. On which day were the most students in school?

    _____ Wednesday _____

17. On which day were the fewest students in school?

    _____ Thursday _____

For questions 18–20, use the Venn diagram.

Sports Played by Boys and Girls

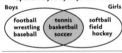

Boys   Girls

football   tennis   softball
wrestling   basketball field
baseball   soccer   hockey

18. In which sports are there only girls' teams?

    _____ field hockey and softball _____

19. In which sports are there only boys' teams?

    _____ football, wrestling, and baseball _____

20. In which sports are there both girls' teams and boys' teams?

    _____ tennis, basketball, and soccer _____

Form B • Free-Response   B164   ▶ **Stop!**

CHAPTER 8 TEST PAGE 1

Write the correct answer.

1. Which unit of time would you use to measure how long it takes to pop popcorn in a microwave?

   _____ minutes _____

2. Which unit of time would you use to measure how long it takes to dial a telephone number?

   _____ seconds _____

3. Show 25 minutes past six on the digital clock below.

   `6:25`

4. Write the time shown on the clock.

   _____ 1:15 _____

5. Kevin leaves for school every day at the time shown on the clock. Write the time Kevin leaves.

   _____ 7:45 _____

6. Mrs. Wu is taking her family to a movie at the time shown on the clock. Write the time that the movie begins.

   _____ 10:00 _____

7. The first star was seen at 9:00. Was this A.M. or P.M.?

   _____ P.M. _____

8. Peggy eats breakfast at 8 o'clock. Is this A.M. or P.M.?

   _____ A.M. _____

9. Patty practiced the piano from 7:30 P.M. to 8:10 P.M. How many minutes did she practice?

   _____ 40 minutes _____

10. The movie began at 9:00 A.M. and ended at 10:35 A.M. How many minutes elapsed from the time the movie began until it ended?

    _____ 95 minutes _____

Form B • Free-Response   B165   Go on. ▶

CHAPTER 8 TEST PAGE 2

For questions 11–16, use the schedule.

NEW YORK – WASHINGTON, D.C.		
Flight	Leave NY	Arrive D.C.
A	7:10 A.M.	8:30 A.M.
B	10:30 A.M.	?
C	4:15 P.M.	?
D	6:45 P.M.	8:05 P.M.
All flights last 1 hour 20 minutes.		

11. What time does Flight B arrive in Washington, D.C.?

    _____ 11:50 A.M. _____

12. What time does Flight C arrive in Washington, D.C.?

    _____ 5:35 P.M. _____

13. Mr. Gomez has to attend a meeting at 11:00 A.M. in Washington, D.C. What flight should he take?

    _____ Flight A _____

14. It takes Mrs. Paul 45 min to drive from her house to the airport. What is the latest she can leave and still catch Flight B?

    _____ 9:45 A.M. _____

15. The Stuarts take Flight A to begin an early tour. Their tour ends at 6:45 P.M. How long is the tour?

    _____ 10 hours 15 minutes _____

16. It takes Mrs. Poski 35 minutes to drive from the Washington airport to her home. If she takes Flight D, what is the earliest she will arrive home?

    _____ 8:40 P.M. _____

For questions 17–20, use the calendars.

August

school starts
September

17. Super Buys department store is having a 3-day back-to-school sale starting on August 23. On what date will the sale end?

    _____ August 25 _____

18. Charles will attend camp from August 4 to August 18. How many weeks will he spend there?

    _____ 2 weeks _____

19. Charles returns from camp on August 18. How many days will he have before school starts?

    _____ 15 days _____

20. The Pirates played their last home game two weeks before school started. What was the date?

    _____ August 20 _____

Form B • Free-Response   B166   ▶ Stop!

TEST • CHAPTERS 5–8 PAGE 1

Write the correct answer.

For questions 1–2, use the grid.

▲ = School
■ = Library
● = Park
♦ = Museum

1. Which ordered pair shows the location of the library?

   _____ (6,7) _____
   5-A.1

2. What is located at (3,4)?

   _____ the park _____
   5-A.1

3. How many thousands are in 4,987?

   _____ 4 thousands _____
   5-A.2

4. During vacation Mayra read 4 times as many books as Kirk. Kirk read 6 books. How many books did Mayra read?

   _____ 24 books _____
   5-A.3

5. Which benchmark number can you use to estimate the number of pogs on Side 1 and Side 2?

   Side 1   Side 2

   _____ Possible answer: 4 pogs _____
   5-A.3

6. A 3-pack of yogurt costs $1.79. About how much should a 9-pack cost?

   _____ Possible answer: about $6.00 _____
   5-A.3

7. Write seven hundred fourteen in standard form.

   _____ 714 _____
   6-A.1

8. Write 4,161 in expanded form.

   _____ 4,000 + 100 + 60 + 1 _____
   6-A.1

9. What is another name for 7,200?

   _____ Possible answer: 72 hundreds _____
   6-A.1

For questions 10–11, use the table.

SALES AT STEVE'S PIZZA SHOP	
Year	Sales
1994	14,163
1995	15,476
1996	16,597
1997	17,779

10. Between which two years did the number of sales increase the most?

    _____ 1994 and 1995 _____
    6-A.2

11. How many more pizzas were sold in 1997 than in 1996?

    _____ 1,182 more pizzas _____
    6-A.2

12. Use the numbers 714 and 741 to complete the statement correctly.

    _____ 741 > 714 _____
    7-A.2

Form B • Free-Response   B167   Go on. ▶

TEST • CHAPTERS 5–8 PAGE 2

13. Write the greatest place-value position in which the digits differ in these numbers.
    5,534
    5,543

    _____ tens position _____
    7-A.2

14. Write the numbers in order from the greatest to the least.
    1,561; 1,591; 1,516

    1,500 1,510 1,520 1,530 1,540 1,550 1,560 1,570 1,580 1,590

    _____ 1,591; 1,561; 1,516 _____
    7-A.3

For questions 15–16, use the Venn diagram.

Students Who Play Sports
Basketball   Track

Bill   Jena
Craig   Scott   Tom
Pam   Leon   Lisa
                    Brian

15. Which students play only basketball?

    _____ Bill, Craig, Pam _____
    7-A.4

16. Which students participate in both basketball and track?

    _____ Jena, Scott, Leon _____
    7-A.4

17. Show 14 minutes past twelve on the digital clock.

    `12:14`
    8-A.1

18. Bobby rode the school bus from 2:55 P.M. to 3:25 P.M. How many minutes was he on the bus?

    _____ 30 min _____
    8-A.1

For questions 19–20, use the calendars.

January   February

19. How many days is it from January 29 to the first Friday in February?

    _____ 9 days _____
    8-A.4

20. How many days are there from the first day of school on January 6 until the first test on January 27?

    _____ 21 days _____
    8-A.4

Form B • Free-Response   B168   ▶ Stop!

Free-Response Format • Test Answers   257

Write the correct answer.

1.
$$\begin{array}{r} 59 \\ 17 \\ +25 \\ \hline 101 \end{array}$$
1-A.1

2. Estimate the difference to the nearest ten dollars.
$$\begin{array}{r} \$58.25 \\ -\ 33.79 \\ \hline \$30.00 \end{array}$$
1-A.3

3.
$$\begin{array}{r} \$3.56 \\ 3.93 \\ +\ 2.11 \\ \hline \$9.60 \end{array}$$
1-A.4

4.
$$\begin{array}{r} 700 \\ -116 \\ \hline 584 \end{array}$$
2-A.2

5. Estimate the difference to the nearest hundred.
$$\begin{array}{r} 611 \\ -209 \\ \hline 400 \end{array}$$
2-A.3

6. Jill has 3 jars with 4 marbles in each jar. Write a number sentence that shows how many marbles Jill has in all.

Possible answer: $3 \times 4 = 12$
3-A.1

7. Use the numbers 7 and 5 to write a number sentence that shows the Order Property of Multiplication.

$7 \times 5 = 5 \times 7$
3-A.2

8. $(5 \times 3) \times 2 =$ ___?

30
3-A.3

9. A library has 9 rows of bookcases. There are 8 bookcases in each row. Write a number sentence and find how many bookcases there are in all.

$9 \times 8 = 72$; 72 bookcases
3-A.4

10. On Saturday 3 friends went fishing. Each of the 3 friends caught 6 fish. How many fish did they catch in all?

18 fish
4-A.1

11. What is a number sentence that is in the same fact family as $3 \times 9 = 27$?

$9 \times 3 = 27, 27 \div 9 = 3$,
or $27 \div 3 = 9$
4-A.2

---

12. Use the model to find the quotient.
$25 \div 7 =$ ___?

3 r4
4-A.3

For questions 13–14, use the multiplication table to find the quotient.

×	3	4	5
3	9	12	15
4	12	16	20
5	15	20	25

13. $12 \div 4 =$ ___?

3
4-A.4

14. $15 \div 3 =$ ___?

5
4-A.4

15. $6\overline{)30}$

5
4-A.5

16. Mrs. Kaufman's students earned $63 at a car wash. They were paid $3 for each car they washed. How many cars in all did the students wash?

21 cars
4-A.6

17. Write whether the number is a cardinal, ordinal, or nominal number.

ordinal number
5-A.1

18. What digit is in the tens place in 2,876?

7
5-A.2

19. There are 30 marbles in a jar now. About how many marbles could the jar hold?

about 90 marbles
5-A.3

20. What is the value of the digit 5 in the number 543?

500
6-A.1

---

21. What is five hundred ninety-two written in standard form?

592
6-A.1

22. What is seven million, three hundred thirty-five thousand, nine hundred seventy-four written in standard form?

7,335,974
6-A.2

23. How do you write 8,463,587 with period names?

8 million, 463 thousand, 587
6-A.2

For questions 24–25, use mental math.

24.
$$\begin{array}{r} 800 \\ +300 \\ \hline 1,100 \end{array}$$
6-A.2

25.
$$\begin{array}{r} 9,000 \\ +3,000 \\ \hline 12,000 \end{array}$$
6-A.2

26. Use the number line to compare. Write < or > for the ●.

20 30 40 50 60 70 80

40 ● 70

<
7-A.1

27. Use the numbers 756 and 765 to complete the statement.

765 > 756
7-A.2

28. Write < or > for the ●.
432 ● 423

>
7-A.2

For questions 29–30, use the table.

VISITORS TO THE SCIENCE MUSEUM	
Week	Number of Visitors
1	1,291
2	1,452
3	1,312
4	1,276
5	1,495

29. During which week did the most visitors go to the Science Museum?

Week 5
7-A.3

30. During which week did the fewest visitors go to the Science Museum?

Week 4
7-A.3

For questions 31–32, use the Venn diagram.

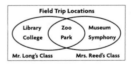

Field Trip Locations
Library College / Zoo Park / Museum Symphony
Mr. Long's Class   Mrs. Reed's Class

31. To which locations did only Mr. Long's class go?

library, college
7-A.4

32. To which locations did both classes go?

zoo, park
7-A.4

33. Show 45 minutes past eight on the digital clock.

8:45

8-A.1

34. You look in the sky and see a rainbow at 10:00. Is this A.M. or P.M.?

A.M.
8-A.2

For questions 35–36, use the schedule.

CITY SIGHTSEEING TOUR		
Tour	Start Time	Finish Time
A	11:15 A.M.	1:45 P.M.
B	11:45 A.M.	?
C	12:15 P.M.	2:45 P.M.
D	?	6:15 P.M.
All tours last 2 hours 30 minutes.		

35. At what time does Tour B finish?

2:15 P.M.
8-A.3

36. At what time does Tour D start?

3:45 P.M.
8-A.3

For questions 37–38, use the calendars.

May						
Su	M	T	W	Th	F	Sa
				1	2	3
4	5	6	7	8	9	10
11	12	13	14	15	16	17
18	19	20	21	22	23	24
25	26	27	28	29	30	31

June						
Su	M	T	W	Th	F	Sa
1	2	3	4	5	6	7
8	9	10	11	12	13	14
15	16	17	18	19	20	21
22	23	24	25	26	27	28
29	30					

37. The circus will be in town for 6 days starting on June 4. What date will be the last day for the circus to be in town?

June 9
8-A.4

38. Caroline is going to visit her cousin from May 24 to June 7. How many weeks will she spend with her cousin?

2 weeks
8-A.4

Write the correct answer.

For questions 1–3, use the frequency table.

NUMBER OF MILES TERESA JOGGED

Week	Miles (Frequency)	Cumulative Frequency
1	14	14
2	11	25
3	20	?
4	18	?

1. During which week did Teresa jog farthest?

   ___Week 3___

2. How many more miles did Teresa jog in Week 1 than in Week 2?

   ___3 more miles___

3. What is the cumulative frequency for the miles jogged in all 4 weeks?

   ___63 miles___

4. You can order a turkey, tuna, peanut butter, or cheese sandwich on white bread or on rye bread. How many sandwich choices are there?

   ___8 choices___

5. Bob can play with his toy trucks, cars, motorcycles, and vans in a toy garage, roadway, or car wash or in a sandbox. How many ways can he spend his time playing?

   ___16 ways___

6. Mr. Eng is having a picnic. He must decide if he should prepare beef, chicken, lamb, or veal. What survey question should he ask his guests?

   ___Possible question: Which do you prefer; beef, chicken, lamb, or veal?___

For questions 7–8, use the data in the table.

FAVORITE JUICE

Choice	Votes
Orange	ЖЖ ЖЖ IIII
Apple	ЖЖ II
Grape	ЖЖ I
Pineapple	ЖЖ IIII

7. Which juice was chosen as the favorite by the greatest number of people?

   ___Orange juice___

8. Which juice was the favorite of the fewest people?

   ___Grape juice___

Form B • Free-Response   B173   Go on. ▶

For questions 9–11, use the graph.

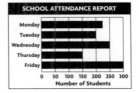

SCHOOL ATTENDANCE REPORT

Monday, Tuesday, Wednesday, Thursday, Friday
0 50 100 150 200 250 300
Number of Students

9. How many students were in school on Thursday?

   ___150 students___

10. What interval is used in the scale of the graph?

   ___50___

11. How many more students were in school on Wednesday than on Monday?

   ___25 more students___

For questions 12–15, use the graph.

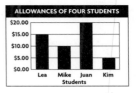

ALLOWANCES OF FOUR STUDENTS

$20.00 $15.00 $10.00 $5.00 $0.00
Lea Mike Juan Kim
Students

12. What interval is used in the scale of the graph?

   ___$5.00___

13. How would the length of the bars change if an interval of $1.00 were used in the graph?

   ___The bars would be longer.___

14. How much more is Lea's allowance than Kim's?

   ___$10.00___

15. How much do all 4 students combined receive each week?

   ___$50.00___

Form B • Free-Response   B174   ▶ Stop!

Write the correct answer.

For questions 1–6, use the line graph.

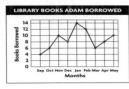

LIBRARY BOOKS ADAM BORROWED

14 12 10 8 6 4 2 0
Books Borrowed
Sep Oct Nov Dec Jan Feb Mar Apr May
Months

1. Why is a line graph a good choice for showing this information?

   ___It shows changes over time.___

2. What interval is used on the scale of this graph?

   ___2___

3. How many books did Adam borrow in November?

   ___10 books___

4. In which month did Adam borrow the most books?

   ___January___

5. In how many months did Adam borrow exactly 6 books?

   ___2 months___

6. How many more books did Adam borrow in February than in April?

   ___4 more books___

For questions 7–11, use the line plot. There is one X for each student.

X X
X X X X
X X X X X X
X X X X X X X X X X
0 1 2 3 4 5 6 7 8 9 10
Books Read

7. What do the numbers on the line plot represent?

   ___number of books read___

8. What is the range of data used in this line plot?

   ___10___

9. How many students read 6 books?

   ___3 students___

10. What was the greatest number of books read?

   ___10 books___

11. How many books were read in all by students who read 4 books?

   ___16 books___

Form B • Free-Response   B175   Go on. ▶

For questions 12–16, use the stem-and-leaf plot.

SCORES ON SCIENCE TEST

Stem	Leaves
6	2 6 8
7	0 0 2 2 4 4 6 6
8	0 1 2 2 2 4 4 8 8
9	0 2 4 4 6

12. How would you find the highest score on the test?

   ___by looking at the last number in the plot___

13. What is the middle number in this set of data called?

   ___median___

14. What is the mode for this data?

   ___82___

15. What is the median for this data?

   ___81___

16. What is the difference between the highest score and the lowest score?

   ___34___

For questions 17–20, choose the type of graph that would be best to display the data described.

17. What kind of graph would be best to show the favorite school subjects of 100 fourth-grade students?

   ___bar graph___

18. What kind of graph would be best to show how much a baby has grown over time?

   ___line graph___

19. Would a bar graph or a stem-and-leaf plot be better to compare the heights in inches of 30 fourth-grade students?

   ___bar graph___

20. What kind of graph would be best to display the data in the table?

FAVORITE RADIO STATIONS OF FOURTH-GRADE BOYS AND GIRLS

Station	Boys	Girls
103 AM	11	6
107.5 FM	9	18
98.9 FM	3	7

   ___double-bar graph___

Form B • Free-Response   B176   ▶ Stop!

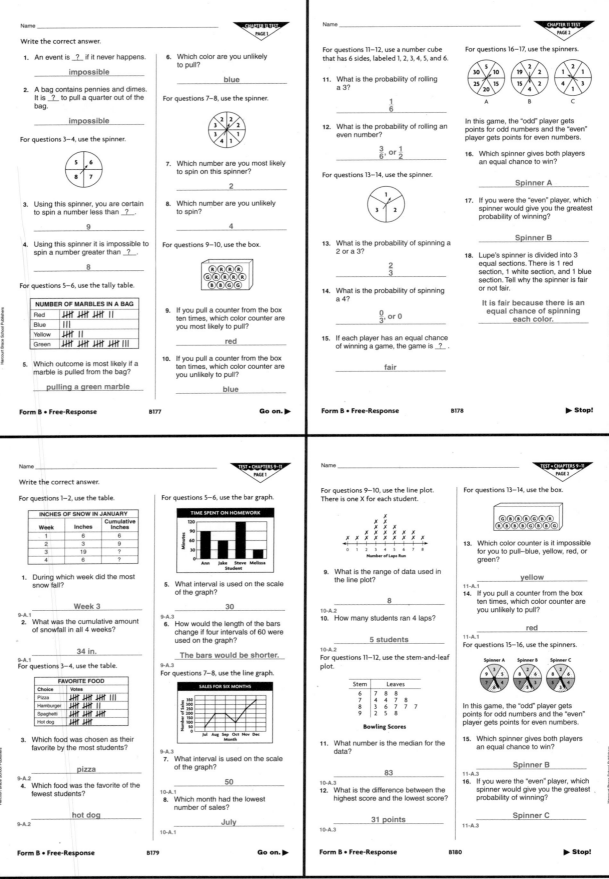

Name _____

Write the correct answer.

1. An event is __?__ if it never happens.

    impossible

2. A bag contains pennies and dimes. It is __?__ to pull a quarter out of the bag.

    impossible

For questions 3–4, use the spinner.

3. Using this spinner, you are certain to spin a number less than __?__.

    9

4. Using this spinner it is impossible to spin a number greater than __?__.

    8

For questions 5–6, use the tally table.

NUMBER OF MARBLES IN A BAG

Red	ЖЖ ЖЖ ЖЖ II
Blue	III
Yellow	ЖЖ II
Green	ЖЖ ЖЖ ЖЖ ЖЖ III

5. Which outcome is most likely if a marble is pulled from the bag?

    pulling a green marble

6. Which color are you unlikely to pull?

    blue

For questions 7–8, use the spinner.

7. Which number are you most likely to spin on this spinner?

    2

8. Which number are you unlikely to spin?

    4

For questions 9–10, use the box.

9. If you pull a counter from the box ten times, which color counter are you most likely to pull?

    red

10. If you pull a counter from the box ten times, which color counter are you unlikely to pull?

    blue

Form B • Free-Response   B177   Go on. ▶

Name _____

For questions 11–12, use a number cube that has 6 sides, labeled 1, 2, 3, 4, 5, and 6.

11. What is the probability of rolling a 3?

    $\frac{1}{6}$

12. What is the probability of rolling an even number?

    $\frac{3}{6}$, or $\frac{1}{2}$

For questions 13–14, use the spinner.

13. What is the probability of spinning a 2 or a 3?

    $\frac{2}{3}$

14. What is the probability of spinning a 4?

    $\frac{0}{3}$, or 0

15. If each player has an equal chance of winning a game, the game is __?__.

    fair

For questions 16–17, use the spinners.

A   B   C

In this game, the "odd" player gets points for odd numbers and the "even" player gets points for even numbers.

16. Which spinner gives both players an equal chance to win?

    Spinner A

17. If you were the "even" player, which spinner would give you the greatest probability of winning?

    Spinner B

18. Lupe's spinner is divided into 3 equal sections. There is 1 red section, 1 white section, and 1 blue section. Tell why the spinner is fair or not fair.

    It is fair because there is an equal chance of spinning each color.

Form B • Free-Response   B178   ▶ Stop!

Name _____

Write the correct answer.

For questions 1–2, use the table.

INCHES OF SNOW IN JANUARY

Week	Inches	Cumulative Inches
1	6	6
2	3	9
3	19	?
4	6	?

1. During which week did the most snow fall?

    Week 3
9-A.1

2. What was the cumulative amount of snowfall in all 4 weeks?

    34 in.
9-A.1

For questions 3–4, use the table.

FAVORITE FOOD

Choice	Votes
Pizza	ЖЖ ЖЖ ЖЖ III
Hamburger	ЖЖ ЖЖ II
Spaghetti	ЖЖ ЖЖ ЖЖ
Hot dog	ЖЖ ЖЖ

3. Which food was chosen as their favorite by the most students?

    pizza
9-A.2

4. Which food was the favorite of the fewest students?

    hot dog
9-A.2

For questions 5–6, use the bar graph.

TIME SPENT ON HOMEWORK

5. What interval is used on the scale of the graph?

    30
9-A.3

6. How would the length of the bars change if four intervals of 60 were used on the graph?

    The bars would be shorter.
9-A.3

For questions 7–8, use the line graph.

SALES FOR SIX MONTHS

7. What interval is used on the scale of the graph?

    50
10-A.1

8. Which month had the lowest number of sales?

    July
10-A.1

Form B • Free-Response   B179   Go on. ▶

Name _____

For questions 9–10, use the line plot. There is one X for each student.

9. What is the range of data used in the line plot?

    8
10-A.2

10. How many students ran 4 laps?

    5 students
10-A.2

For questions 11–12, use the stem-and-leaf plot.

Stem	Leaves
6	7 8 8
7	4 4 7 8
8	3 6 7 7 7
9	2 5 8

Bowling Scores

11. What number is the median for the data?

    83
10-A.3

12. What is the difference between the highest score and the lowest score?

    31 points
10-A.3

For questions 13–14, use the box.

13. Which color counter is it impossible for you to pull—blue, yellow, red, or green?

    yellow
11-A.1

14. If you pull a counter from the box ten times, which color counter are you unlikely to pull?

    red
11-A.1

For questions 15–16, use the spinners.

Spinner A   Spinner B   Spinner C

In this game, the "odd" player gets points for odd numbers and the "even" player gets points for even numbers.

15. Which spinner gives both players an equal chance to win?

    Spinner B
11-A.3

16. If you were the "even" player, which spinner would give you the greatest probability of winning?

    Spinner C
11-A.3

Form B • Free-Response   B180   ▶ Stop!

Free-Response Format • Test Answers

Write the correct answer.

1. What is a reasonable estimate of the sum?

212
396
+101

_____ 700

1-A.3

2. 6,000
−3,987

_____ 2,013

2-A.2

3. A farmer has 3 barns. He has 5 cows in each barn. How many cows does he have in all?

_____ 15 cows

3-A.1

4. $(4 \times 2) \times 7 =$?

_____ 56

3-A.3

5. There are 54 students taking a trip. They will go in 6 vans. How many students will ride in each van?

_____ 9 students

4-A.1

6. What number sentence is in the same fact family as these number sentences?

$3 \times 4 = 12$
$4 \times 3 = 12$
$12 \div 4 = 3$

_____ $12 \div 4 = 3$

4-A.2

7. $14 \div 3 =$?

_____ 4 r2

4-A.3

For questions 8–9, use the multiplication table to find the quotient.

×	2	3	4
2	4	6	8
3	6	9	12
4	8	12	16

8. $16 \div 4 =$?

_____ 4

4-A.4

9. $9 \div 3 =$?

_____ 3

4-A.4

10. Earl has 18 books stored on 3 shelves. He put the same number on each shelf. How many books are on each shelf?

_____ 6 books

4-A.6

11. Sue Ellen is 25 years old. Is the number 25 *cardinal, ordinal,* or *nominal*?

_____ cardinal

5-A.1

12. How many tens are in 9,265?

_____ 6 tens

5-A.2

13. In the number 400, what is the value of 4?

_____ 4 hundreds

6-A.1

14. What are these numbers in order from the least to the greatest?

872, 869, 857

_____ 857, 869, 872

7-A.3

For questions 15–16, use the Venn diagram.

Six States

Texas   Florida   Maine
Arizona Georgia   Delaware

Southern States   Eastern States

15. Which states are eastern states only?

_____ Maine, Delaware

7-A.4

16. Which states are both southern states and eastern states?

_____ Florida, Georgia

7-A.4

17. What unit of time would you use to measure how long it takes to prepare a bowl of cereal?

_____ minutes

8-A.1

18. Which time is closer to the time that school starts—8:00 A.M. or 8:00 P.M.?

_____ 8:00 A.M.

8-A.2

For questions 19–20, use the schedule.

Bus	Leave Johnson City	Arrive Fosterville
A	8:00 A.M.	9:50 A.M.
B	9:30 A.M.	?
C	11:10 A.M.	?
D	1:45 P.M.	?
Each trip lasts 1 hour and 50 minutes.		

19. At what time does Bus B arrive in Fosterville?

_____ 11:20 A.M.

8-A.3

20. Mr. Lorenzo has a meeting in Fosterville at 2:00 P.M. Which is the latest bus he could take to arrive at the meeting on time?

_____ Bus C

8-A.3

For questions 21–22, use the table.

BOXES OF COOKIES SOLD		
Week	Number Sold (Frequency)	Cumulative Frequency
1	235	235
2	175	410
3	150	?

21. During which week were the most boxes of cookies sold?

_____ Week 1

9-A.1

22. What was the total number of boxes of cookies sold during the 3 weeks?

_____ 560 boxes of cookies

9-A.1

23. A teacher will survey students to find out whether they want to play soccer, basketball, or baseball on Sports Day. What survey question would be the most useful for the teacher to ask?

_____ Possible answer: What sport do you prefer to play on Sports Day—soccer, baseball, or basketball?

9-A.2

For questions 24–25, use the graph.

COMPUTER SALES

24. What interval is used in the scale of the graph?

_____ 10

9-A.3

25. How many more computers were sold on Saturday than were sold on Friday?

_____ 10 more computers

9-A.3

For questions 26–27, use the line graph.

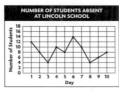

NUMBER OF STUDENTS ABSENT AT LINCOLN SCHOOL

26. How many students were absent on Day 4?

_____ 10 students

10-A.1

27. On which days were the fewest students absent?

_____ Day 3 and Day 8

10-A.1

For questions 28–29, use the line plot. There is one X for each student.

Miles Walked in Walkathon

28. How many students walked 3 miles?

_____ 5 students

10-A.2

29. What was the greatest number of miles walked by any student?

_____ 6 miles

10-A.2

For questions 30–31, use the stem-and-leaf plot.

Stem	Leaves
7	2 4 6 6
8	4 6 6 8 8
9	2 4 4 4 4 6 8

Scores on a Spelling Test for 16 Students

30. What number is the mode for these data?

_____ 94

10-A.3

31. What number is the median for these data?

_____ 88

10-A.3

32. What graph would be best to show how many girls were absent and how many boys were absent each day for a week?

_____ Possible answer: double-line graph

10-A.4

For questions 33–36, use the spinner.

33. Using this spinner, it is impossible to spin a number greater than ? .

_____ 4

11-A.1

34. What number are you most likely to spin on this spinner?

_____ 4

11-A.1

35. What is the probability of spinning a 1?

_____ $\frac{1}{8}$

11-A.2

36. What is the probability of spinning a 3?

_____ $\frac{2}{8}$, or $\frac{1}{4}$

11-A.2

Harcourt Brace School Publishers

Write the correct answer.

For questions 1–2, tell whether the figure is one-dimensional, two-dimensional, or three-dimensional.

1.

two-dimensional

2.

three-dimensional

3. What unit would be used to measure the area of a large blackboard?

square feet

4. What unit would be used to measure the volume of a refrigerator?

cubic feet

For questions 5–6, use the figure.

5. How many faces are on this figure?

5 faces

6. What two plane figures are the faces of this figure?

triangles and square

For questions 7–8, use this figure.

7. How many faces does this figure have?

6 faces

8. Each face on this figure is a __?__.

square

For questions 9–11, use the figure.

9. How many faces does this figure have?

5 faces

10. How many edges does this figure have?

9 edges

11. How many vertices does this figure have?

6 vertices

Form B • Free-Response   B185   **Go on. ▶**

For questions 12–15, use the grid.

12. Write the ordered pair for point x.

(4,9)

13. Write the ordered pairs of the vertices of the square marked on the grid.

(5,5), (5,9), (9,9), (9,5)

14. Write the ordered pairs of the vertices of the triangle marked on the grid.

(3,3), (3,7), (5,5)

15. Which ordered pair identifies the vertex that is shared by the square *and* the triangle?

(5,5)

16. Ralph placed a can of beans, a roll of mints, and a can of soda in his grocery basket. Which term best describes the shapes of these objects?

cylinder

17. What is the shape of a globe, a round balloon, and a marble?

sphere

18. Circle the figure that belongs in the overlapped section of this Venn diagram.

With Triangular and Square Faces

With Triangular Faces   With Square Faces

For questions 19–20, use the organized list.

19. Which heading can be used for the last column?

Rectangular Prisms	Cylinders	?
book candy box ?	lipstick straw pen	party hat ice-cream cone

Cones

20. Which figure listed below could be listed under **Rectangular Prisms**?

pencil	soup can
shoe box	basketball

shoe box

Form B • Free-Response   B186   **▶ Stop!**

Write the correct answer.

1. The part of a line between point *A* and point *B* is called a __?__.

A   B

line segment

2. Is a flat surface with no end called a plane, a line segment, a line, or a point?

plane

3. Are line segments that never cross and are the same distance apart called *parallel lines* or *perpendicular lines*?

parallel lines

4. What term names these figures?

C   D

points

5. What kind of angle is the following?

right angle

6. What is the name of this figure?

X   Y

XY

7. Are lines that cross each other called *parallel lines* or *intersecting lines*?

intersecting lines

8. Are lines that intersect to form four right angles called *parallel lines* or *perpendicular lines*?

perpendicular lines

For questions 9–10, use the map.

Street A
Street B
Street C
Street D

9. Which street is perpendicular to Streets B and C?

Street D

10. Which street is parallel to Street B?

Street C

Form B • Free-Response   B187   **Go on. ▶**

---

11. Do all polygons have straight sides or curved sides?

straight sides

12. What is this figure called?

pentagon

13. An octagon has 8 sides. How many angles does it have?

8 angles

14. A hexagon has 6 angles. How many sides does it have?

6 sides

15. How many angles does a quadrilateral have?

4 angles

16. I am a 4-sided polygon. I have 2 pairs of parallel sides. I have 2 congruent acute angles and 2 congruent obtuse angles. What am I?

parallelogram

17. What is the name of this figure?

trapezoid

18. What is the name of this figure?

parallelogram

19. Circle the figure that does *not* have 4 right angles.

20. Martin drew a 4-sided figure. It had 4 right angles and 2 sets of parallel lines of equal length. What shape was his figure?

square

Form B • Free-Response   B188   **▶ Stop!**

Free-Response Format • Test Answers

Write the correct answer.

1. Write a number sentence to find the perimeter of this figure.

Possible answer:
$1 + 1 + 1 + 1 + 1 + 1 + 3 + 3 = 12$

2. Write a number sentence to find the perimeter of this figure.

Possible answer:
$(2 \times 3) + (2 \times 5) = 16$

For questions 3–4, find the perimeter.

3.

4m

6m

_____ 20 m

4.

4 cm

1 cm   1 cm
2 cm   2 cm

5 cm

_____ 15 cm

5. A garden is 62 feet long and 25 feet wide. How many feet of fencing are needed to go around the garden?

_____ 174 ft

6. Students are hanging a banner all the way around the four walls of their classroom. Each wall is 40 feet long. How long is the banner?

_____ 160 ft

For questions 7–8, find the area.

7.

_____ 8 sq units

8.

_____ 10 sq units

9. Estimate the area.

Possible answer: 12 sq units

Form B • Free-Response   B189   **Go on.** ▶

10. Estimate the area.

Possible answer: 9 sq units

11. Find the area.

7m

7m

_____ 49 sq m

12. Find the area.

5 ft

8 ft

_____ 40 sq ft

13. How many square feet of wallpaper do you need to cover a wall that is 8 feet high and 10 feet wide?

_____ 80 sq ft

14. The dog's pen is 7 yards by 9 yards. How much area does the dog have?

_____ 63 sq yd

For questions 15–18, use the shaded figures below.

A   B   C   D

15. What is the perimeter of Figure B?

_____ 12 units

16. What is the area of Figure C?

_____ 7 sq units

17. Which figure has the same area as Figure D but a different perimeter?

_____ Figure C

18. Which two figures have the same area and the same perimeter?

_____ Figures A and D

19. Screen costs $2.00 per square foot. The screen door is 7 feet by 3 feet. How much does screen for the door cost?

_____ $42.00

20. Pia has a rope that is 48 feet long. What is the greatest square area she can rope off?

_____ 144 sq ft (12 ft by 12 ft)

Form B • Free-Response   B190   ▶ **Stop!**

Write the correct answer.

1. A figure that has been turned around a point or vertex is called a __?__.

_____ rotation

For questions 2–3, use the figures.

A   B

2. Figure A is an example of a __?__.

_____ translation, or slide

3. Figure B is an example of a __?__.

_____ reflection

4. If two figures have the same size and shape, they are __?__.

_____ congruent

5. Circle the two figures that are congruent.

6. Draw a figure that is congruent to the figure shown.

Check students' figures.

7. Circle the figure that has point symmetry.

8. Draw a line of symmetry through this figure.

Check students' lines of symmetry.

9. Circle the figure that has line symmetry.

Form B • Free-Response   B191   **Go on.** ▶

10. A pattern of repeated polygons with no gaps or overlaps is called a __?__.

_____ tessellation

11. Draw the figure that tessellates in this design.

12. Circle the figure that will tessellate.

13. What figures are used in this tessellation?

_____ triangles and squares

14. A figure is drawn on 1-cm grid paper. If you copy the figure on 2-cm paper, it will be the same but __?__.

_____ larger

For questions 15–17, use the pairs of figures.

A   B
C   D

15. In which pair are the figures congruent?

_____ A

16. In which pair are the figures similar but not congruent?

_____ C

17. You could describe the figures in pair B as neither similar nor __?__.

_____ congruent

18. Luz has a design on grid paper. How can she reduce the size of the design and be sure it is the same as the original design?

_____ She can copy it onto
_____ smaller grid paper.

Form B • Free-Response   B192   ▶ **Stop!**

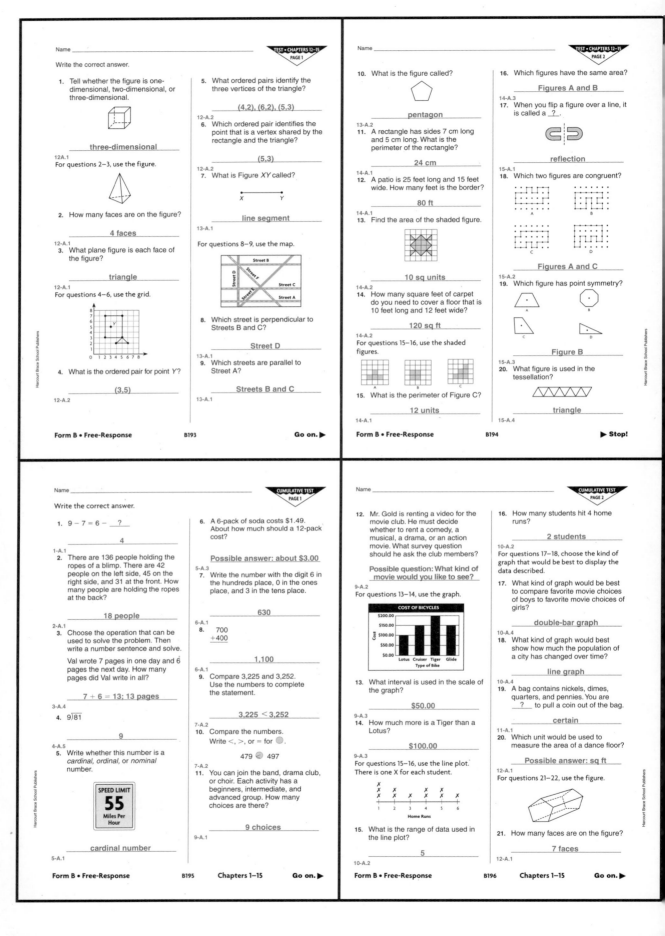

Name _____

Write the correct answer.

1. Tell whether the figure is one-dimensional, two-dimensional, or three-dimensional.

three-dimensional
12A.1

For questions 2–3, use the figure.

2. How many faces are on the figure?

4 faces
12-A.1

3. What plane figure is each face of the figure?

triangle
12-A.1

For questions 4–6, use the grid.

4. What is the ordered pair for point Y?

(3,5)
12-A.2

5. What ordered pairs identify the three vertices of the triangle?

(4,2), (6,2), (5,3)
12-A.2

6. Which ordered pair identifies the point that is a vertex shared by the rectangle and the triangle?

(5,3)
12-A.2

7. What is Figure XY called?

X ———— Y

line segment
13-A.1

For questions 8–9, use the map.

8. Which street is perpendicular to Streets B and C?

Street D
13-A.1

9. Which streets are parallel to Street A?

Streets B and C
13-A.1

Form B • Free-Response   B193   **Go on. ▶**

Name _____

10. What is the figure called?

pentagon
13-A.2

11. A rectangle has sides 7 cm long and 5 cm long. What is the perimeter of the rectangle?

24 cm
14-A.1

12. A patio is 25 feet long and 15 feet wide. How many feet is the border?

80 ft
14-A.1

13. Find the area of the shaded figure.

10 sq units
14-A.2

14. How many square feet of carpet do you need to cover a floor that is 10 feet long and 12 feet wide?

120 sq ft
14-A.2

For questions 15–16, use the shaded figures.

15. What is the perimeter of Figure C?

12 units
14-A.1

16. Which figures have the same area?

Figures A and B
14-A.3

17. When you flip a figure over a line, it is called a _?_.

reflection
15-A.1

18. Which two figures are congruent?

Figures A and C
15-A.2

19. Which figure has point symmetry?

Figure B
15-A.3

20. What figure is used in the tessellation?

triangle
15-A.4

Form B • Free-Response   B194   **▶ Stop!**

Name _____

Write the correct answer.

1. $9 - 7 = 6 - \underline{?}$

4
1-A.1

2. There are 136 people holding the ropes of a blimp. There are 42 people on the left side, 45 on the right side, and 31 at the front. How many people are holding the ropes at the back?

18 people
2-A.1

3. Choose the operation that can be used to solve the problem. Then write a number sentence and solve.

Val wrote 7 pages in one day and 6 pages the next day. How many pages did Val write in all?

7 + 6 = 13; 13 pages
3-A.4

4. 9)81

9
4-A.5

5. Write whether this number is a *cardinal*, *ordinal*, or *nominal* number.

SPEED LIMIT **55** Miles Per Hour

cardinal number
5-A.1

6. A 6-pack of soda costs $1.49. About how much should a 12-pack cost?

Possible answer: about $3.00
5-A.3

7. Write the number with the digit 6 in the hundreds place, 0 in the ones place, and 3 in the tens place.

630
6-A.1

8. 700
  +400

1,100
6-A.1

9. Compare 3,225 and 3,252. Use the numbers to complete the statement.

3,225 < 3,252
7-A.2

10. Compare the numbers. Write <, >, or = for ◯.

479 ◯ 497

7-A.2

11. You can join the band, drama club, or choir. Each activity has a beginners, intermediate, and advanced group. How many choices are there?

9 choices
9-A.1

Form B • Free-Response   B195   **Chapters 1–15**   **Go on. ▶**

Name _____

12. Mr. Gold is renting a video for the movie club. He must decide whether to rent a comedy, a musical, a drama, or an action movie. What survey question should he ask the club members?

Possible question: What kind of movie would you like to see?
9-A.2

For questions 13–14, use the graph.

13. What interval is used in the scale of the graph?

$50.00
9-A.3

14. How much more is a Tiger than a Lotus?

$100.00
9-A.3

For questions 15–16, use the line plot. There is one X for each student.

15. What is the range of data used in the line plot?

5
10-A.2

16. How many students hit 4 home runs?

2 students
10-A.2

For questions 17–18, choose the kind of graph that would be best to display the data described.

17. What kind of graph would be best to compare favorite movie choices of boys to favorite movie choices of girls?

double-bar graph
10-A.4

18. What kind of graph would best show how much the population of a city has changed over time?

line graph
10-A.4

19. A bag contains nickels, dimes, quarters, and pennies. You are _?_ to pull a coin out of the bag.

certain
11-A.1

20. Which unit would be used to measure the area of a dance floor?

Possible answer: sq ft
12-A.1

For questions 21–22, use the figure.

21. How many faces are on the figure?

7 faces
12-A.1

Form B • Free-Response   B196   **Chapters 1–15**   **Go on. ▶**

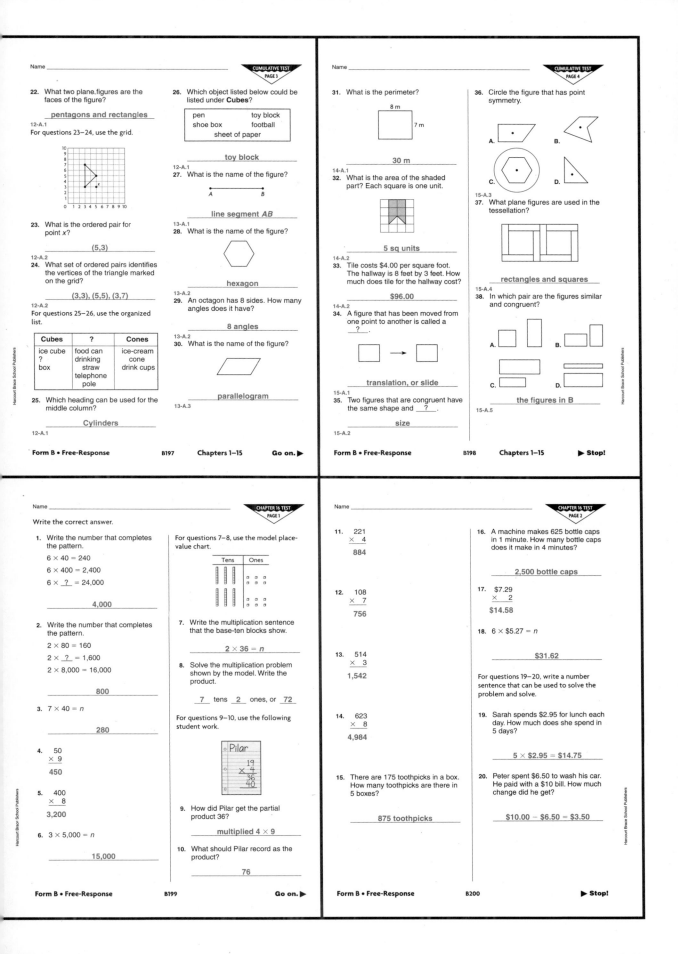

22. What two plane figures are the faces of the figure?

___pentagons and rectangles___
12-A.1

For questions 23–24, use the grid.

23. What is the ordered pair for point *x*?

___(5,3)___
12-A.2

24. What set of ordered pairs identifies the vertices of the triangle marked on the grid?

___(3,3), (5,5), (3,7)___
12-A.2

For questions 25–26, use the organized list.

Cubes	?	Cones
ice cube ? box	food can drinking straw telephone pole	ice-cream cone drink cups

25. Which heading can be used for the middle column?

___Cylinders___
12-A.1

26. Which object listed below could be listed under **Cubes**?

pen	toy block
shoe box	football
	sheet of paper

___toy block___
12-A.1

27. What is the name of the figure?

___line segment *AB*___
13-A.1

28. What is the name of the figure?

___hexagon___
13-A.2

29. An octagon has 8 sides. How many angles does it have?

___8 angles___
13-A.2

30. What is the name of the figure?

___parallelogram___
13-A.3

Form B • Free-Response   B197   **Chapters 1–15**   **Go on. ▶**

31. What is the perimeter?

8 m

7 m

___30 m___
14-A.1

32. What is the area of the shaded part? Each square is one unit.

___5 sq units___
14-A.2

33. Tile costs $4.00 per square foot. The hallway is 8 feet by 3 feet. How much does tile for the hallway cost?

___$96.00___
14-A.2

34. A figure that has been moved from one point to another is called a ___?___ .

___translation, or slide___
15-A.1

35. Two figures that are congruent have the same shape and ___?___ .

___size___
15-A.2

36. Circle the figure that has point symmetry.

A.   B.

C.   D.
15-A.3

37. What plane figures are used in the tessellation?

___rectangles and squares___
15-A.4

38. In which pair are the figures similar and congruent?

A.   B.

C.   D.

___the figures in B___
15-A.5

Form B • Free-Response   B198   **Chapters 1–15**   **▶ Stop!**

Write the correct answer.

1. Write the number that completes the pattern.

$6 \times 40 = 240$
$6 \times 400 = 2,400$
$6 \times \underline{?} = 24,000$

___4,000___

2. Write the number that completes the pattern.

$2 \times 80 = 160$
$2 \times \underline{?} = 1,600$
$2 \times 8,000 = 16,000$

___800___

3. $7 \times 40 = n$

___280___

4. 50
   $\times 9$
   450

5. 400
   $\times 8$
   3,200

6. $3 \times 5,000 = n$

___15,000___

7. Write the multiplication sentence that the base-ten blocks show.

For questions 7–8, use the model place-value chart.

Tens	Ones

___$2 \times 36 = n$___

8. Solve the multiplication problem shown by the model. Write the product.

___7___ tens ___2___ ones, or ___72___

For questions 9–10, use the following student work.

Pilar
  19
 $\times 4$
  36
  40

9. How did Pilar get the partial product 36?

___multiplied 4×9___

10. What should Pilar record as the product?

___76___

Form B • Free-Response   B199   **Go on. ▶**

11. 221
    $\times 4$
    884

12. 108
    $\times 7$
    756

13. 514
    $\times 3$
    1,542

14. 623
    $\times 8$
    4,984

15. There are 175 toothpicks in a box. How many toothpicks are there in 5 boxes?

___875 toothpicks___

16. A machine makes 625 bottle caps in 1 minute. How many bottle caps does it make in 4 minutes?

___2,500 bottle caps___

17. $7.29
    $\times 2$
    $14.58

18. $6 \times \$5.27 = n$

___$31.62___

For questions 19–20, write a number sentence that can be used to solve the problem and solve.

19. Sarah spends $2.95 for lunch each day. How much does she spend in 5 days?

___$5 \times \$2.95 = \$14.75$___

20. Peter spent $6.50 to wash his car. He paid with a $10 bill. How much change did he get?

___$\$10.00 - \$6.50 = \$3.50$___

Form B • Free-Response   B200   **▶ Stop!**

Free-Response Format • Test Answers

265

Write the correct answer.

For questions 1–3, find the product by using a basic fact and a pattern of zeros.

1. $5 \times 7 = 35$

   $5 \times 70 = 350$

   $50 \times 70 = 3,500$

   $50 \times 700 = n$

   _____ $n = 35,000$ _____

2. $80 \times 60 = n$

   _____ $n = 4,800$ _____

3. $40 \times 500 = n$

   _____ $n = 20,000$ _____

4. A building has 20 sets of stairs. Each set of stairs has 30 steps. How many steps does the building have?

   _____ 600 steps _____

5. Debra has a puzzle. When she says 5, the answer is 150. When she says 10, the answer is 300. When she says 20, the answer is 600. What is the pattern?

   _____ multiply by 30 _____

6. Write a number sentence to estimate the product of 57×31.

   _____ $60 \times 30 = 1,800$ _____

For questions 7–8, write a reasonable estimate for the product.

7. $82 \times 23 = n;$

   _____ $n \approx 1,600$ _____

8. 493
   $\times\ 71$

   _____ 35,000 _____

9. An airplane makes 12 flights a week and carries 103 people on each flight. What is a reasonable estimate of the number of people the airplane carries?

   _____ about 1,200 people _____

10. A rain forest averages 39 inches of rain per month. What is a reasonable estimate of the amount of rain that would fall in 12 months?

    _____ about 480 in. _____

Form B • Free-Response   B201   **Go on. ▶**

---

11. Sarah is using the partial-products method to multiply 73 and 48. Her next step should be to multiply __?__ by 40.

    ```
    73
    × 48
    24
    560
    ```

    _____ 3 _____

12. John is using a shorter way to multiply 73 and 48. His next step should be to multiply __?__ by 40.

    ```
    73
    × 48
    584
    ```

    _____ 73 _____

13. 53
    $\times\ 76$

    _____ 4,028 _____

14. $39
    $\times\ 26$

    _____ $1,014 _____

15. $55 \times 82 = n$

    _____ 4,510 _____

16. Carol is multiplying 219 by 18. Which operation should she perform next?

    ```
    219
    × 18
    1752
    2190
    ```

    _____ addition _____

17. 456
    $\times\ 38$

    _____ 17,328 _____

18. $2.38
    $\times\ \ 59$

    _____ $140.42 _____

19. A bicycle wheel has 112 spokes. How many spokes are on 6 bicycle wheels?

    _____ 672 spokes _____

20. A telephone book has 270 names on each page. How many names are on 95 pages?

    _____ 25,650 names _____

Form B • Free-Response   B202   **▶ Stop!**

Write the correct answer.

1. To check the quotient for this division problem, first multiply 5 times __?__.

   ```
     5 r1
   8)41
   ```

   _____ 8 _____

2. An even number can be divided by 2 with no __?__.

   _____ remainder _____

3. ```
     6 r5
   7)47
   ```

4. ```
     7 r1
   4)29
   ```

5. When you divide by 7, what is the largest possible remainder?

   _____ 6 _____

6. The next step in solving this problem is to divide __?__ by 4.

   ```
      1
   4)78
   -4
    38
   ```

   _____ 38 _____

7. ```
     12 r1
   7)85
   ```

8. ```
     18 r3
   5)93
   ```

9. The first digit in the quotient should be placed in the __?__ place.

   ```
   5)76
   ```

   _____ tens _____

10. How many digits will be in the quotient?

    ```
    4)93
    ```

    _____ 2 digits _____

11. Six friends are having a bake sale. They want a total of 120 cookies to sell. How many cookies should each person bake?

    _____ 20 cookies _____

12. There were 266 crackers in a carton. They were divided equally among 7 people. How many crackers did each person receive?

    _____ 38 crackers _____

Form B • Free-Response   B203   **Go on. ▶**

---

13. At the end of art class, the students put an equal number of crayons into each box. All but 1 of the 118 crayons fit into the boxes. How many boxes were used?
    Possible answers:
    3 boxes (of 39),
    9 boxes (of 13), or
    13 boxes (of 9)

14. The first digit of the quotient should be placed over the __?__.

    ```
    8)753
    ```

    _____ 5 _____

Divide.

15. ```
    7)58
    ```

    _____ 8 r2 _____

16. $374 \div 4 = n$

    _____ 93 r2 _____

17. $319 \div 6 = n$

    _____ 53 r1 _____

18. A table in the lunchroom has space for 6 students. How many tables are needed to hold 126 students?

    _____ 21 tables _____

19. A gallon of milk contains 8 pints. If 128 students each drink 1 pint of milk, how many gallons will they drink?

    _____ 16 gallons _____

20. Mike has 528 baseball cards. He has an equal number in each of 4 shoe boxes. How many baseball cards are in each shoe box?

    _____ 132 baseball cards _____

Form B • Free-Response   B204   **▶ Stop!**

Free-Response Format • Test Answer
    ```

Write the correct answer.

For questions 1–2, use a basic fact and a pattern of zeros to find the quotient.

1. $24 \div 6 = 4$

   $2{,}400 \div 6 = n$

   _____ 400 _____

2. $21 \div 7 = 3$

   $21{,}000 \div 7 = n$

   _____ 3,000 _____

For questions 3–4, estimate. Use a basic fact and a pattern of zeros to estimate the quotient.

3. $63{,}017 \div 9 = n$

   _____ 7,000 _____

4. $4{,}123 \div 7 = n$

   _____ 600 _____

5. What number belongs in the tens place of the quotient?

   _____ 0 _____

6. $4\overline{)824}$

   _____ 206 _____

7. $7\overline{)985}$

   _____ 140 r5 _____

8. A farmer picks 125 pumpkins in 5 days. How many pumpkins does he pick each day?

   _____ 25 pumpkins _____

9. On sports day the P.E. teacher separated 176 students into teams of 8. How many teams were there?

   _____ 22 teams _____

10. $3\overline{)\$18.03}$

    _____ \$6.01 _____

11. $6\overline{)\$13.80}$

    _____ \$2.30 _____

12. $9\overline{)\$7.29}$

    _____ \$0.81 _____

13. Baseball cards cost \$4.50 for 6. What is the cost for each card?

    _____ \$0.75 _____

14. Mr. Waller is buying 3 bags of sand for \$25.50. What is the cost for each bag?

    _____ \$8.50 _____

Form B • Free-Response   B205   Go on. ▶

For questions 15–16, tell how you interpret the remainder.

15. Larry has 250 pieces of candy and 3 bags. He wants to put an equal amount of candy in each bag. How many pieces of candy will he put in each bag?

    _____ 83 pieces/Drop the remainder. _____

16. Mrs. Fox needs 135 pencils for her class. There are 6 pencils in a package. How many packages does she need to buy?

    23 packages/Round the quotient to the next greater whole number.

17. Mr. Robinson bought 475 feet of rope. He will cut the rope into 6-foot lengths. How many 6-foot lengths can he cut?

    _____ 79 lengths _____

18. Sue Ellen has to do 144 math problems. How many problems should she do each day to be sure she finishes in 5 days?

    _____ 29 problems _____

19. Sandra can make 1 bracelet in 7 minutes. How many bracelets can she make in 130 minutes?

    _____ 18 bracelets _____

20. Pete can make a key chain in 9 minutes. How many key chains can he make in 162 minutes?

    _____ 18 key chains _____

For questions 21–24, solve. Name the operation you used.

21. Jose's family recycled 120 pounds of newspaper in June, 136 pounds in July, and 163 pounds in August. How many pounds did they recycle in all?

    _____ 419 lb; addition _____

22. The basketball game lasts 48 minutes. Each of the 4 quarters takes the same amount of time. How long is each quarter?

    _____ 12 min; division _____

23. Josh is climbing a mountain that is 953 feet high. He has climbed 208 feet. How many more feet does he have to climb?

    _____ 745 ft; subtraction _____

24. Delia does 45 minutes of homework each night after school. How many minutes of homework will she do in 20 school nights?

    _____ 900 min; multiplication _____

Form B • Free-Response   B206   ▶ Stop!

Write the correct answer.

1. Write the number that completes the pattern.
   $3 \times 40 = 120$
   $3 \times 400 = 1{,}200$
   $3 \times \underline{\ ?\ } = 12{,}000$

   _____ 4,000 _____
   16-A.1

2. $\begin{array}{r} 500 \\ \times\ 6 \\ \hline \end{array}$

   _____ 3,000 _____
   16-A.1

3. $\begin{array}{r} 278 \\ \times\ 4 \\ \hline \end{array}$

   _____ 1,112 _____
   16-A.2

4. There are 150 seats in each section of a ball park. How many seats are in 7 sections?

   _____ 1,050 seats _____
   16-A.2

5. $5 \times \$4.95 = \underline{\ ?\ }$

   _____ \$24.75 _____
   16-A.3

6. Write a number sentence that can be used to solve the problem and solve.

   Bobby saves \$1.75 of his allowance each week. How much does he save in 3 weeks?

   _____ $3 \times \$1.75 = \$5.25$ _____
   16-A.3

7. $20 \times 600 = n$

   _____ $n = 12{,}000$ _____
   17-A.1

8. Lauren was putting pennies in penny wrappers. Each penny wrapper held 50 pennies. Lauren filled 20 penny wrappers. How many pennies did Lauren have?

   _____ 1,000 pennies _____
   17-A.1

9. A truck makes 7 trips a month and carries 53 packages on each trip. What is a reasonable estimate of the number of packages the truck carries each month?

   _____ about 350 packages _____
   17-A.2

10. $\begin{array}{r} 35 \\ \times 58 \\ \hline \end{array}$

    _____ 2,030 _____
    17-A.3

11. $\begin{array}{r} \$4.37 \\ \times\ 26 \\ \hline \end{array}$

    _____ \$113.62 _____
    17-A.3

12. A library has 175 books on each shelf. How many books are on 80 shelves?

    _____ 14,000 books _____
    17-A.4

Form B • Free-Response   B207   Go on. ▶

---

13. $6\overline{)39}$

    _____ 6 r3 _____
    18-A.1

14. When you divide by 6, what is the largest possible remainder?

    _____ 5 _____
    18-A.2

15. $8\overline{)62}$

    _____ 7 r6 _____
    18-A.1

16. At the end of computer class, the students put an equal number of diskettes into each box. All but 2 of the 121 diskettes fit into the boxes. How many boxes were used?

    7 boxes (of 17), or 17 boxes (of 7)
    18-A.3

17. $172 \div 5 = n$

    _____ $n = 34$ r2 _____
    18-A.4

18. A school plans to use 4 buses for a field trip. If 220 students go on the field trip, how many will ride in each bus?

    _____ 55 students _____
    18-A.4

19. Use a basic fact and a pattern of zeros to find the quotient.
    $27 \div 9 = 3$
    $270 \div 9 = 30$
    $2{,}700 \div 9 = n$
    $27{,}000 \div 9 = 3{,}000$

    _____ $n = 300$ _____
    19-A.1

20. $2\overline{)416}$

    _____ 208 _____
    19-A.2

21. $3\overline{)572}$

    _____ 190 r2 _____
    19-A.2

22. $6\overline{)\$4.38}$

    _____ \$0.73 _____
    19-A.3

23. A farmer bought 225 gallons of fertilizer. He will pour the fertilizer into 8-gallon containers. How many 8-gallon containers can he fill? How much fertilizer will be left over?

    28 containers; 1 gallon of fertilizer
    19-A.4

24. Solve and name the operation you used.

    A school play lasts 42 minutes. Each of the 6 scenes takes the same amount of time. How long is each scene?

    _____ 7 minutes; division _____
    19-A.5

Form B • Free-Response   B208   ▶ Stop!

Free-Response Format • Test Answers

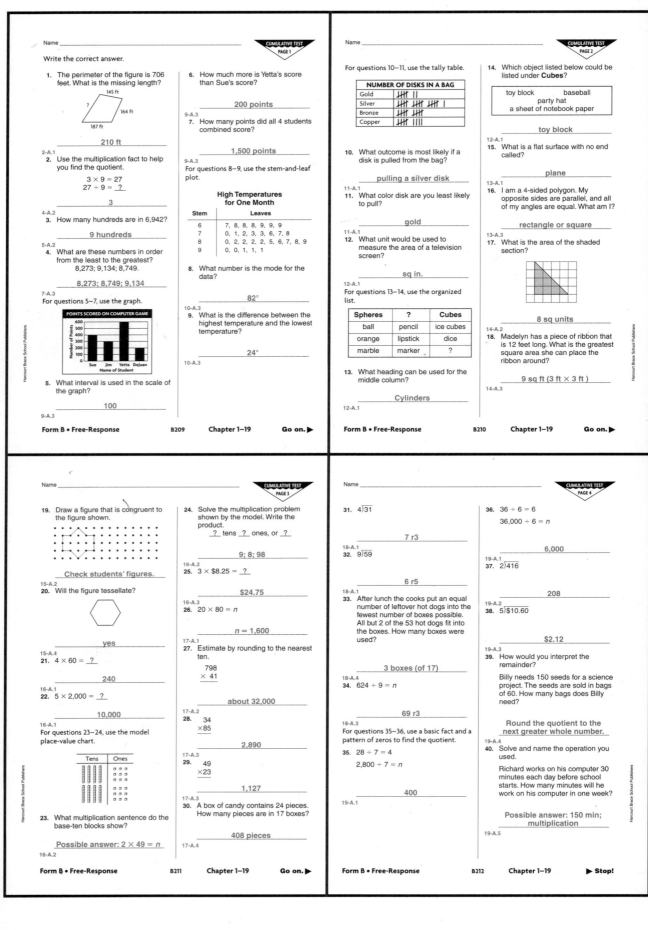

Write the correct answer.

1. The perimeter of the figure is 706 feet. What is the missing length?

145 ft
?
164 ft
187 ft

210 ft

2-A.1

2. Use the multiplication fact to help you find the quotient.

$3 \times 9 = 27$
$27 \div 9 = \underline{?}$

3

4-A.2

3. How many hundreds are in 6,942?

9 hundreds

5-A.2

4. What are these numbers in order from the least to the greatest?
8,273; 9,134; 8,749.

8,273; 8,749; 9,134

7-A.3

For questions 5–7, use the graph.

POINTS SCORED ON COMPUTER GAME

Sue   Jim   Yetta   DeJuan
Name of Student

5. What interval is used in the scale of the graph?

100

9-A.3

6. How much more is Yetta's score than Sue's score?

200 points

9-A.3

7. How many points did all 4 students combined score?

1,500 points

9-A.3

For questions 8–9, use the stem-and-leaf plot.

High Temperatures for One Month

Stem	Leaves
6	7, 8, 8, 8, 9, 9, 9
7	0, 1, 2, 3, 3, 6, 7, 8
8	0, 2, 2, 2, 2, 5, 6, 7, 8, 9
9	0, 0, 1, 1, 1

8. What number is the mode for the data?

82°

10-A.3

9. What is the difference between the highest temperature and the lowest temperature?

24°

10-A.3

For questions 10–11, use the tally table.

NUMBER OF DISKS IN A BAG

Gold						
Silver	|||| |||| ||||	
Bronze									
Copper									

10. What outcome is most likely if a disk is pulled from the bag?

pulling a silver disk

11-A.1

11. What color disk are you least likely to pull?

gold

11-A.1

12. What unit would be used to measure the area of a television screen?

sq in.

12-A.1

For questions 13–14, use the organized list.

Spheres	?	Cubes
ball	pencil	ice cubes
orange	lipstick	dice
marble	marker	?

13. What heading can be used for the middle column?

Cylinders

12-A.1

14. Which object listed below could be listed under **Cubes**?

toy block   baseball
party hat
a sheet of notebook paper

toy block

12-A.1

15. What is a flat surface with no end called?

plane

13-A.1

16. I am a 4-sided polygon. My opposite sides are parallel, and all of my angles are equal. What am I?

rectangle or square

13-A.3

17. What is the area of the shaded section?

8 sq units

14-A.2

18. Madelyn has a piece of ribbon that is 12 feet long. What is the greatest square area she can place the ribbon around?

9 sq ft (3 ft × 3 ft)

14-A.3

19. Draw a figure that is congruent to the figure shown.

Check students' figures.

15-A.2

20. Will the figure tessellate?

yes

15-A.4

21. $4 \times 60 = \underline{?}$

240

16-A.1

22. $5 \times 2,000 = \underline{?}$

10,000

16-A.1

For questions 23–24, use the model place-value chart.

Tens	Ones

23. What multiplication sentence do the base-ten blocks show?

Possible answer: $2 \times 49 = n$

16-A.2

24. Solve the multiplication problem shown by the model. Write the product.

$\underline{?}$ tens $\underline{?}$ ones, or $\underline{?}$

9; 8; 98

16-A.2

25. $3 \times \$8.25 = \underline{?}$

$24.75

16-A.3

26. $20 \times 80 = n$

$n = 1,600$

17-A.1

27. Estimate by rounding to the nearest ten.

798
× 41

about 32,000

17-A.2

28. 34
×85

2,890

17-A.3

29. 49
×23

1,127

17-A.3

30. A box of candy contains 24 pieces. How many pieces are in 17 boxes?

408 pieces

17-A.4

31. $4\overline{)31}$

7 r3

18-A.1

32. $9\overline{)59}$

6 r5

18-A.1

33. After lunch the cooks put an equal number of leftover hot dogs into the fewest number of boxes possible. All but 2 of the 53 hot dogs fit into the boxes. How many boxes were used?

3 boxes (of 17)

18-A.4

34. $624 \div 9 = n$

69 r3

18-A.3

For questions 35–36, use a basic fact and a pattern of zeros to find the quotient.

35. $28 \div 7 = 4$
$2,800 \div 7 = n$

400

19-A.1

36. $36 \div 6 = 6$
$36,000 \div 6 = n$

6,000

19-A.1

37. $2\overline{)416}$

208

19-A.2

38. $5\overline{)\$10.60}$

$2.12

19-A.3

39. How would you interpret the remainder?

Billy needs 150 seeds for a science project. The seeds are sold in bags of 60. How many bags does Billy need?

Round the quotient to the next greater whole number.

19-A.4

40. Solve and name the operation you used.

Richard works on his computer 30 minutes each day before school starts. How many minutes will he work on his computer in one week?

Possible answer: 150 min; multiplication

19-A.5

Free-Response Format • Test Answers

Name _____

Write the correct answer.

1. What fraction of the circle is shaded?

$\frac{1}{4}$

2. What fraction of the bar is shaded?

$\frac{1}{3}$

3. What fraction of the rectangle is shaded?

$\frac{5}{6}$

4. What fraction means the same as three out of four?

$\frac{3}{4}$

For questions 5–6, use the figure.

5. What fraction of the figure is striped?

$\frac{2}{8}$, or $\frac{1}{4}$

6. What fraction of the figure is *not* striped or shaded?

$\frac{3}{8}$

For questions 7–10, write the fraction that represents the group that is shaded.

7.

$\frac{1}{4}$

8.

$\frac{1}{3}$

9.

$\frac{5}{6}$

Form B • Free-Response   B213   **Go on. ▶**

Name _____

10.

$\frac{4}{5}$

11. Mrs. Sentra bought 12 eggs. She used 4 of them for breakfast. What fraction of the eggs did she use?

$\frac{4}{12}$, or $\frac{1}{3}$

12. Kendal bought a six-pack of soda. He kept one can and gave the rest to his mother. What fraction did he keep?

$\frac{1}{6}$

For questions 13–14, use the fraction bars to compare the fractions. Write $<$, $>$, or $=$.

13.

$\frac{8}{10}$ ◯ $\frac{3}{4}$

$>$

14.

$\frac{4}{6}$ ◯ $\frac{2}{3}$

$=$

15. Arrange the fractions in order from least to greatest.

$\frac{2}{3}, \frac{1}{2}, \frac{1}{3}$

$\frac{1}{3}, \frac{1}{2}, \frac{2}{3}$

16. Arrange the fractions in order from greatest to least.

$\frac{1}{4}, \frac{3}{8}, \frac{3}{4}$

$\frac{3}{4}, \frac{3}{8}, \frac{1}{4}$

17. Shawna bought $\frac{1}{8}$ pound of peanuts, $\frac{3}{8}$ pound of almonds, and $\frac{3}{4}$ pound of cashews. List the nuts she bought in order from greatest to least.

cashews, almonds, peanuts

18. A spinner has 8 equal sections. Of the sections, 1 is blue, 3 are yellow, 1 is white, and 3 are red. Which two colors together cover more than $\frac{1}{2}$ of the spinner?

yellow and red

Form B • Free-Response   B214   **Go on. ▶**

Name _____

For questions 19–20, write the mixed number for the shaded part of the picture.

19.

$1\frac{1}{4}$

20.

$4\frac{3}{6}$, or $4\frac{1}{2}$

For questions 21–24, rename each fraction as a mixed number.

21. $\frac{7}{5}$ = _?_

$1\frac{2}{5}$

22. $\frac{9}{4}$ = _?_

$2\frac{1}{4}$

23. $\frac{8}{3}$ = _?_

$2\frac{2}{3}$

24. $\frac{11}{8}$ = _?_

$1\frac{3}{8}$

Form B • Free-Response   B215   **▶ Stop!**

Name _____

Write the correct answer.

1. Use the fraction bars to help you find the sum.

$\frac{1}{3} + \frac{2}{3} = n$

$\frac{3}{3}$, or 1

2. Use the fraction bars to help you find the sum.

$\frac{1}{4} + \frac{2}{4} = n$

$\frac{3}{4}$

3. Write the number sentence for the problem and solve.

two sixths plus three sixths

$\frac{2}{6} + \frac{3}{6} = \frac{5}{6}$

4. Is the sum greater than 1 or less than 1?

$\frac{6}{8} + \frac{3}{8}$ = _?_

greater than 1

5. $\frac{1}{5} + \frac{3}{5} = n$

$\frac{4}{5}$

6. $\frac{4}{10} + \frac{3}{10} = n$

$\frac{7}{10}$

7. Felix ate $\frac{2}{5}$ cup of raisins before the game. He ate $\frac{1}{5}$ cup of raisins after the game. How much of a cup of raisins did Felix eat?

$\frac{3}{5}$ cup

8. Before dinner Mary played outside for $\frac{1}{3}$ hour. After dinner she played outside for $\frac{1}{3}$ hour. How long did Mary play outside in all?

$\frac{2}{3}$ hr

9. Use the model to help you find the difference.

$\frac{4}{5} - \frac{3}{5} = n$

$\frac{1}{5}$

Form B • Free-Response   B216   **Go on. ▶**

Free-Response Format • Test Answers

10. Use the model to help you find the difference.

$\frac{7}{8} - \frac{4}{8} = n$

$\frac{3}{8}$

11. Betty has read $\frac{2}{3}$ of her book. How much is left to read?

$\frac{1}{3}$ of the book

12. Julio ate $\frac{3}{8}$ of a pizza. What fraction of the pizza is left?

$\frac{5}{8}$ of the pizza

13. Use the model to help you find the sum.

$3\frac{1}{4}$
$+1\frac{2}{4}$
$\overline{4\frac{3}{4}}$

14. $7\frac{1}{9}$
$+2\frac{3}{9}$
$\overline{9\frac{4}{9}}$

15. $5\frac{7}{12}$
$+4\frac{4}{12}$
$\overline{9\frac{11}{12}}$

16. $3\frac{4}{6} + 2\frac{1}{6} = n$

$5\frac{5}{6}$

17. Jason did homework for $1\frac{1}{4}$ hours before dinner and $1\frac{3}{4}$ after dinner. How much time did Jason spend on homework?

$2\frac{4}{4}$, or 3, hours

18. Shelly jogged $1\frac{1}{5}$ miles on Tuesday and $2\frac{2}{5}$ miles on Wednesday. How far did Shelly jog in all?

$3\frac{3}{5}$ miles

19. Use the model to help you find the difference.

$2\frac{3}{4}$
$-1\frac{1}{4}$
$\overline{1\frac{2}{4}}$, or $1\frac{1}{2}$

20. $9\frac{3}{6}$
$-1\frac{2}{6}$
$\overline{8\frac{1}{6}}$

21. $6\frac{7}{10}$
$-5\frac{2}{10}$
$\overline{1\frac{5}{10}}$, or $1\frac{1}{2}$

22. $3\frac{6}{8} - 1\frac{3}{8} = n$

$2\frac{3}{8}$

23. Oscar grew $5\frac{3}{4}$ inches in one year. His sister Shawna grew $2\frac{1}{4}$ inches. How much more did Oscar grow than Shawna?

$3\frac{2}{4}$, or $3\frac{1}{2}$, inches

24. The trail up the mountain is $6\frac{4}{10}$ miles. The trail down is $5\frac{2}{10}$ miles. How much shorter is the trail down?

$1\frac{2}{10}$, or $1\frac{1}{5}$, miles

Write the correct answer.

1. The model shows 0.6. Write the fraction for the shaded part.

$\frac{6}{10}$

2. The model shows $\frac{75}{100}$. Write the decimal for the shaded part.

0.75

3. Write $\frac{7}{10}$ as a decimal.

0.7

4. Write 0.35 as a fraction.

$\frac{35}{100}$

5. Write the decimal name for the shaded part of the model.

0.16

6. Write the decimal name for the shaded part of the model.

0.5

7. Write 8 pennies as a money amount.

$0.08

8. Write 5 dimes as a money amount.

$0.50

9. Trey has 83 pennies. Write that amount as a decimal.

0.83

10. Dina has $\frac{25}{100}$ of a dollar. How many pennies is that?

25 pennies

For questions 11–12, use the number line.

11. The number line has small ticks and large ticks. Do the large ticks show hundreds, tens, ones, or tenths?

tenths

12. Write another decimal number that would be at the same place on the number line as 0.40.

Possible answer: 0.4

13. Write the number that is greater.

0.41, 0.2

0.41

14. Write the number that is greater.

0.8, 0.18

0.8

15. Write 0.5, 0.21, 0.9, and 0.62 in order from least to greatest.

0.21, 0.5, 0.62, 0.9

16. Write 0.08, 0.01, 0.19, and 0.70 in order from greatest to least.

0.70, 0.19, 0.08, 0.01

17. Write the mixed decimal shown by the model.

2.3, or 2.30

18. Write an equivalent mixed decimal for 4.10.

Possible answer: 4.1

19. Write an equivalent mixed decimal for 6.30.

Possible answer: 6.3

20. Write $5\frac{5}{10}$ as a mixed decimal.

Possible answer: 5.5

21. Write 14.07 as a mixed number.

Possible answer: $14\frac{7}{100}$

22. Write 8.32 as a mixed number.

$8\frac{32}{100}$

23. In a swimming race, Phil finished in 20.09 seconds. Raj finished in 22.10 seconds, Jorge finished in 19.75 seconds, and Chal finished in 21.60 seconds. Who finished the race in the least amount of time?

Jorge

24. Four girls counted their money. Samara has $2.91, Gina has $2.56, Carmen has $2.73, and Patty has $2.65. Which girl has the least amount of money?

Gina

Free-Response Format • Test Answers

Write the correct answer.

For questions 1–2, use the decimal-square model.

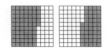

1. Write a number sentence that matches the model.

$$0.65 + 0.46 = n$$

2. What is the sum of the shaded parts of the model?

1.11

3. 0.8
   +0.5

   1.3

4. 0.23
   +0.72

   0.95

5. 2.65
   +0.54

   3.19

6. Bill has 2.5 pounds of bananas and 2.3 pounds of grapes. How many pounds of fruit does he have in all?

4.8 lb

7. Becky runs the first half of a race in 1.35 minutes and the second half in 1.70 minutes. What is her total time?

3.05 min

8. Use the model to find the difference.

$$0.6 - 0.4 = n$$

0.2

9. Use the model to find the difference.

$$0.70 - 0.40 = n$$

0.30

10. 1.5
    −0.7

    0.8

---

11. 0.83
    −0.19

    0.64

12. 3.02
    −0.75

    2.27

13. Ruth ran a race in 1.85 minutes. Jan ran the same race in 1.63 minutes. What is the difference in their times?

0.22 min

14. Drew lives 1.8 miles from school. Mark lives 0.9 miles from school. How many miles farther from school does Drew live?

0.9 mi farther

15. 0.77
    +0.57

    1.34

16. 0.60
    −0.35

    0.25

17. 1.90
    −0.06

    1.84

18. $0.43 + 0.2 = n$

0.63

For questions 19–20, write a number sentence that shows how to solve the problem.

19. George walked 3.5 miles. Bert walked 2.1 miles. How many more miles did George walk?

$$3.5 - 2.1 = n$$

20. Alice practiced her guitar for 1.7 hours on Saturday and 1.2 hours on Sunday. How many hours did she practice in all?

$$1.7 + 1.2 = n$$

21. What is 8.8 rounded to the nearest whole number?

9

For questions 22–24, estimate the sum or difference by rounding to the nearest whole number.

22. 2.8
    +1.9

    5

23. 5.7
    −2.3

    4

24. Alonzo and Marci worked on a puzzle for 2.9 hours on Saturday, 2.8 hours on Sunday, and 1.7 hours on Monday. About how many hours in all did they work on the puzzle?

about 8 hr

Write the correct answer.

1. What fraction of the circle is shaded?

$\frac{1}{3}$

20-A.1

2. What fraction represents the group that is shaded?

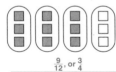

$\frac{9}{12}$, or $\frac{3}{4}$

20-A.1

3. Donald checked out 4 books from the library. He read 2 of them. What fraction of the books did he read?

$\frac{1}{2}$

20-A.1

4. Write the fractions in order from greatest to least.

$\frac{1}{6}$, $\frac{1}{4}$, $\frac{3}{4}$

$\frac{3}{4}$, $\frac{1}{4}$, $\frac{1}{6}$

20-A.2

5. What is the mixed number for the shaded part of the picture?

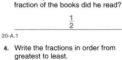

$2\frac{1}{3}$

20-A.3

6. $\frac{3}{5} + \frac{4}{5} = $?

$\frac{7}{5}$, or $1\frac{2}{5}$

21-A.1

7. $4\frac{2}{7} + 2\frac{3}{7} = $?

$6\frac{5}{7}$

21-A.1

8. Barbara went swimming for $1\frac{2}{4}$ hours in the morning. She went swimming for $1\frac{1}{4}$ hours in the afternoon. How many hours in all did Barbara go swimming?

$2\frac{3}{4}$ hours

21-A.1

9. A recipe uses $1\frac{1}{8}$ cups of wheat flour and $2\frac{3}{8}$ cups of white flour. How much flour does the recipe use?

$3\frac{4}{8}$, or $3\frac{1}{2}$, cups

21-A.1

---

10. $5\frac{4}{5} - 2\frac{1}{5} = $?

$3\frac{3}{5}$

21-A.2

11. Scouts hiked $8\frac{5}{8}$ miles the first day and $6\frac{3}{8}$ miles the second day. How much more did they hike the first day?

$2\frac{2}{8}$, or $2\frac{1}{4}$, more mi

21-A.2

12. Write $\frac{43}{100}$ as a decimal.

0.43

22-A.1

13. Write 4 nickels as a money amount.

$0.20

22-A.1

14. Write 5.37 as a mixed number.

$5\frac{37}{100}$

22-A.3

15. Write 0.29, 0.5, 0.73, and 0.4 in order from greatest to least.

0.73, 0.5, 0.4, 0.29

22-A.4

16. What is a mixed decimal equivalent to 2.50?

Possible answer: 2.5

22-A.4

17. In a track meet, Julio finished in 40.09 seconds, Ricky finished in 39.85 seconds, Brent finished in 42.26 seconds, and Andy finished in 41.70 seconds. Who finished the race in the least amount of time?

Ricky

22-A.4

18. Write a number sentence that matches the model.

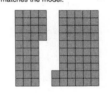

Possible answer:
$0.34 + 0.52 = n$

23-A.1

19. 1.74
    +2.53

    4.27

23-A.1

20. 1.3
    −0.8

    0.5

23-A.1

21. What is 6.7 rounded to the nearest whole number?

7

23-A.2

Estimate the sum or difference by rounding to the nearest whole number.

22. Rebecca collected 2.1 lb of cans on Friday, 4.8 lb of cans on Saturday, and 3.9 lb of cans on Sunday. About how many pounds did she collect on the three days?

about 11 lb

23-A.2

Free-Response Format • Test Answers

271

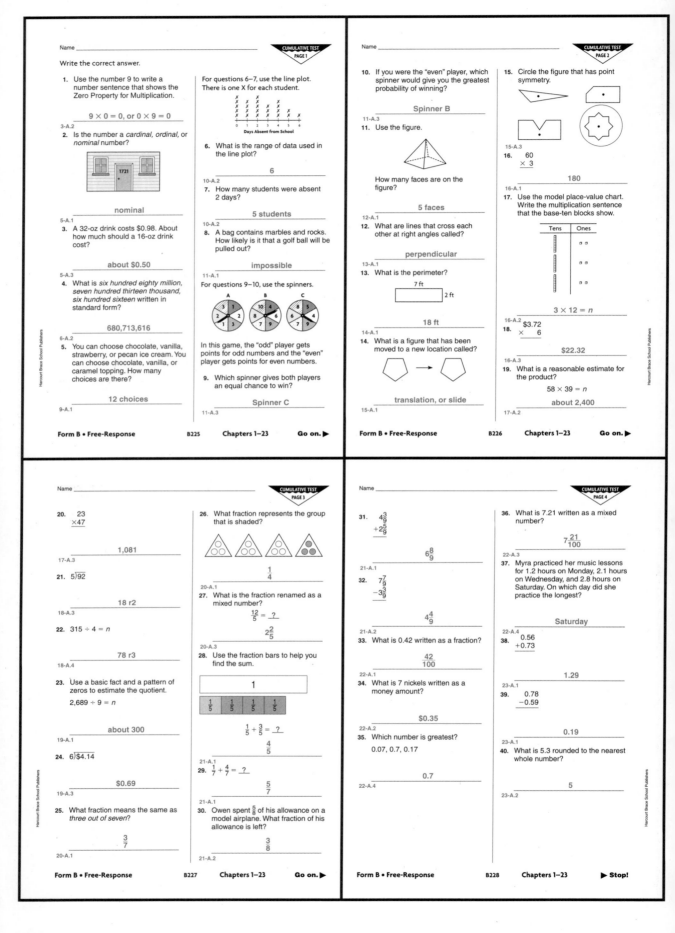

Write the correct answer.

1. Use the number 9 to write a number sentence that shows the Zero Property for Multiplication.

$9 \times 0 = 0$, or $0 \times 9 = 0$

3-A.2

2. Is the number a *cardinal*, *ordinal*, or *nominal* number?

1721

nominal

5-A.1

3. A 32-oz drink costs $0.98. About how much should a 16-oz drink cost?

about $0.50

5-A.3

4. What is *six hundred eighty million, seven hundred thirteen thousand, six hundred sixteen* written in standard form?

680,713,616

6-A.2

5. You can choose chocolate, vanilla, strawberry, or pecan ice cream. You can choose chocolate, vanilla, or caramel topping. How many choices are there?

12 choices

9-A.1

For questions 6–7, use the line plot. There is one X for each student.

Days Absent from School

6. What is the range of data used in the line plot?

6

10-A.1

7. How many students were absent 2 days?

5 students

10-A.2

8. A bag contains marbles and rocks. How likely is it that a golf ball will be pulled out?

impossible

11-A.1

For questions 9–10, use the spinners.

A   B   C

In this game, the "odd" player gets points for odd numbers and the "even" player gets points for even numbers.

9. Which spinner gives both players an equal chance to win?

Spinner C

11-A.3

Form B • Free-Response   B225   **Chapters 1–23**   **Go on.** ▶

10. If you were the "even" player, which spinner would give you the greatest probability of winning?

Spinner B

11-A.3

11. Use the figure.

How many faces are on the figure?

5 faces

12-A.1

12. What are lines that cross each other at right angles called?

perpendicular

13-A.1

13. What is the perimeter?

7 ft
2 ft

18 ft

14-A.1

14. What is a figure that has been moved to a new location called?

translation, or slide

15-A.1

15. Circle the figure that has point symmetry.

15-A.3

16.   60
    $\times 3$

180

16-A.1

17. Use the model place-value chart. Write the multiplication sentence that the base-ten blocks show.

Tens	Ones

$3 \times 12 = n$

16-A.2

18. $3.72
    $\times \quad 6$

$22.32

16-A.3

19. What is a reasonable estimate for the product?

$58 \times 39 = n$

about 2,400

17-A.2

Form B • Free-Response   B226   **Chapters 1–23**   **Go on.** ▶

20.   23
    $\times 47$

1,081

17-A.3

21. $5\overline{)92}$

18 r2

18-A.3

22. $315 \div 4 = n$

78 r3

18-A.4

23. Use a basic fact and a pattern of zeros to estimate the quotient.

$2,689 \div 9 = n$

about 300

19-A.1

24. $6\overline{)$4.14}$

$0.69

19-A.3

25. What fraction means the same as *three out of seven*?

$\frac{3}{7}$

20-A.1

26. What fraction represents the group that is shaded?

$\frac{1}{4}$

20-A.1

27. What is the fraction renamed as a mixed number?

$\frac{12}{5} = \underline{?}$

$2\frac{2}{5}$

20-A.3

28. Use the fraction bars to help you find the sum.

1

| $\frac{1}{5}$ | $\frac{1}{5}$ | $\frac{1}{5}$ | $\frac{1}{5}$ |

$\frac{1}{5} + \frac{3}{5} = \underline{?}$

$\frac{4}{5}$

21-A.1

29. $\frac{1}{7} + \frac{4}{7} = \underline{?}$

$\frac{5}{7}$

21-A.1

30. Owen spent $\frac{5}{8}$ of his allowance on a model airplane. What fraction of his allowance is left?

$\frac{3}{8}$

21-A.2

Form B • Free-Response   B227   **Chapters 1–23**   **Go on.** ▶

31. $4\frac{3}{9}$
    $+2\frac{5}{9}$

$6\frac{8}{9}$

21-A.1

32. $7\frac{7}{9}$
    $-3\frac{3}{9}$

$4\frac{4}{9}$

21-A.2

33. What is 0.42 written as a fraction?

$\frac{42}{100}$

22-A.1

34. What is 7 nickels written as a money amount?

$0.35

22-A.2

35. Which number is greatest?

0.07, 0.7, 0.17

0.7

22-A.4

36. What is 7.21 written as a mixed number?

$7\frac{21}{100}$

22-A.3

37. Myra practiced her music lessons for 1.2 hours on Monday, 2.1 hours on Wednesday, and 2.8 hours on Saturday. On which day did she practice the longest?

Saturday

22-A.4

38.   0.56
    $+0.73$

1.29

23-A.1

39.   0.78
    -0.59

0.19

23-A.1

40. What is 5.3 rounded to the nearest whole number?

5

23-A.2

Form B • Free-Response   B228   **Chapters 1–23**   ▶ **Stop!**

Name _____

Write the correct answer.
For some items, an inch ruler may be needed.

1. Name a linear unit of measurement.

   Possible answers: inch, foot,
   yard, mile

2. Use a ruler to measure the length of this ribbon.

   3 in.

For questions 3–4, write the reasonable unit of measure.

3. A new pencil is about 6 _?_ long.

   inches

4. A baseball bat is about 1 _?_ long.

   yard

5. The Amazon is the longest river in South America. Which unit is best for describing its length?

   miles

6. Mr. Black is buying some rope. Which unit is best for describing the length of the rope?

   Possible answers:
   feet or yards

For questions 7–9, find the equivalent measurement.

7. 60 ft = ___ yd

   20

8. 5 yd = ___ ft

   15

9. 33 ft = ___ yd

   11

For questions 10–11, use the diagram.

Mrs. Garcia's Yard

1 square = 1 yard

10. How many trees are in Mrs. Garcia's yard?

   6 trees

11. About how far is it from the tree at D to the tree at F?

   about 10 yd

Form B • Free-Response   B229   Go on. ▶

Name _____

12. How long is the crayon to the nearest $\frac{1}{4}$ in.?

   CRAYON

   $2\frac{3}{4}$ in.

13. How long is the string to the nearest $\frac{1}{2}$ in.?

   $2\frac{1}{2}$ in.

For questions 14–16, use an inch ruler to measure length.

14. How long is this paper clip to the nearest $\frac{1}{4}$ in.?

   $1\frac{1}{4}$ in.

15. How long is this pencil to the nearest $\frac{1}{2}$ in.?

   $1\frac{1}{2}$ in.

16. How long is this line to the nearest $\frac{1}{4}$ in.?

   $2\frac{1}{4}$ in.

17. To change pounds to tons, _?_ by 2,000.

   divide

18. A good estimate of the weight of a medium-size turkey is about 10 _?_.

   pounds

19. A good estimate of the weight of a small car is about 1 _?_.

   ton

20. Find the equivalent measure.

   2 pounds = _?_ oz

   32

21. Mrs. Slotsky bought a case of 24 cans of soda. Each can contains 12 ounces. How many ounces of soda are in the whole case?

   288 ounces

22. Kim bought 3 lb of birdseed for her feeder. Her feeder holds 8 oz. How many times can she fill her feeder?

   6 times

Form B • Free-Response   B230   ▶ Stop!

Name _____

Write the correct answer.

1. Arrange the metric units in order from largest to smallest.

   cm, m, dm

   m, dm, cm

For questions 2–8, write the equivalent measurement.

2. 1 dm = ____ cm

   10

3. 1 m = ____ dm

   10

4. 1 dm = ____ m

   0.1

5. 2 cm = ____ dm

   0.2

6. 5 dm = ____ m

   0.5

7. Darla's poster is 2 times longer than Cassie's poster. Cassie's poster is 6 dm long. How long is Darla's poster in meters?

   1.2 m

8. Frank needs 1 m of rope. He has 4 dm of rope. How much more rope does he need?

   6 dm

9. To change 2 m to cm, multiply 2 by ____.

   100

10. Write a number sentence that shows how to change 3 m to dm.

   $3 \times 10 = 30$

For questions 11–14, write the equivalent measurement.

11. 8 dm = ____ cm

   80

12. 5 m = ____ dm

   50

13. 15 m = ____ cm

   1,500

14. 9 m = ____ dm

   90

Form B • Free-Response   B231   Go on. ▶

Name _____

For questions 15–16, use the diagram.

Floor Plan of Mrs. Bell's Office

15. About how far is the desk from the door?

   about 3 m

16. How much wider is the bookcase than the doorway?

   2 m

17. What is a common metric unit of measure of capacity?

   Possible answer: liter

18. A good estimate of the amount of water in the glass is 250 _?_.

   mL

19. A good estimate of the amount of medicine in an eyedropper is 5 _?_.

   mL

For questions 20–21, find the equivalent measure.

20. 10 liters = ____ milliliters

   10,000

21. 8 metric cups = ____ L

   2

22. After practice, each of 8 tennis players drank 3 cups of water. How many quarts of water did all the players drink?

   6 qt

23. Soda costs $0.89 for a 2-L bottle and $0.59 for a 1-L bottle. Janie bought two 2-L bottles and one 1-L bottle. How much money did she spend?

   $2.37

24. A soccer player's water bottle holds 500 mL. How many liters are needed to fill the water bottles of 6 players?

   3 L

Form B • Free-Response   B232   ▶ Stop!

Free-Response Format • Test Answers

CHAPTER 26 TEST — PAGE 1

Write the correct answer.

For questions 1–2, draw the minute hand and hour hand to show the correct time.

1. a quarter to three

2. half past ten

3. What is another way to write *a quarter past five*?

Possible answer: 5:15

4. What is another way to write *half past twelve*?

Possible answer: 12:30

5. What is another way to write 4:45?

Possible answer: a quarter to five

6. What is another way to write 2:15?

Possible answer: a quarter past two

7. The perimeter of a square is 50 cm. If the same square is measured in inches, would the number of units be *greater than* or *less than* 50?

5 in.   12.5 cm

5 in.   12.5 cm

less than

8. A reasonable estimate for the length of this line is 2 _?_.

in.

9. A reasonable estimate for the length of the rope is 5 _?_.

cm

10. A reasonable estimate for the length of the ribbon is 6 _?_.

cm

11. Use the ruler to find the perimeter of the rectangle in inches.

6 in.

Form B • Free-Response   B233   Go on. ▶

CHAPTER 26 TEST — PAGE 2

12. Sonia caught a fish 6 in. long. Fran caught one 6 cm long. Who caught the longer fish?

Sonia

13. Marco's book is 4 cm longer than Billy's book. Billy's book is 34 cm long. How long is Marco's book?

38 cm

14. Henry wants to buy 4 books that cost $5.00 each. The store is having a sale of $1.00 off each book purchased. What price will he pay for all 4 books?

$16.00

15. Sally is putting a border around her flower bed. Two sides are 24 ft long, and two sides are 12 ft long. How many yards of border does she need?

24 yd

16. What temperature does this thermometer show?

30°F

17. Which temperature is colder: 8°F or −8°F?

−8°F

18. What is the difference between the temperatures?

30°F

19. What is the difference between the temperatures?

50°C

20. At sunrise the temperature was 35°F. At noon it was 20 degrees warmer. By six o'clock in the evening, it had cooled off 15 degrees. What was the evening temperature?

40°F

Form B • Free-Response   B234   ▶ Stop!

TEST • CHAPTERS 24–26 — PAGE 1

Write the correct answer.

For some items, an inch ruler may be needed.

1. An inch is a _?_ unit of measurement.

linear

24-A.1

2. What unit of measure is reasonable to measure the distance from one end of town to the other?

mi

24-A.1

3. 36 in. = _?_ ft

3

24-A.2

4. How long is the leaf to the nearest $\frac{1}{4}$ in.?

$1\frac{3}{4}$ in.

24-A.3

5. How long is the string to the nearest $\frac{1}{2}$ in.?

$2\frac{1}{2}$ in.

24-A.3

6. To change pounds to tons, divide the number of pounds by _?_.

2,000

24-A.2

7. Mr. Rey used 30 bags of mulch in his garden. One bag weighs 20 pounds. How many pounds of mulch did Mr. Rey use?

600 lb

24-A.4

8. Jill bought 3 lb of bread for a party. Each loaf of bread weighed 8 oz. How many loaves did she buy?

6 loaves

24-A.4

9. 1 cm = _?_ m

0.01

25-A.1

10. Lenno's older brother is 20 dm tall. His younger brother is one half as tall. How tall is Lenno's younger brother in centimeters?

100 cm

25-A.1

11. To change 3 m to dm, multiply 3 by _?_.

10

25-A.1

Form B • Free-Response   B235   Go on. ▶

TEST • CHAPTERS 24–26 — PAGE 2

12. 4 m = _?_ cm

400

25-A.1

For questions 13–14, use the diagram.

The Bryants' Kitchen

13. The stove is 8 dm long. How much longer is the sink than the stove?

2 dm

25-A.2

14. The table is 11 dm wide. How long is the table in decimeters?

20 dm

25-A.2

15. A reasonable estimate of the amount of soda in a can is 350 _?_.

mL

25-A.3

16. A cup holds 250 mL. How many liters are needed to fill 4 cups?

1 L

25-A.3

17. What is another way to write a quarter to six?

Possible answer: 5:45

26-A.1

18. What is another way to write 2:30?

Possible answer: half past two

26-A.1

19. Raul's picture is 5 cm wide and 9 cm long. He wants to glue a border of yarn around the picture. How many centimeters of yarn does Raul need?

28 cm

26-A.3

20. At sunrise the temperature was 60°F. At noon it was 20 degrees warmer. By six o'clock in the evening, it had cooled off 15 degrees. What was the evening temperature?

65°F

26-A.4

Form B • Free-Response   B236   ▶ Stop!

Free-Response Format • Test Answers

Write the correct answer.

1. 67
26
+39

_____

132

1-A.2

2. A bakery puts 8 donuts in each box. The bakery has 16 boxes of donuts. How many donuts does the bakery have in all?

_____

128 donuts

3-A.4

3. How many thousands are in 8,615?

_____

8 thousands

5-A.2

4. What number has the digit 3 in the hundreds place, 8 in the ones place, and 1 in the tens place?

_____

318

6-A.1

5. What is the greatest place-value position in which the digits are different?
5,673
5,764

_____

hundreds position

7-A.2

For questions 6–7, use the frequency table.

INCHES OF SNOWFALL DURING JANUARY

Week	Inches (Frequency)	Cumulative Frequency
1	11	14
2	8	22
3	17	?
4	15	?

6. How much more snow fell in Week 3 than in Week 1?

_____

6 in.

9-A.1

7. What is the cumulative frequency for the snow that fell in all 4 weeks?

_____

54 in.

9-A.1

For questions 8–9, use the stem-and-leaf plot.

High Temperatures

Stem	Leaves
7	4 5 5 7 8 9 9
8	3 3 4 5 6 6 8 8 8
9	1 1 2 3 4 4

8. What number is the mode for the data?

_____

88

10-A.3

9. What is the difference between the highest and the lowest temperature?

_____

20°

10-A.3

For questions 10–11, use the grid.

10. What is the ordered pair for point x?

_____

(6,2)

12-A.2

11. What is the set of ordered pairs that identifies the vertices of the square marked on the grid?

_____

(3,4), (3,8), (7,8), (7,4)

12-A.2

12. A large painting is 5 feet by 7 feet. What is the area of the painting?

_____

35 sq ft

14-A.2

13. Draw a line of symmetry through the figure.

15-A.3

14. 453
× 7

_____

3,171

16-A.2

15. Find the product by using a basic fact and a pattern of zeros.
90 × 300 = n

_____

n = 27,000

17-A.1

16. $53
× 32

_____

$1,696

17-A.3

17. In which place should the first digit in the quotient be placed?
7)63

_____

ones place

18-A.3

18. 8)537

_____

67 r1

19-A.2

19. A train has to travel 179 miles in 3 hours. How many miles should it travel each hour to reach its destination on time?

_____

60 miles

19-A.4

20. A car had a flat tire. What fraction of the car's 4 tires was flat?

_____

$\frac{1}{4}$

20-A.1

21. What is the fraction renamed as a mixed number?
$\frac{11}{3} = $?

_____

$3\frac{2}{3}$

20-A.3

22. Use the fraction bars to help you find the sum.

$\frac{2}{5} + \frac{1}{5} = $?

_____

$\frac{3}{5}$

21-A.1

23. Use the model to help you find the difference.

$\frac{4}{5} - \frac{1}{5} = $?

_____

$\frac{3}{5}$

21-A.1

24. What is 0.55 written as a fraction?

_____

$\frac{55}{100}$

22-A.1

25. What are 0.44, 0.7, 0.64, and 0.5 written in order from least to greatest?

_____

0.44, 0.5, 0.64, 0.7

22-B.1

26. 1.71
+1.52

_____

3.23

23-A.1

27. 3.19
−1.42

_____

1.77

23-A.1

28. A reasonable unit of measure for a hot dog is about 5 ? .

_____

in.

24-A.1

29. How long is the string to the nearest $\frac{1}{2}$ in.?

_____

$2\frac{1}{2}$ in.

24-A.3

30. 36 in. = ? yd

_____

1

24-A.2

For questions 31–32, use the diagram.

Darts on a Dartboard

1 square = 1 inch

31. How many darts are on the dart board?

_____

14 darts

24-A.3

32. How far is it from the dart at A to the dart at B?

_____

7 in.

24-A.3

33. 4 lb = ? oz

_____

64 oz

24-A.4

34. 0.07 m = ? cm

_____

7

25-A.1

35. 90 cm = ? dm

_____

9 dm

25-A.1

36. 3,000 milliliters = ? liters

_____

3

25-A.3

37. What is another way to write half past seven?

_____

Possible answer: 7:30

26-A.1

38. A reasonable estimate for the length of the string is 3 ? .

_____

in.

26-A.2

39. Tickets to a movie theater cost $5. The price is reduced by $2 for tickets bought before 6 P.M. How much would 3 tickets bought at 5 P.M. cost?

_____

$9

26-A.3

40. What is the difference between the temperatures on the thermometers?

_____

70°

26-A.4

Name _____

Write the correct answer.

1. What numbers should you use to estimate the quotient for this division problem?

   $415 \div 48 = n$

   _____ $400 \div 50 = 8$ _____

2. What basic fact helps find these quotients?

$360 \div 40 = n$
$3,600 \div 40 = n$
$36,000 \div 40 = n$

   _____ $36 \div 4 = 9$ _____

For questions 3–4, estimate the quotient by rounding to the nearest ten.

3. $796 \div 38 = n$

   _____ 20 _____

4. $203 \div 52 = n$

   _____ 4 _____

For questions 5–6, estimate by rounding to the nearest ten or hundred.

5. There are 302 CDs. About 58 CDs fit in a box. About how many boxes are needed to pack the CDs?

   _____ about 5 boxes _____

6. At a basketball camp, 107 players are divided into groups of 12. About how many groups are there?

   _____ about 10 groups _____

7. Should the first digit in the quotient be placed in the hundreds, tens, or ones place?

   $21\overline{)480}$

   _____ tens place _____

8. Should the first digit in the quotient be placed in the hundreds, tens, or ones place?

   $70\overline{)258}$

   _____ ones place _____

9. $60\overline{)686}$

   _____ 11 r26 _____

10. $30\overline{)215}$

    _____ 7 r5 _____

11. $90\overline{)847}$

    _____ 9 r37 _____

Form B • Free-Response   B241   **Go on.** ▶

Name _____

12. A troop of 30 Scouts sold 630 boxes of popcorn. Each Scout sold the same number of boxes. How many boxes did each Scout sell?

    _____ 21 boxes _____

13. Tim must solve the division problem below. What is the first step he should take after estimating the quotient?

    $42\overline{)506}$

    Decide where to place the first digit in the quotient.

14. Mary started doing the problem below. What should she do next?

    _____ Subtract 14 from 15. _____

15. $21\overline{)257}$

    _____ 12 r5 _____

16. $36\overline{)184}$

    _____ 5 r4 _____

17. $72\overline{)890}$

    _____ 12 r26 _____

18. $55\overline{)739}$

    _____ 13 r24 _____

19. Celine swam one lap in 124 seconds. How many minutes and seconds is this?

    _____ 2 min 4 sec _____

20. Eric's bed is 77 inches long. How long is his bed in feet and inches?

    _____ 6 ft 5 in. _____

For questions 21–24, decide if each estimate is *too high, too low,* or *just right.*

21. $19\overline{)178}$ $\;^{8}$

    _____ too low _____

22. $21\overline{)162}$ $\;^{9}$

    _____ too high _____

23. $82\overline{)193}$ $\;^{2}$

    _____ just right _____

24. $59\overline{)183}$ $\;^{4}$

    _____ too high _____

Form B • Free-Response   B242   ▶ **Stop!**

Name _____

Write the correct answer.

For questions 1–2, use the circle graph.

28 Pets at the Pet Fair

1. What does the whole circle represent?

   _____ 28 pets at the pet fair _____

2. What is something you can tell by looking at the graph?

   Possible answer: There are more dogs than either cats or birds at the pet fair.

For questions 3–6, use the circle graph.

Favorite Sport Choices of 25 Students

3. What fraction of the 25 students chose baseball as their favorite sport?

   _____ $\frac{2}{5}$ _____

4. What fraction of the 25 students chose soccer as their favorite sport?

   _____ $\frac{1}{5}$ _____

5. What fraction represents all the students in the survey?

   _____ $\frac{5}{5}$ _____

6. Which sport was chosen by the most students?

   _____ baseball _____

For questions 7–8, use the circle.

7. What decimal represents 1 part of the circle?

   _____ 0.25 _____

8. What is the sum of the decimals that represents 3 parts of the circle?

   _____ 0.75 _____

Form B • Free-Response   B243   **Go on.** ▶

Name _____

For questions 9–12, use the graph.

Favorite Colors of Fourth Graders

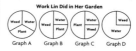

9. What decimal tells how many students chose green?

   _____ 0.3 _____

10. What decimal tells how many students chose blue?

    _____ 0.4 _____

11. What decimal tells how many students chose red?

    _____ 0.2 _____

12. What decimal tells how many students chose yellow?

    _____ 0.1 _____

For questions 13–14, use the graphs.

Graph A   Graph B   Graph C

13. Which graph can be used to show that $\frac{1}{2}$ of the students in a class are boys and $\frac{1}{2}$ are girls?

    _____ Graph B _____

14. Which graph can be used to show that $\frac{1}{2}$ the members of the school band are sixth graders, $\frac{1}{4}$ are fifth graders, and $\frac{1}{4}$ are fourth graders?

    _____ Graph C _____

For questions 15–18, choose the graph that matches the data.

Work Lin Did in Her Garden

Graph A   Graph B   Graph C   Graph D

15. Which graph shows that Lin spent $\frac{1}{3}$ of her time planting, $\frac{1}{3}$ weeding, and $\frac{1}{3}$ watering?

    _____ Graph A _____

16. Which graph shows that Lin spent $\frac{1}{4}$ of her time weeding and $\frac{3}{4}$ watering?

    _____ Graph D _____

17. Which graph shows that Lin spent $\frac{1}{2}$ of her time weeding, $\frac{1}{4}$ planting, and $\frac{1}{4}$ watering?

    _____ Graph B _____

18. Which graph shows that Lin spent $\frac{1}{4}$ of her time weeding, $\frac{1}{2}$ planting, and $\frac{1}{4}$ watering?

    _____ Graph C _____

Form B • Free-Response   B244   ▶ **Stop!**

Write the correct answer.

1. What numbers should you use to estimate the quotient?

$811 \div 79 = n$

$800 \div 80 = 10$

27-A.1

2. Estimate the quotient by rounding to the nearest ten or hundred.

$603 \div 19 = n$

30

27-A.1

3. At a recreation center, 39 players are divided into groups of 9. About how many groups are there?

about 4 groups

27-A.1

4. $80\overline{)752}$

9 r32

27-A.2

5. Luisa must solve this problem. She starts by estimating. What is the next step?

$19\overline{)212}$

Decide where to place the first digit in the quotient.

27-A.3

6. $16\overline{)249}$

15 r9

27-A.3

7. Riley likes a song that plays for 207 seconds. How many minutes and seconds is this?

3 min 27 sec

27-A.3

8. Nova can jump a distance of 59 inches. How long is this in feet and inches?

4 ft 11 in.

27-A.3

For questions 9–10, decide whether the estimate is *too high, too low,* or *just right.*

9. $39\overline{)248}$

too high

27-A.4

10. $19\overline{)212}$

too low

27-A.4

For questions 11–12, use the circle graph.

FAVORITE ACTIVITY OF 30 STUDENTS

11. What fraction of the 30 students chose basketball as their favorite activity?

$\frac{1}{6}$

28-A.1

---

12. What fraction of the 30 students chose hobbies as their favorite?

$\frac{2}{6}$, or $\frac{1}{3}$

28-A.1

For questions 13–14, use the circle.

13. What decimal represents 1 part of the circle?

0.25

28-A.2

14. What is the sum of the decimals that represent 4 parts of the circle?

1.00

28-A.2

For questions 15–16, use the circle graph.

FAVORITE PET

15. What decimal tells how many chose a dog as their favorite pet?

0.4

28-A.2

16. What decimal tells how many chose a cat as their favorite pet?

0.2

28-A.2

For questions 17–18, use the circle graphs.

Graph A   Graph B   Graph C

17. Which graph can be used to show that $\frac{3}{4}$ of the students play baseball and $\frac{1}{4}$ play football?

Graph B

28-A.3

18. Which graph can be used to show that $\frac{1}{4}$ of the students prefer pizza, $\frac{1}{2}$ prefer hamburgers, and $\frac{1}{4}$ prefer peanut butter sandwiches?

Graph A

28-A.3

For questions 19–20, choose the graph that matches the data.

Graph A   Graph B   Graph C   Graph D

19. Which graph shows that $\frac{1}{4}$ of the students like red cars and $\frac{3}{4}$ like both red cars and blue cars?

Graph D

28-A.3

20. Which graph shows that $\frac{1}{3}$ of the students like red cars, $\frac{1}{3}$ like blue cars, and $\frac{1}{3}$ like both red cars and blue cars?

Graph B

28-A.3

Write the correct answer.

1. Estimate the difference to the nearest thousand.

6,281
$-4,873$

1,000

2-A.3

2. Use the model to find the quotient.

$14 \div 3 =$?

4 r2

4-A.3

3. What is the value of the digit 6 in the number 861?

60 (6 × 10)

6-A.1

Compare the numbers and write <, >, or =.

4. 923 ● 932

<

7-A.2

5. The flag at many schools is raised every day at about 8:00. Is this A.M. or P.M.?

A.M.

8-A.2

For questions 6–7, use the calendar.

July

Su	M	T	W	Th	F	Sa
			1	2	3	4	5
6	7	8	9	10	11	12
13	14	15	16	17	18	19
20	21	22	23	24	25	26
27	28	29	30	31		

6. If a space shuttle is launched on July 4 and returns 7 days later, on what date will it land?

July 11

8-A.4

7. On July 15 Laura will sign up for swimming lessons that begin on July 26. How many days will she have to wait for the lessons to start?

11 days

8-A.4

8. What kind of graph would be best to compare the changing times at which the sun sets each day during a month?

line graph

10-A.4

For questions 9–10, use the spinner.

9. What is the probability of spinning a 2?

$\frac{1}{4}$

11-A.2

10. What is the probability of spinning a 1 or a 3?

$\frac{2}{4}$, or $\frac{1}{2}$

11-A.2

---

11. Parallel lines are lines that are the same distance apart and that never ? .

cross, or intersect

13-A.1

12. If a figure on 0.5-cm grid paper is copied onto another page of 0.5-cm paper, the two figures will be ? .

congruent

15-A.5

13. 329
× 3

987

16-A.2

14. $7\overline{)41}$

5 r6

18-A.1

15. $4\overline{)\$19.72}$

$4.93

19-A.3

16. Arrange the fractions in order from least to greatest.

$\frac{5}{6}, \frac{1}{3}, \frac{3}{6}$

$\frac{1}{3}, \frac{3}{6}, \frac{5}{6}$

20-A.2

17. $\frac{2}{9} + \frac{5}{9} =$?

$\frac{7}{9}$

21-A.1

18. 0.81
-0.26

0.55

23-A.1

19. Find the equivalent measurement.

2 mi = ? ft

10,560

24-A.2

20. To change tons to pounds, ? the number of tons by 2,000.

multiply

24-A.2

Free-Response Format • Test Answers

21. 190 cm = __?__ dm

_____19_____
25-A.1

For questions 22–23, use the diagram.

Plan of Flo's Family Room

22. About how far is it from the bookcase to the TV cabinet?

_____about 5 m_____
25-A.2

23. Which piece of furniture is the longest?

_____sofa_____
25-A.2

24. Wendy saw a bird that was 18 in. long. Edra saw a bird that was 18 cm long. Who saw the longer bird?

_____Wendy_____
26-A.2

25. Which temperature is warmer: 2°F or ⁻2°F?

_____2°F_____
26-A.3

For questions 26–27, write the best estimate of the quotient.

26. 889 ÷ 29 = n

_____n = 30_____
27-A.1

27. 298 ÷ 62 = n

_____n = 5_____
27-A.1

28. 50)847

_____16 r47_____
27-A.2

29. 20)546

_____27 r6_____
27-A.2

30. 19)263

_____13 r16_____
27-A.3

For questions 31–32, write whether each estimate is *too high, too low,* or *just right.*

31. 15)139   9

_____just right_____
27-A.4

32. 34)199   6

_____too high_____
27-A.4

33. A visit to a museum lasts 126 minutes. How long is this in hours and minutes?

_____2 hours 6 minutes_____
27-A.3

34. A tennis ball bounced 73 inches. How far is this in feet and inches?

_____6 feet 1 inch_____
27-A.3

For questions 35–36, use the circle graph.

FAVORITE SPORT CHOICES OF 30 STUDENTS

35. Write the fraction of the 30 students who chose baseball as their favorite sport.

$\frac{2}{6}$, or $\frac{1}{3}$
28-A.1

36. Write the fraction of the 30 students who chose soccer as their favorite sport.

$\frac{1}{6}$
28-A.1

For questions 37–38, use the graph.

DISTANCES STUDENTS TRAVEL TO SCHOOL

37. What is the decimal that tells how many students travel 2–3 miles?

_____0.4_____
28-A.2

38. What is the decimal that tells how many students travel 3–4 miles?

_____0.1_____
28-A.2

For questions 39–40, choose the graph that matches the data.

Graph A   Graph B   Graph C   Graph D

39. Which graph shows that $\frac{1}{3}$ chose TV, $\frac{1}{3}$ chose Radio, and $\frac{1}{3}$ chose Book?

_____Graph C_____
28-A.3

40. Which graph shows that $\frac{1}{2}$ chose TV and $\frac{1}{2}$ chose Book?

_____Graph B_____
28-A.3

Management Forms

Test Answer Sheet

This copying master is an individual recording sheet for up to 50 items on the multiple-choice (standardized) format tests.

Grading Made Easy

This percent converter can be used for all quizzes and tests. The percents given are based on all problems having equal value. Percents are rounded to the nearest whole percent giving the benefit of 0.5 percent.

Individual Record Form

One copying master for each content cluster of chapters is provided. Criterion scores for each learning goal are given for the chapter test. The student's total scores are recorded at the top of the page for chapter tests, the multi-chapter test and the cumulative test. The scores for each learning goal can also be recorded. You can use the Review Options that are listed on the form to assign additional review for the student unable to pass the test.

Formal Assessment Class Record Form

The scores for all the tests can be recorded for your class on these record forms. The Criterion Score for each test is given.

Learning Goals

The learning goals for the entire grade level are provided. These goals are referenced throughout the program. Each test item is referenced to a learning goal. You may wish to use these pages to cross-reference the Math Advantage Learning Goals with local, district, or statewide benchmarks.

Test Answer Sheet

MATH ADVANTAGE

Test Title_____

1. (A) (B) (C) (D)
2. (A) (B) (C) (D)
3. (A) (B) (C) (D)
4. (A) (B) (C) (D)
5. (A) (B) (C) (D)

6. (A) (B) (C) (D)
7. (A) (B) (C) (D)
8. (A) (B) (C) (D)
9. (A) (B) (C) (D)
10. (A) (B) (C) (D)

11. (A) (B) (C) (D)
12. (A) (B) (C) (D)
13. (A) (B) (C) (D)
14. (A) (B) (C) (D)
15. (A) (B) (C) (D)

16. (A) (B) (C) (D)
17. (A) (B) (C) (D)
18. (A) (B) (C) (D)
19. (A) (B) (C) (D)
20. (A) (B) (C) (D)

21. (A) (B) (C) (D)
22. (A) (B) (C) (D)
23. (A) (B) (C) (D)
24. (A) (B) (C) (D)
25. (A) (B) (C) (D)

26. (A) (B) (C) (D)
27. (A) (B) (C) (D)
28. (A) (B) (C) (D)
29. (A) (B) (C) (D)
30. (A) (B) (C) (D)

31. (A) (B) (C) (D)
32. (A) (B) (C) (D)
33. (A) (B) (C) (D)
34. (A) (B) (C) (D)
35. (A) (B) (C) (D)

36. (A) (B) (C) (D)
37. (A) (B) (C) (D)
38. (A) (B) (C) (D)
39. (A) (B) (C) (D)
40. (A) (B) (C) (D)

41. (A) (B) (C) (D)
42. (A) (B) (C) (D)
43. (A) (B) (C) (D)
44. (A) (B) (C) (D)
45. (A) (B) (C) (D)

46. (A) (B) (C) (D)
47. (A) (B) (C) (D)
48. (A) (B) (C) (D)
49. (A) (B) (C) (D)
50. (A) (B) (C) (D)

Total Number of Test Items

Number of Test Items Wrong

	4	5	6	7	8	9	10	11	12	13	14	15	16	17	18	19	20	21	22	23	24	25	26	27	28	29	30
1	75	80	83	86	88	89	90	91	92	92	93	93	94	94	94	95	95	95	95	96	96	96	96	96	96	97	97
2	50	60	67	71	75	78	80	82	83	85	86	87	88	88	89	89	89	90	90	91	91	92	92	93	93	93	93
3	25	40	50	57	63	67	70	73	75	77	79	80	81	82	83	84	85	86	86	87	88	88	88	89	89	90	90
4	0	20	33	43	50	56	60	64	67	69	71	73	75	76	78	79	80	81	82	83	83	84	85	85	86	86	87
5		0	17	29	38	44	50	55	58	62	64	67	69	71	72	74	75	76	77	78	79	80	81	81	82	83	83
6			0	14	25	33	40	45	50	54	57	60	63	65	67	68	70	71	73	74	75	76	77	78	79	79	80
7				0	13	22	30	36	42	46	50	53	56	59	61	63	65	67	68	70	71	72	73	74	75	76	77
8					0	11	20	27	33	38	43	47	50	53	56	58	60	62	64	65	67	68	69	70	71	72	73
9						0	10	18	25	31	36	40	44	47	50	53	55	57	59	61	63	64	65	67	68	69	70
10							0	9	17	23	29	33	38	41	44	47	50	52	55	57	58	60	62	63	64	66	67
11								0	8	15	21	27	31	35	39	42	45	48	50	52	54	56	58	59	61	62	63
12									0	8	14	20	25	29	33	37	40	43	45	48	50	52	54	56	57	59	60
13										0	7	13	19	24	28	32	35	38	41	43	46	48	50	52	54	55	57
14											0	7	13	18	22	26	30	33	36	39	42	44	46	48	50	52	53
15												0	6	12	17	21	25	29	32	35	38	40	42	44	46	48	50
16													0	6	11	16	20	24	27	30	33	36	38	41	43	45	47
17														0	6	11	15	19	23	26	29	32	35	37	39	41	43
18															0	5	10	14	18	22	25	28	31	33	36	38	40
19																0	5	10	14	17	21	24	27	30	32	34	37
20																	0	5	9	13	17	20	23	26	29	31	33
21																		0	5	9	13	16	19	22	25	28	0
22																			0	4	8	12	15	19	21	24	27
23																				0	4	8	12	15	18	21	23
24																					0	4	8	11	14	17	20
25																						0	4	7	11	14	17
26																							0	4	7	10	13
27																								0	4	7	10
28																									0	3	8
29																										0	3
30																											0
31																											
32																											

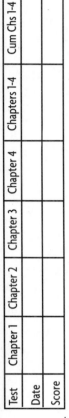

Individual Record Form

GRADE 4 • Chapters 1-4

Student Name _____

Test	Chapter 1	Chapter 2	Chapter 3	Chapter 4	Chapters 1-4	Cum Chs 1-4
Date						
Score						

LEARNING GOALS

		FORM A CHAPTER TEST				REVIEW OPTIONS			MATH ADVANTAGE			
		Test Items			Criterion	Lesson			Workbooks			
Goal #	Learning Goal	Concept	Skills	PSolv	Scores	page #	PE	TE	P	R	E	PS
1-A.1	To use addition and subtraction to make equations equal		1-4		3/4	4-5	EL-1 MP-H68		1.2	1.2	1.2	1.2
1-A.2	To find sums by adding three or more addends	5-6	7-10	11-12	5/8	6-7 8-9	C-H62 MP-H68	CC-p7 LC-1	1.3.1 1.3.2	1.3.1 1.3.2	1.3.1 1.3.2	1.3.1 1.3.2
1-A.3	To use rounding to estimate sums and differences	13-14	15-16	17-18	4/6	10-11	MP-H69	SSC-p11	1.4	1.4	1.4	1.4
1-A.4	To add and subtract two-, three-, and four-digit numbers and money amounts with and without regrouping		19-22	23-24	4/6	12-13	MP-H69	CC-p13	1.5	1.5	1.5	1.5
2-A.1	To use addition and subtraction to solve problems	1-2		3-4	3/4	18-21	MP-H69	PA-18A G-2 AWL-p21	2.1	2.1	2.1	2.1
2-A.2	To subtract across zeros with multiple regroupings	5	6-9	10-11 12-13	6/9	24-25 26-27	EL-2 MP-H70	CC-p25	2.3.1 2.3.2	2.3.1 2.3.2	2.3.1 2.3.2	2.3.1 2.3.2
2-A.3	To use rounding to estimate sums and differences	14-15	16-18		3/5	28-29	MP-H70	WIM-p29	2.4	2.4	2.4	2.4
2-A.4	To choose the operation to solve problems and then find the sums or differences			19-20	2/2	30-31	MP-H70-71		2.5	2.5	2.5	2.5
3-A.1	To model multiplication problems	1-3		4-5	3/5	36-37	MP-H71 EL-3	LL-3	3.1	3.1	3.1	3.1
3-A.2	To use the Property of One, the Zero Property, and the Order Property to find products	6-8	9-10		3/5	38-39	MP-H71	WIM-p39	3.2	3.2	3.2	3.2
3-A.3	To multiply three factors		11-15	16-17	5/7	42-43 44-45	MP-H72	PA-2A G3	3.4.1 3.4.2	3.4.1 3.4.2	3.4.1 3.4.2	3.4.1 3.4.2
3-A.4	To choose the operation to solve problems			18-22	2/5	46-47	MP-H72		3.5	3.5	3.5	3.5

Key: EL–E-Lab **MP**–More Practice **SH**–Student Handbook **C**–Calculator **LC**–Learning Center **PA**–Practice Activities **LL**–Lit Link **G**–Games
BB–Bulletin Board **CC**–Calculator Connection **SSC**–Social Studies Connection **AWL**–Another Way to Learn **WIM**–Writing in Mathematics

Individual Record Form

GRADE 4 • Chapters 1-4 (continued)

Student Name _____

MATH ADVANTAGE

LEARNING GOALS

FORM A CHAPTER TEST

REVIEW OPTIONS

Goal #	Learning Goal	Concept	Test Items Skills	PSolv	Criterion Scores	Lesson page #	PE	TE	Workbooks P	R	E	PS
4-A.1	To decide whether a problem can be solved by using division			1-2	2/2	52-53	SH-H8-9 MP-H72	TR-C8-9	4.1	4.1	4.1	4.1
4-A.2	To use inverse operations to solve problems	3-4	5-6		3/4	54-55	MP-H73	LC-4	4.2	4.2	4.2	4.2
4-A.3	To divide with remainders and make a table to solve problems	7-8		9-10	3/4	56-57 58-59	EL-4 MP-H73	LC-4	4.3.1 4.3.2	4.3.1 4.3.1	4.3.1 4.3.2	4.3.2
4-A.4	To use a multiplication table to find quotients		11-14		3/4	60-61	MP-H73	PA-3A WIM-p61	4.4	4.4	4.4	4.4
4-A.5	To divide with 1 and practice basic division facts		15-16		2/2	62-63	MP-H73		4.5	4.5	4.5	4.5
4-A.6	To choose the operation to solve problems		17-18	19-20	3/4	64-65	MP-H74	CON-p65	4.6	4.6	4.6	4.6

Key: EL–E-Lab   **MP**–More Practice   **SH**–Student Handbook   **C**–Calculator   **LC**–Learning Center   **PA**–Practice Activities   **LL**–Lit Link   **G**–Games
BB–Bulletin Board   **TR**–Troubleshooting   **WIM**–Writing in Mathematics   **CON**–Consumer Connection

Individual Record Form

GRADE 4 • Chapters 5-8

Student Name _____

Test	Chapter 5	Chapter 6	Chapter 7	Chapter 8	Chapters 5-8	Cum Chs 1-8
Date						
Score						

LEARNING GOALS

Goal #	Learning Goal	FORM A CHAPTER TEST Test Items Concept	Skills	PSolv	Criterion Scores	REVIEW OPTIONS Lesson page #	PE	TE	Workbooks P	R	E	PS
5-A.1	To learn different meanings and uses of numbers	1-2	3-6		4/6	76-79	MP-H74-75	RAL-p78	5.1.1 5.1.2	5.1.1 5.1.2	5.1.1 5.1.2	5.1.1 5.1.2
5-A.2	To model, read, and write numbers to 9,999	7-8	9-12	13-14	5/8	82-83 84-85	MP-H75-76 SH-H10-11	TR-C10-11	5.3.1 5.3.2	5.3.1 5.3.2	5.3.1 5.3.2	5.3.1 5.3.2
5-A.3	To use benchmark numbers to show relationships among numbers	15-16	17-18	19-20	4/6	86-87	MP-H76	SC-p81	5.4	5.4	5.4	5.4
6-A.1	To identify place value and represent numbers through 9,999 in standard, expanded, and written form	3-4	1-2 5-8		5/8	92-93 94-95	SH-H12-13 MP-H76-77	TR-C12-13 PA-8	6.1 6.2	6.1 6.2	6.1 6.2	6.1 6.2
6-A.2	To read and write numbers to millions	9-10 13-14	11-12 15-18	19-20	8/12	96-97 100-101 102-103	MP-H77-78	CAR-p97	6.3 6.5.1 6.5.2	6.3 6.5.1 6.5.2	6.3 6.5.1 6.5.2	6.3 6.5.1 6.5.2

Key: **EL**–E-Lab **MP**–More Practice **SH**–Student Handbook **C**–Calculator **LC**–Learning Center **PA**–Practice Activities **LL**–Lit Link **G**–Games
BB–Bulletin Board **RAL**–Reaching All Learners **TR**–Troubleshooting **SC**–Science Connection **CAR**–Career Connection

Individual Record Form

GRADE 4 • Chapters 5–8 (continued)

Student Name _____

LEARNING GOALS

Goal #	Learning Goal	FORM A CHAPTER TEST Test Items Concept	Skills	PSolv	Criterion Scores	Lesson page #	REVIEW OPTIONS PE	TE	Workbooks P	R	E	PS
7-A.1	To use a number line to compare numbers	1-2	3-5		3/5	108-109	MP-H78-79	SSC-p109	7.1	7.1	7.1	7.1
7-A.2	To use place value to compare numbers	6-7	8-9	10-11	4/6	110-111 112-113	SH-H14-15 MP-H79	TR-C14-15 LC-7	7.2.1 7.2.2	7.2.1 7.2.2	7.2.1 7.2.2	7.2.1 7.2.2
7-A.3	To use number lines and place value to order numbers	12-13	14-15	16-17	4/6	116-119	EL-7 MP-H79	G-7 AWL-p119	7.4	7.4	7.4	7.4
7-A.4	To sort and compare sets of numbers using a Venn diagram			18-20	2/3	120-121	MP-H80	WIM-p121	7.5	7.5	7.5	7.5
8-A.1	To tell time to the minute and second and give reasonable units of time for activities	1-2	3-4	5-6	4/6	126-127	MP-H80 SH-H16-17	PA-9 TR-C16-17	8.1	8.1	8.1	8.1
8-A.2	To tell the difference between A.M. and P.M.	7-8		9-10	3/4	128-129	MP-H80 EL-8		8.2	8.2	8.2	8.2
8-A.3	To read and use a schedule to solve problems		11-12	13-16	4/6	132-133 134-135	MP-H81	CUL-p134	8.4.1 8.4.2	8.4.1 8.4.2	8.4.1 8.4.2	8.4.1 8.4.2
8-A.4	To use a calendar to measure elapsed time		17-18	19-20	3/4	136-137	MP-H81 SH-H16-17	TR-C16-17	8.5	8.5	8.5	8.5

Key: EL–E-Lab   **MP**–More Practice   **SH**–Student Handbook   **C**–Calculator   **LC**–Learning Center   **PA**–Practice Activities   **LL**–Lit Link   **G**–Games
BB–Bulletin Board   **SSC**–Social Studies Connection   **TR**–Troubleshooting   **WIM**–Writing In Mathematics   **AWL**–Another Way to Learn   **CUL**–Cultural Connection

Individual Record Form

GRADE 4 • Chapters 9-11

Student Name _____

MATH ADVANTAGE

Test	Chapter 9	Chapter 10	Chapter 11	Chapters 9-11	Cum Chs 1-11
Date					
Score					

LEARNING GOALS

Goal #	Learning Goal	FORM A CHAPTER TEST — Test Items — Concept	Skills	PSolv	Criterion Scores	REVIEW OPTIONS — Lesson page #	PE	TE	Workbooks P	R	E	PS
9-A.1	To organize data in tables and use the data to solve problems		1-3	4-5	3/5	148-149 150-153	MP-H82 EL-9	SC-p151 LL-9	9.1 9.2.1 9.2.2	9.1 9.2.1 9.2.2	9.1 9.2.1 9.2.2	9.1 9.2.1 9.2.2
9-A.2	To evaluate surveys for usefulness in appropriate data	6	7-8		2/3	154-155	MP-H83	EXT-p155	9.3	9.3	9.3	9.3
9-A.3	To interpret data in bar graphs		9-11 12-16		5/8	156-157 158-159	MP-H83-84	HC-p159	9.4 9.5	9.4 9.5	9.4 9.5	9.4 9.5
10-A.1	To read and interpret data on a line graph	1-2	3-6		4/6	166-167	MP-H84	CUL-p167	10.2	10.2	10.2	10.2
10-A.2	To read and interpret data on a line plot	7	8-11		3/5	168-169	MP-H85	BB-9	10.3	10.3	10.3	10.3
10-A.3	To read and interpret data on a stem-and-leaf plot	12-13	14-15	16	3/5	170-171	MP-H85		10.4	10.4	10.4	10.4
10-A.4	To choose an appropriate graph to represent data		17-20		3/4	172-175	MP-H85-86 SH-H20-21	TR-C20-21 G-10 RAL-p174	10.5.1 10.5.2	10.5.1 10.5.2	10.5.1 10.5.2	10.5.1 10.5.2
11-A.1	To determine whether events are certain or impossible, likely or unlikely	1-2	3-4 5-10		7/10	180-181 182-183	MP-H86 EL-11 SH-H22-23	TR-C22-23 LL-11 SC-p183	11.1 11.2	11.1 11.2	11.1 11.2	11.1 11.2
11-A.2	To determine the probability of an event		11-14		3/4	186-187	MP-H87	LAC-p187 G-11	11.4	11.4	11.4	11.4
11-A.3	To determine whether or not a game is fair	15	16-17	18	3/4	188-189 190-191	MP-H87	RAL-p190	11.5.1 11.5.2	11.5.1 11.5.2	11.5.1 11.5.2	11.5.1 11.5.2

Key: EL–E-Lab **MP**–More Practice **SH**–Student Handbook **C**–Calculator **LAC**–Language Arts Connection **LC**–Learning Center **RAL**–Reaching All Learners **PA**–Practice Activities **LL**–Lit Link **G**–Games **BB**–Bulletin Board **TR**–Troubleshooting **SC**–Science Connection **EXT**–Extension **HC**–Home Connection **CUL**–Cultural Connection

Individual Record Form

GRADE 4 • Chapters 12–15

Student Name _____

MATH ADVANTAGE

Test	Chapter 12	Chapter 13	Chapter 14	Chapter 15	Chapters 12-15	Cum Chs 1-15
Date						
Score						

LEARNING GOALS

Goal #	Learning Goal	FORM A CHAPTER TEST — Test Items — Concept	Skills	PSolv	Criterion Scores	REVIEW OPTIONS — Lesson page #	PE	TE	Workbooks P	R	E	PS
12-A.1	To identify and distinguish between one-, two-, and three-dimensional figures and their properties	1 16	2-4 5-6 7-11	17-20	11/16	202-203 206-207 208-209 212-213 214-215	MP-H88-90 EL-12 SH-H36-37	SSC-p205 BB-12 EXT-C54-55	12.1 12.3.1 12.3.2 12.5.1 12.5.2	12.1 12.3.1 12.3.2 12.5.1 12.5.2	12.1 12.3.1 12.3.2 12.5.1 12.5.2	12.1 12.3.1 12.3.2 12.5.1 12.5.2
12-A.2	To locate points on a coordinate grid and identify plane figures made by connecting points		12-15		3/4	210-211	MP-H89	AC-p211 LL-12	12.4	12.4	12.4	12.4
13-A.1	To identify points, planes, lines, line segments, angles and angle relationships	7-8	1-4 5-6	9-10	7/10	220-221 222-223 224-225	MP-H90-91	LWC-p221 G-13 LL-13	13.1 13.2.1 13.2.2	13.1 13.2.1 13.2.2	13.1 13.2.1 13.2.2	13.1 13.2.1 13.2.2
13-A.2	To identify and classify polygons		11-14		3/4	228-229	SH-H24-25 MP-H91	TR-C26-27	13.4	13.4	13.4	13.4
13-A.3	To identify and classify quadrilaterals	15-16	17-18	19-20	4/6	230-233	MP-H92		13.5.1 13.5.2	13.5.1 13.5.2	13.5.1 13.5.2	13.5.1 13.5.2
14-A.1	To find the perimeter of a figure	1-2	3-4	5-6	4/6	238-239	MP-H92	G-14	14.1	14.1	14.1	14.1
14-A.2	To find the area of regular and irregular figures		7-10 11-12	13-14	5/8	240-243 244-245	EL-14 MP-H93	AC-p241 G-14	14.3 14.4	14.3 14.4	14.3 14.4	14.3 14.4
14-A.3	To find the perimeter and area of the same figure and predict how changing the shape of the figure will change its area and perimeter		15-18	19-20	4/6	246-247 248-249	MP-H94 SH-H38-39	LL-14 RAL-p248 EXT-C58-59	14.5.1 14.5.2	14.5.1 14.5.2	14.5.1 14.5.2	14.5.1 14.5.2

Key: **EL**–E-Lab **MP**–More Practice **SH**–Student Handbook **C**–Calculator **LC**–Learning Center **RAL**–Reaching All Learners **PA**–Practice Activities **LL**–Lit Link
G–Games **BB**–Bulletin Board **EXT**–Extension Lesson **SSC**–Social Studies Connection **AC**–Art Connection **LWC**–Literature/Writing Connection

Individual Record Form

GRADE 4 • Chapters 12-15 (continued)

Student Name _____

LEARNING GOALS

Goal #	Learning Goal	FORM A CHAPTER TEST Test Items: Concept	Skills	PSolv	Criterion Scores	Lesson page #	REVIEW OPTIONS PE	TE	Workbooks P	R	E	PS
15-A.1	To translate, reflect, and rotate figures and determine that the figure's size and shape do not change	1	2-3		2/3	254-255	MP-H94 SH-H40-41	G-15 LL-15 EXT-C60-61	15.1	15.1	15.1	15.1
15-A.2	To identify and construct congruent figures	4	5-6		2/3	256-257	MP-H94	HC-p257 LL-15	15.2	15.2	15.2	15.2
15-A.3	To identify figures with point symmetry and figures with line symmetry	7 8-9			2/3	258-259 260-261	MP-H95 EL-15	SC-p259 RAL-p260	15.3.1 15.3.2	15.3.1 15.3.2	15.3.1 15.3.2	15.3.1
15-A.4	To identify tessellations and properties of figures that tessellate	10	11-14		3/5	262-263	MP-H95		15.4	15.4	15.4	15.4
15-A.5	To identify similar figures and solve problems using the *make a model* strategy		15-17	18	3/4	264-265 266-267	MP-H95-96	EXT-p265	15.5.1 15.5.2	15.5.1 15.5.2	15.5.1 15.5.2	15.5.1 15.5.2

Key: EL–E-Lab   **MP**–More Practice   **SH**–Student Handbook   **C**–Calculator   **LC**–Learning Center   **RAL**–Reaching All Learners   **PA**–Practice Activities   **LL**–Lit Link   **G**–Games   **BB**–Bulletin Board   **HC**–Home Connection   **SC**–Science Connection   **EXT**–Extension

Individual Record Form

GRADE 4 • Chapters 16-19

Student Name _____

MATH ADVANTAGE

Test	Chapter 16	Chapter 17	Chapter 18	Chapter 19	Chapters 16-19	Cum Chs 1-19
Date						
Score						

LEARNING GOALS

Goal #	Learning Goal	FORM A CHAPTER TEST — Test Items — Concept	Skills	PSolv	Criterion Scores	REVIEW OPTIONS — Lesson page #	PE	TE	Workbooks P	R	E	PS
16-A.1	To multiply a one-digit number by 10, 100, and 1,000	1-2	3-6		4/6	278-279	C-H58 MP-H96 EL-16	CC-p279	16.1	16.1	16.1	16.1
16-A.2	To multiply a one-digit number by a two- or three-digit number	7-10	11-14	15-16	7/10	282-285 286-287	MP-H97 SH-H26-27	TR-C64-65 RAL-p284 AWL-p285	16.3 16.4	16.3 16.4	16.3 16.4	16.3 16.4
16-A.3	To multiply a whole number by amounts of money to solve problems		17-18	19-20	3/4	288-289 290-291	MP-H97	RAL-p290	16.5.1 16.5.2	16.5.1 16.5.2	16.5.1 16.5.2	16.5.1 16.5.2
17-A.1	To use basic facts and patterns of tens to multiply two-digit numbers and solve problems		1-3	4 5	3/5	296-297 298-299	MP-H97-98 EL-17 SH-H42-43	PA-17A ATS-p297 G-17 RAL-p298 EXT-C92-93	17.1.1 17.1.2	17.1.1 17.1.2	17.1.1 17.1.2	17.1.1 17.1.2
17-A.2	To estimate products of two-digit numbers by rounding factors	6	7-8	9-10	3/5	300-301	MP-H98		17.2	17.2	17.2	17.2
17-A.3	To multiply by two-digit numbers using partial products	11-12	13-15		3/5	304-307	MP-H99	TR-C66-67 RAL-p306 AWL-p307	17.4	17.4	17.4	17.4
17-A.4	To solve problems by multiplying two-digit numbers	16	17-18	19-20	3/5	308-309	MP-H99	LL-17 CC-p309	17.5	17.5	17.5	17.5

Key: EL–E-Lab **MP**–More Practice **SH**–Student Handbook **C**–Calculator **LC**–Learning Center **TR**–Troubleshooting **PA**–Practice Activities **LL**–Lit Link **G**–Games **EXT**–Extension **CC**–Calculator Connection **RAL**–Reaching All Learners **ATS**–Alternative Teaching Strategy **SSC**–Social Studies Connection **AWL**–Another Way to Learn

Individual Record Form

GRADE 4 • Chapters 16-19 (continued)

Student Name _____

LEARNING GOALS

Goal #	Learning Goal	FORM A CHAPTER TEST				REVIEW OPTIONS						
		Test Items			Criterion Scores	Lesson page #	PE	TE	Workbooks			
		Concept	Skills	PSolv					P	R	E	PS
18-A.1	To use basic facts to divide with remainders	1-2	3-4		3/4	316-319	EL-17 MP-H99 C-H60	PA-4A CON-p315 AWL-p319	18.2	18.2	18.2	18.2
18-A.2	To divide a two-digit number by a one-digit number without a remainder	5-6	7-8		3/4	320-321	MP-H99-100 SH-H28-29	TR-C68-69	18.3	18.3	18.3	18.3
18-A.3	To divide two-digit numbers using partial products	9	10	11-12 13	3/5	322-323 324-325	MP-H100		18.4.1 18.4.2	18.4.1 18.4.2	18.4.1 18.4.2	18.4.1 18.4.2
18-A.4	To solve problems by dividing two- and three-digit numbers	14	15-16 17	18-20	5/7	326-327 328-329	MP-H100	G-18 ATS-p323	18.5 18.6	18.5 18.6	18.5 18.6	18.5 18.6
19-A.1	To use basic facts and patterns of zeros to estimate quotients	1-2	3-4		3/4	334-335	MP-H101		19.1	19.1	19.1	19.1
19-A.2	To divide when a zero is in the dividend or in the quotient	5	6-7	8-9	3/5	336-339	MP-H101	EXT-p337 RAL-p338 PA-17A AWL-p339	19.2	19.2	19.2	19.2
19-A.3	To divide amounts of money		10-12	13-14	3/5	340-341	MP-H101		19.3	19.3	19.3	19.3
19-A.4	To interpret the remainder when solving division problems	15-16		17 18-20	4/6	342-343 344-345	C-H60 MP-H101-102	LL-19 WIM-p343	19.4.1 19.4.2	19.4.1 19.4.2	19.4.1 19.4.2	19.4.1 19.4.2
19-A.5	To choose the operation to solve problems			21-24	3/4	348-349	MP-H102		19.6	19.6	19.6	19.6

Key: EL–E-Lab **MP**–More Practice **SH**–Student Handbook **C**–Calculator **LC**–Learning Center **TR**–Troubleshooting **PA**–Practice Activities **LL**–Lit Link **G**–Games
BB–Bulletin Board **CON**–Consumer Connection **ATS**–Alternative Teaching Strategy **EXT**–Extension **WIM**–Writing In Mathematics **AWL**–Another Way to Learn

Individual Record Form

GRADE 4 • Chapters 20–23

Student Name _____

Test	Chapter 20	Chapter 21	Chapter 22	Chapter 23	Chapters 20–23	Cum Chs 1–23
Date						
Score						

LEARNING GOALS

Goal #	Learning Goal	FORM A CHAPTER TEST — Test Items: Concept	Skills	PSolv	Criterion Scores	REVIEW OPTIONS — Lesson page #	PE	TE	Workbooks P	R	E	PS
20-A.1	To identify the fractional part of a whole or group	1-4 7-10	5-6	11-12	8/12	360-361 362-363	MP-H102-103 EL-20 C-H64	PA-21 EXT-p363 LL-20	20.1 20.2	20.1 20.2	20.1 20.2	20.1 20.2
20-A.2	To compare and order fractions	13-14	15-16	17-18	4/6	366-367 368-369	MP-H103	RAL-p368	20.4.1 20.4.2	20.4.1 20.4.2	20.4.1 20.4.2	20.4.1 20.4.2
20-A.3	To identify, read, and write mixed numbers and change fractions greater than 1 to mixed numbers	19-20	21-24		4/6	370-371	C-H65 MP-H104		20.5	20.5	20.5	20.5
21-A.1	To solve problems by adding fractions and mixed numbers with like denominators	1-2 3-4 13	5-6 14-16	7-8 17-18	9/14	376-377 378-379 384-385	MP-H104-105	PA-22 EXT-p379 G-21 MC-p381	21.1 21.2 21.4	21.1 21.2 21.4	21.1 21.2 21.4	21.1 21.2 21.4
21-A.2	To solve problems by subtracting fractions and mixed numbers with like denominators	9-10 19	20-22	11-12 23-24	7/10	380-381 382-383 386-387	EL-21 MP-H105-106		21.3.1 21.3.2 21.5	21.3.1 21.3.2 21.5	21.3.1 21.3.2 21.5	21.3.1 21.3.2 21.5
22-A.1	To relate fractions and decimals	1-2	3-4		3/4	392-393	C-H63 MP-H106	CC-p393	22.1	22.1	22.1	22.1
22-A.2	To identify, read, and write decimals to hundredths	5-6	7-8	9-10	4/6	394-397	MP-H106-107 EL-22	LL-22	22.2	22.2	22.2	22.2
22-A.3	To identify, read, and write mixed decimals	17	18-22		4/6	402-405	MP-H107	EXT-p403	22.5.1 22.5.2	22.5.1 22.5.2	22.5.1 22.5.2	22.5.1 22.5.2
22-A.4	To compare and order decimals and mixed decimals	11-12	13-16 23-24		5/8	398-401	MP-H107	AWL-p401	22.4	22.4	22.4	22.4
23-A.1	To solve problems by adding and subtracting decimals	1-2 8-9	3-5 10-12 15-18	6-7 13-14 19-20	14/20	412-413 414-415 416-417 418-418	EL-23 MP-H108 C-H66 C-H62	MC-p411 G-23 CC-p413	23.2 23.3 23.4.1 23.4.2	23.2 23.3 23.4.1 23.4.2	23.2 23.3 23.4.1 23.4.2	23.2 23.3 23.4.1 23.4.2
23-A.2	To estimate decimal sums and differences by rounding	21	22-23	24	3/4	420-421	C-H67	EXT-p421	23.5	23.5	23.5	23.5

Key: EL–E-Lab **MP**–More Practice **SH**–Student Handbook **C**–Calculator **LC**–Learning Center **PA**–Practice Activities **LL**–Lit Link **MC**–Math Connection
G–Games **BB**–Bulletin Board **EXT**–Extension **CC**–Calculator Connection **AWL**–Another Way to Learn **RAL**–Reaching All Learners

Individual Record Form

GRADE 4 • Chapters 24–26

Student Name _____

MATH ADVANTAGE

Test	Chapter 24	Chapter 25	Chapter 26	Chapters 24-26	Cum Chs 1-26
Date					
Score					

LEARNING GOALS

FORM A CHAPTER TEST   REVIEW OPTIONS

Goal #	Learning Goal	Concept	Skills	PSolv	Criterion Scores	Lesson page #	PE	TE	P	R	E	PS
24-A.1	To measure length in linear units to the nearest unit or fraction of a unit	1	2-4 12-16	5-6	8/11	432-435 440-441	MP-H109 MP-H110 SH-H32-33	TR-C80-81 RAL-p434 LC-24 AWL-p435	24.1 24.3	24.1 24.3	24.1 24.3	24.1 24.3
24-A.2	To use multiplication and division to change units of measure		7-9		2/3	436-437	MP-H109 EL24	LL-24 CUL-p437	24.2.1	24.2.1	24.2.1	24.2.1
24-A.3	To use diagrams to solve problems			10-11	2/2	438-439	MP-H109	RAL-p438	24.2.2	24.2.2	24.2.2	24.2.2
24-A.4	To use appropriate units to measure weight	17	18-20	21-22	4/6	444-445	MP-H110	EXT-p445	24.5	24.5	24.5	24.5
25-A.1	To use multiplication to change units of measure	1 9-10	2-6 11-14	7-8	9/14	452-453 454-455	MP-H-111 SH-H52-53	G-25 EXT-C108-109	25.2 25.3.1	25.2 25.3.1	25.2 25.3.1	25.2 25.3.1
25-A.2	To use the strategy *solve a simpler problem* to solve problems			15-16	2/2	456-457	MP-H111		25.3.2	25.3.2	25.3.2	25.3.2
25-A.3	To use appropriate units to measure capacity	17	18-21	22-24	5/8	458-459	MP-H111	CUL-p459	25.4	25.4	25.4	25.4
26-A.1	To express time by using fractions of an hour	1-2	3-6		4/6	466-467	MP-H112 SH-H54-55	PA-9 EXT-C110-111	26.1	26.1	26.1	26.1
26-A.2	To compare customary and metric linear units of measure	7	8-11	12-13	5/7	468-469	MP-H112	RAL-p470	26.2.1	26.2.1	26.2.1	26.2.1
26-A.3	To write a number sentence to solve problems			14-15	2/2	470-471	MP-H113	LL-26	26.2.2	26.2.2	26.2.2	26.2.2
26-A.4	To read a Fahrenheit thermometer and compare the difference in degrees of two temperatures	16-17	18-19	20	3/5	472-473	MP-H113	G-26	26.3	26.3	26.3	26.3

(Test Items column group: Concept, Skills, PSolv. Workbooks column group: P, R, E, PS.)

Key: **EL**–E-Lab   **MP**–More Practice   **SH**–Student Handbook   **C**–Calculator   **LC**–Learning Center   **RAL**–Reaching All Learners   **PA**–Practice Activities   **LL**–Lit Link
G–Games   **BB**–Bulletin Board   **CUL**–Cultural Connection   **EXT**–Extension   **AWL**–Another Way to Learn

Individual Record Form

GRADE 4 • Chapters 27-28

Student Name _____

Test	Chapter 27	Chapter 28	Chapters 27-28	Cum Chs 1-28
Date				
Score				

LEARNING GOALS

FORM A CHAPTER TEST / REVIEW OPTIONS

Goal #	Learning Goal	Test Items Concept	Test Items Skills	Test Items PSolv	Criterion Scores	Lesson page #	PE	TE	Workbooks P	Workbooks R	Workbooks E	Workbooks PS
27-A.1	To use multiples of 10 and a pattern of zeros to estimate quotients	1-2	3-4	5-6	4/6	486-487	MP-H113	PA-17A	27.1	27.1	27.1	27.1
27-A.2	To divide by multiples of 10	7-8	9-11	12	4/6	488-489	MP-H114	ATS-p489	27.2	27.2	27.2	27.2
27-A.3	To divide three-digit numbers by two digit divisors	13-14	15-18		4/6	492-493	EL-27 MP-H114 SH-H34-35	TR-C86-87 LC-27 WIM-p491	27.4.1	27.4.1	27.4.1	27.4.1
27-A.4	To correct the estimated quotient if it is too high or too low	21-24			3/4	496-499	MP-H115	EXT-p497 AWL-p499	27.5	27.5	27.5	27.5
27-A.5	To write a number sentence to solve problems			19-20	2/2	494-495	MP-H114	LL-27	27.4.2	27.4.2	27.4.2	27.4.2
28-A.1	To use fractions to identify data represented in a circle graph	1-2	3-6		4/6	506-507	EL-28 MP-H115 SH-H56-57	PA-21 G-28 CUL-p507 EXT-C114-115	28.2	28.2	28.2	28.2
28-A.2	To use decimals to identify data represented in a circle graph	7-8	9-12	13-14	5/8	508-511	MP-H116		28.3.1 28.3.2	28.3.1 28.3.2	28.3.1 28.3.2	28.3.1 28.3.2
28-A.3	To choose a graph that represents the given data		15-18		3/4	512-513	MP-H116	LAC-p513	28.4	28.4	28.4	28.4

Key: EL–E-Lab **MP**–More Practice **SH**–Student Handbook **C**–Calculator **LC**–Learning Center **TR**–Troubleshooting **PA**–Practice Activities **LL**–Lit Link **G**–Games
BB–Bulletin Board **ATS**–Alternative Teaching Strategy **WIM**–Writing In Mathematics **LAC**–Language Arts Connection **EXT**–Extension **CUL**–Cultural Connection
AWL–Another Way to Learn

		Inventory	Chapter 1	Chapter 2	Chapter 3	Chapter 4	Chapters 1-4	Cumulatives 1-4	Chapter 5	Chapter 6	Chapter 7	Chapter 8	Chapters 5-8
ol													
her													
Criterion Score		23/34	16/24	14/20	15/22	14/20	16/24	28/40	14/20	14/20	14/20	14/20	14/20
ES	**Date**												

Formal Assessment

Class Record Form (continued)

School / Teacher	Cumulatives 1-8	Chapter 9	Chapter 10	Chapter 11	Chapters 9-11	Cumulatives 1-11	Chapter 12	Chapter 13	Chapter 14	Chapter 15	Chapters 12-15
Criterion Score	26/38	11/16	14/20	12/18	11/16	25/36	14/20	14/20	14/20	12/18	13/19
NAMES — **Date**											

	Chapter 16	Chapter 17	Chapter 18	Chapter 19	Chapters 16-19	Cumulatives 1-19	Chapter 20	Chapter 21	Chapter 22	Chapter 23	Chapters 20-23	Cumulatives 1-23
Criterion Score	14/20	14/20	14/20	16/24	16/24	28/40	16/24	16/24	16/24	16/24	15/22	28/40
S Date												

Formal Assessment

Class Record Form (continued)

School Teacher	Chapter 24	Chapter 25	Chapter 26	Chapters 24-26	Cumulatives 1-26	Chapter 27	Chapter 28	Chapters 27-28	Cumulatives 1-28
Criterion Score	15/22	16/24	14/20	14/20	28/40	16/24	12/18	14/20	28/40
NAMES Date									